MANCHESTER ROYAL EYE HOSPITAL

Manchester Royal Eye Hospital 1814–2014: An Inside View

A history of the life and times of the Manchester Royal Eye Hospital to mark its bicentenary

NICHOLAS JONES

First published in 2014 on behalf of the author by

Scotforth Books (www.scotforthbooks.com)

ISBN   978-1-909817-08-1

Typesetting and design by Carnegie Book Production, Lancaster.

Manufacturing Managed by Jellyfish Print Solutions Ltd

Printed in Malta by Gutenberg Press

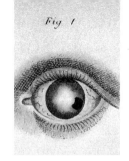

Contents

The author

Preface

I SHOULD BEGIN IMMEDIATELY by stating that this has been done before. In 1964, Frederick Stancliffe Stancliffe, a solicitor and published local historian, was asked to write a history of the Manchester Royal Eye Hospital (MREH) to celebrate its 150th anniversary. He had previously written the history of *John Shaw's 1738–1938* (the Manchester club), and *The Birthplace of the Manchester Royal Infirmary*. Eminently qualified therefore as a Manchester man with a record of historical publishing, he was commissioned by the Board of MREH to produce a concise record of the first 150 years of the Hospital's existence. He met his brief admirably, from the perspective of a non-medical man. A brief appendix to the book was written by one of my predecessor consultants at MREH, Max Duthie, to give a little medical flavour to the largely organisational record of the institution.

I have chosen to write a second history of my Hospital for several reasons. Firstly, MREH is now celebrating its bicentenary, and arguably has changed as much in the past 50 years as it did in its first 150. Secondly, I read Stancliffe's book many years ago with interest, as a record of historical events, but wondered what personalities and contemporaneous circumstances lay behind his portrayal. My extensive reading over the years has revealed a wealth of information about the characters associated with the hospital, their beliefs, strengths and achievements, and also their very different personalities. Some major conflicts have been euphemistically referred to by Stancliffe, probably with the view that such matters are better left undisturbed. My colleagues here at MREH will know that I have no such compunctions. The wealth of detail about people and places, I hope, brings alive the story for all with an interest in this hospital.

Thirdly, as an ophthalmic surgeon with a deep interest in the historical development of both my specialty and my profession, I hope that I am able to place into historical context the developing levels of skill, instrumentation and knowledge of eye disease and its treatment, as the years have advanced. Fourthly, no institution evolves in isolation, and MREH is above all else a part of Manchester, involved at all levels in Manchester history and with Manchester people, good and bad. I have tried to bring relevant social, medical and political events into perspective, partly in the narrative itself, but initially in a pair of Prologues: the first giving a brief history of the town and city of Manchester up to its zenith as Cottonopolis in the nineteenth century; the second a history of the way in which eye care was provided in the century or so up to the creation of MREH, with its focus on Manchester itself.

Lastly, I have benefitted enormously from access to sources that Mr Stancliffe, notwithstanding his enormous diligence in trawling through paper records, did not. Had I not had online access to so many archival sources this book would have been impossible for a full-time consultant. In particular the *British Newspaper Archive* has permitted detailed searching of printed articles as far back as the early eighteenth century, and *Google Books* has enabled direct access to old texts that would otherwise have been too difficult to locate. The wealth of genealogical, local history and association records now presenting from simple word searches has rendered more detail than Stancliffe could have contemplated. As a result not only is more known now about my hospital's history, but rare errors can be corrected. That is not to say that paper is not involved; my reading of archives and references is not counted in pages, but in shelf-metres, and exposure to some antigens also cheerfully celebrating their bicentenary, is in itself a challenge to a chronic asthmatic. I have diligently recorded my sources of information in a bibliography, but have chosen neither to reference nor annotate the text; this is not a scientific discourse and I felt that to treat it as such would reduce its legibility.

My previous writing experience, of ophthalmological textbooks, chapters and research papers, requires a discipline which is both highly structured and restrictive of style. A simple chronological recapitulation of our history, using these same disciplines, would have created a disjointed and cumbersome text. I have therefore taken some liberties with storylines; on introducing some characters, their future stories are sometimes dealt with there and then instead of fragmenting them into the timeline. I sometimes pass laterally into subject matter that is only partially related to MREH, but which I hope gives a flavour of contemporaneous healthcare or social history; leeches, Engels and artificial eyes are but three examples. To those frustrated by this style and by my self-indulgent diversions, my apologies. To those who feel that my approach is too doctor-centred, I only apologise in part; the doctors have been, and remain, at the heart of ophthalmological and organisational developments, both at MREH and at every hospital.

I have been helped in writing this book by several individuals: the late Professor John Pickstone has given me helpful advice and much reference source on the history of Manchester healthcare; retired colleagues have been badgered for information and memories, and I thank Alan Ridgway, David McLeod and Chris Dodd in particular; Anna Goddard, Lucy Frontani and the team at Carnegie have guided me diligently through the publishing process; several sources have kindly given permission for me to reproduce illustrations without charge, including the Royal College of Ophthalmolgists, and I am particularly grateful to Richard Keeler, whose collection of ophthalmic instrument images is without peer, and whose generosity knows no bounds; and finally my wife, who is now so used to my evening absences in my study, writing this and that, and who now hardly knows whether it is history this time, or a paper or chapter on uveitis, or merely yet another lecture. I treasure her tolerance. To all, my thanks.

In 2014 the Manchester Royal Eye Hospital should be proud to be one of the oldest eye hospitals in the world to remain in existence; to be one of the busiest and well-regarded in the world; and to be a flagship for eye care in the North of England, a centre of training to which many gravitate from around the world. In 1814 the hospital started with one Honorary Surgeon. There are now 32 Consultants, providing the highest-quality care to patients both nationally and internationally. As part of our bicentenary celebrations, a charitable appeal has been initiated, to help to fund the creation of an enhanced paediatric genetics service. The proceeds from this book will all go towards that appeal, and I hope the reader will feel satisfied that in indulging this author his opportunity to write about a topic close to his heart, at least some good has come of it.

Nicholas Jones
Wilmslow 2014

Mamucium to Cottonopolis

LONDINIUM WAS ESTABLISHED AS a Roman town in 43AD. Initially secondary to Camulodunum (Colchester) in importance, it later took over as the administrative centre of Roman occupation. Following the consolidation of a road link to its main channel port, Portus Dubris (Dover), forays North were in due course followed by the establishment of major garrisons at Diva (Chester) and Eboracum (York). Agricola, having failed to secure an amicable treaty with the indigenous Brigantes, required these two major northern Roman settlements to be securely interconnected by a new road, and during its construction a chain of defensive forts was erected. It was during one of the required scouting expeditions that a very suitable sandstone hill was found, situated close to an already established river crossing of the river Medlock near its junction with the Irwell, and in excellent strategic position not only between the road forts of Condate (Northwich) to the West and Castleshaw to the East, but also guarding a road crossing to Coccium (Wigan) and Bremetannacum (Ribchester) to the North, and Stockport to the south. The hill upon which the fort was therefore built, in 79AD, was said to resemble a woman's breast, and the Celtic root for said appendage (mamm) was co-opted into the name for the new fort, *Mamucium*, later known as *Mancunium*, possibly owing to nothing more romantic than a transcription error.

The archaeology of pre-Roman settlement in the Mamucium area is sparse, but the region was inhabited by the Setantii, a tribe of the Brigantes. As with all Roman garrisons, an adjacent civilian settlement (vicus) sprang up to supply and trade with the garrison cohort of about 500 auxiliaries. The fort, initially of turf and wood, underwent several adaptations and expansions over 150 years, eventually having stone gatehouses and rampart facings, and extending to about 5 acres. The recession of occupation during the late third century left Mancunium to fall to ruin. Nevertheless, over one thousand years later the medieval remains on this same site, known as the "Castle in the Field" gave that area of Manchester the name that it keeps to this day.

After the abandonment of Mamucium and its vicus, the locals moved somewhat west to the confluence of the Irwell and Irk rivers. The Dark Ages which followed the final Roman abandonment in the fifth century were characterised by aggressive

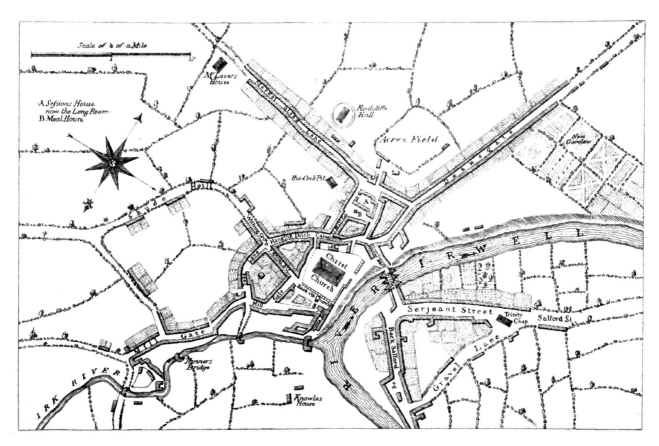

The Manchester of 1650

fluctuations in the boundaries of the territories of the British, Northumbrians, Angles and Danes, those conflicts habitually leading to the exchange of ground in the Northwest, and the repeated sacking of the small civilian settlements in the area, the languages of those occupants being retained in the –tons (British, eg Gorton), the –hulmes (Danish, eg Davyhulme) and other areas which are now suburbs of the city. It is known from the Anglo-Saxon chronicles that in 919 the settlement now known as *Mameceaster* was Northumbrian. Its parish was extensive, yet included only two churches, at Mameceaster and Tameside. Within the parish were up to 40 villages, the most significant being not Mameceaster, but Salford. It was for this reason that Norman reorganisation after 1066, when dividing Lancashire into 4 "hundreds", named the southern, containing the settlement now called *Manchester*, the Salford Hundred.

As was the Norman habit, Lords of the Manor took lands previously British, Danish or Anglo-Saxon and built motte-and-bailey castles to defend and administer them. The Grelleys did so in Manchester, and the settlement expanded gradually, obtaining its charter as a market town in 1301. This status attracted trade, and later in that century a group of Flemish weavers settled in the town, producing both woollen and linen cloth and thereby establishing the roots of the trade that would grow and eventually fuel the explosion of development now called the Industrial Revolution. Manchester's small church of St Mary was no longer appropriate for its status, and in 1510 was completed the new, grand Collegiate Church, now the Cathedral of Manchester. The road leading to the Dean's gate to the church (following the original route of the Roman road between Diva and Eboracum) remains today as Deansgate.

The map of 1650 shows Manchester to be still a small town clustered around its church, its population being less than 10,000. By this time it had acquired a reputation as a centre of textile manufacture, in wool, cotton, linen and silk. By 1729 the cotton trade was sufficiently important for its Guild to erect a Cotton Exchange. One feature of this corner of the Northwest that favoured its development as a centre of cotton manufacturing was its damp climate, and though Manchester has long lost its famed cotton manufacturing industry, the climate strides on resolutely. The second geographical feature placing cotton mills in this particular location was the ready water supply from the Irwell and Irk, of course not unique to Manchester, but a *sine qua non* of all early mills, the resultant civil engineering leaving a plentiful supply of millponds, mill-races and weirs which are a particular feature of the Northwest of England.

In 1781, Richard Arkwright opened the world's first steam-powered cotton mill, in Manchester. He had already become a central figure in the development of the industry, having set up several mills in the midlands and north, and having contributed to the invention of the water-powered spinning frame, and carding machinery. However, steam power permitted the construction of a mill away from a high-volume natural water supply, and the resultant proliferation of mills further from the rivers of Manchester was the real beginning of the industrial revolution. A map of Manchester in 1801 shows its transformation since 1650 into a thriving, rapidly enlarging town of nearly 100,000 souls, the world centre of the cotton trade, the world's first industrial city; *Cottonopolis*. By 1830, astonishingly, the population would be 300,000. It is in this era, the early nineteenth century, into this melting pot of humanity that the Manchester Eye Institution would be created.

Cotton production: its hundreds of spewing chimneys and its thousands of factory workers, children and adult; the burgeoning coal trade that supplied its mills; the expanding canal and railway transport systems; the alehouses and victuallers; the churches and chapels; the gravediggers and navvies; the warehouses and whorehouses; the itinerants and vagrants, and all others attracted into this honeypot of capitalism, swelled the town to bursting. Immigrants from Europe and Ireland flocked to the area, some forming ghettoes including Little Italy and Little Ireland, the latter being located just north of the Medlock, between it and what would later become the Oxford Road railway station. Into this tiny space from 1825 were crammed thousands of emigrant Irishmen and their families, a number to be swelled even further by the potato famines beginning in 1845. Johanna Schopenhauer, mother of the philosopher Arthur, described it as "dark and smoky from the coal vapours, it resembles a huge forge or workshop. Work, profit and greed seem to be the only thoughts here. The clatter of the

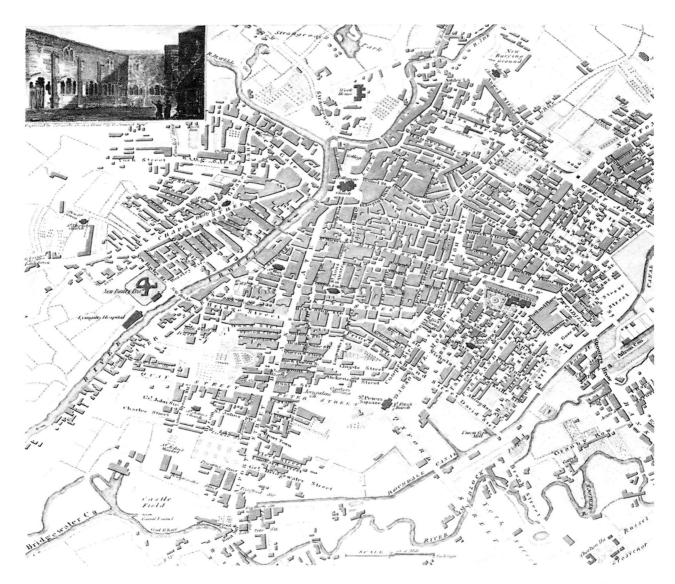

The Manchester of 1801

cotton mills and the looms can be heard everywhere." Hippolyte Taine visited in 1859 and was more direct:

> Manchester: a sky turned coppery red by the setting sun; a cloud, strangely shaped resting upon the plain; and under this motionless cover a bristling of chimneys by hundreds, as tall as obelisks. A mass, a heap, blackish, enormous, endless rows of buildings; and you are there, at the heart of a Babel built of brick… Earth and air seem impregnated with fog and soot. The factories extend their flanks of fouler brick one after another, bare, with shutterless windows, like economical and colossal prisons . . . and inside, lit by gas-jets and deafened by the uproar of their own labour, toil thousands of workmen, penned in, regimented, hands active, feet motionless, all day and every day, mechanically serving their

machines… What dreary streets! Through half-open windows we could see wretched rooms at ground level, or even below the damp earth's surface. Masses of livid children, dirty and flabby of flesh, crowd each threshold and breathe the vile air of the street, less vile than that within. Even to walk in the rich quarter of the town is depressing. But they [the rich] are powerful: there is the compensation. The life of the head of an industrial or commercial house can be compared to that of a princeling. They have the capital sums, the large aims, the responsibilities and dangers, the importance and, from what I hear, the pride of a potentate. They are the generals and rulers of human toil. Quarter of a million sterling, half a million sterling, such are the figures they deal in. The warehouses of finished cotton goods and other fabrics are Babylonian monuments. One of them is two hundred yards long and the bales of cloth are handled by steam-driven machinery. A cotton mill may contain as many as three hundred thousand spindles… Always the same impression: enormousness. But are work and power all that is required to make a man happy?"

The social conditions of Manchester in the early and middle nineteenth century have been well-described, but with particular ire by Friedrich Engels. The father of communism was ironically the scion of a prosperous Prussian family of cotton manufacturers. Already a well-practised radical activist at 22 years of age, and already having been imprisoned for the vandalism of bourgeois property, in 1842 he was sent by his frustrated parents to Manchester, to work in the Erwen & Engels' Victoria Mill, part-owned by his father, in an attempt to instil into him some semblance of corporate responsibility

The Manchester of 1857, drawn by William Wyld; his attempt to inject romance with its bucolic, sunlit foreground cannot hide its forest of "dark, satanic mills"

and social proportion. The experiment failed spectacularly, in that Manchester became the social laboratory of Engels, leading in 1844 to his publication of *The Condition of the Working Class in England*, a scathing attack upon social inequality, poverty and the English bourgeoisie. His experiences and his radical interpretation of them led in due course to the joint authorship, with his friend Karl Marx, of *The Communist Manifesto*. In the preface to an English translation of his work on the working classes in the 1890s, Engels acknowledged his fiery youth in some of the language used, and admitted (somewhat prematurely) that the problems described then were no longer an issue in England. Nevertheless his words still paint a vivid picture of the working poor of Manchester. He said of Little Ireland:

> "It lies in a fairly deep natural depression on a bend of the river and is completely surrounded by tall factories or high banks and embankments covered in buildings. Here lie two groups of about 200 cottages, most of which are built on the back-to-back principle. Some 4,000 people, mostly Irish, inhabit this slum… Heaps of refuse, offal and sickening filth are everywhere interspersed with pools of stagnant liquid. The atmosphere is polluted by the stench and is darkened by the thick smoke of a dozen factory chimneys. A horde of ragged women and children swarm about the streets, and they are just as dirty as the pigs, which wallow happily on the heaps of garbage and in the pools of filth. In short, this horrid little slum affords as hateful and repulsive a spectacle as the worst courts to be found on the Irk… The creatures who inhabit these dwellings and even their dark, wet cellars, and which live confined amongst all this filth and foul air, which cannot be dissipated because of all the surrounding lofty buildings, must surely have sunk to the lowest level of humanity."

Friedrich Engels, an angry young man in Manchester c. 1844

We shall hear from Engels again. Manchester's slums provoked another perceptive observer, one who would express her concerns not by direct critique, but by novel-writing: Elizabeth Gaskell. Born in London, she then lived and married in Knutsford (or as she would later call it, *Cranford*) but moved with her husband William to Manchester in 1828, where he had been appointed minister of Cross Street Unitarian Chapel. She travelled to Germany in the 1840s and was fluent in German, the literature of that country strongly influencing her work. It would be intriguing to know whether she knew Friedrich Engels, either in Germany or Manchester, but as a strong-willed social reformer it can reasonably be assumed that she had read his Manchester-based work (which at that time had not been translated from the German) and it is tempting to think that they influenced each other; they certainly lived within easy walking distance of each other in Manchester. The Gaskells moved to No. 84 Plymouth Grove, a few minutes walk from the current location of the Manchester Royal Eye Hospital, in 1850 and Elizabeth lived there until her death in 1865. She held a wide circle of literary friends, including Charlotte Brontë, who visited several times (and whose father was to have his cataract removed in Manchester). Her novel *Mary Barton; a Tale of Manchester Life* published in 1848, was a harrowing tale highlighting the gulf between

The Irwell, Manchester in the early nineteenth century. An engraving by William Westall

employer and employee in that industrial town. As *Fraser's Magazine* recommended: "Do they want to get a detailed insight into the whole science of starving?... Let them read *Mary Barton*". In its preface she stated her sympathy for the care-worn workers, who "seem to me to be left in a state wherein lamentations and tears are thrown aside as useless, but in which the lips are compressed for curses, and the hands are clenched and ready to smite." Murder and strife ensues, but there is at least a happy ending to the novel – the restoration to sight of Margaret, by an operation for cataract. Where could it have taken place? Where other than at the Manchester Eye Hospital! The Gaskell family were later to form strong links to the Hospital, when Elizabeth's daughter was to become Secretary of the Ladies' Committee for many years.

Quackery, Medicine and Ophthalmology in Manchester prior to 1814

T HROUGHOUT THE EIGHTEENTH CENTURY, a tradition existed of a broad separation of skills, the physicians (those practising the physick) being regarded as practitioners superior to the surgeons, with their more lowly tradition of barber-surgery. The apothecaries, although practising independently, also dispensed on the instruction of physicians. Within these broad areas, though many doctors professed some particular expertise in certain areas, true attempts at specialisation were regarded with high suspicion by the medical profession in general. Such suspicion had some justification, as "specialisation" was practised by the itinerant quacks, especially of the seventeenth century. Some travelling oculists attained an impressive notoriety, their movements skilfully keeping them a step ahead of their creditors, paramours, or dissatisfied patients. One of the more infamous was Henry Blackburne, who, it was said:

> "travelled contynouslye from one market towne to another, who could couche ye Cataracke welle, cure yt, Laye a scar Lippe, set a crockt necke strayght & helpe deafness. Though he could doe good in these cures yet he was soe wickedlye gyven that he would cousen & deceave men of great som of moneys by taken incurable diseases in hand. He was lusty amorously gyven to seueral women so that his cosenynge made him fearfully to flee from place to place & often changed his name and habits in divers places, & was often imprisoned for women. His skille was excelente, but his vices.... His practice was this, yf he made a blind man see; after he had couched ye Cataracke and he...prepare ye lady. He dubled a thicke linen clothe wet in ye white of an ege beaten, & so gave him divers hianst to dresse ye eyes twice a daye for IX dayes together & so he lefte ym, yf he herde they did welle he would see ym agayne, yf not he would neuer come at ym. If cum payne or accedentlyes fell out they receaved no comforte from him"

Notwithstanding the contemporary views of the avarice and dishonesty of the itinerant, there is little evidence that his medical or surgical skills were worse than those of the reputable physicians or surgeons of the time. The latter however, now began to record their careful observations, many of which show that without modern instrumentation, it was possible to discern features of eye disease which are still important today. Richard Bannister, oculist, portrayed the condition *gutta serena* in 1622, and described four features which suggest that the condition was beyond hope of cure (features which indeed were well-observed and largely accurate):

> *"I will show my opinion, where most hope of Cure is; if the humour settled in the hollow Nerves, be grown to any solid, or hard substance, it is not possible to be cured; which may be iudged of, four wayes. First, if it be of long continuance. Secondly if they see no light at all of the sun, fire or candle. Thirdly, if one feele the Eye by rubbing upon the Eie-lids, that the Eye be growne more solid and hard, than naturally it should be. Fourthly, if one perceive no dilatation of the pupilla, then there is no hope of Cure"*

Surgical skills at this time were crude, with poor and unclean instrumentation, and often a trifling knowledge of ocular anatomy. However, one can still find an occasional historical gem, such as this from Daubigney Turberville, Salisbury oculist, also in 1622, making what was almost certainly the first description of the magnetic extraction of a foreign body:

> *"A person in Salisbury had a piece of iron or steel stuck in the iris of the eye which I endeavoured to push out with a small spatula, but could not; but on applying a loadstone it immediately jumped out"*

The eighteenth century saw the appointment of the first ophthalmic surgeons to the established London general hospitals, the most prominent being John Freke, appointed in 1727 at St Bartholomew's (who was paid the princely sum of 6s 8d for each couching of cataract) and William Cheselden, appointed in 1733 at St George's. Such surgeons were aware of the potential complications of the surgery of eye trauma, and Benedict Duddell, oculist from Derbyshire but working in London, describes the condition we know now as sympathetic ophthalmia, though he misunderstood the cause. After a penetrating eye injury:

> *"A busy old woman had applied a plaister. The uvea digested came through the wound in the cornea. The eye that is not hurt must always be drest for fear of a flux of humours upon it: I have seen several that have lost both eyes, though only one has been hurt at first, by reason of bad application, and irregular methods"*

The quacks also appreciated such complications. The rogue itinerant oculist John "Chevalier" Taylor was reviled by the medical establishment (and also by Benjamin Duddell, himself not within the professional mainstream, who said of him "His blunders are so many and so palpable that I blush he should wear a graduate cap"). Yet to the indignation and envy of his critics, he was regularly courted by Royalty and the aristocracy both at home and abroad, to his great enrichment (he always travelled in comfort, in a splendid carriage emblazoned with paintings of eyes, with an itinerary of servants). Indeed he sometimes referred to himself in his advertisements as "Ophthalmiator Royal" and was indeed appointed Oculist-in-Ordinary to George

Chevalier John Taylor, Ophthalmiator Royal

II. His couching of Handel's cataract was a failure, and post-operative complications after his surgery may even have killed JS Bach. He was a popinjay, a macaroni, a theatrical self-publicist. Nevertheless it is clear that despite his disreputability, he had been trained within the establishment (his teachers including Cheselden) and his skills of observation were acute; he could honestly record an incident of the same condition (sympathetic ophthalmia) following a cataract operation:

> *"The Eye continued clear, and the Patient saw for some Days. At which Time an Inflammation came on, which equally affected both Eyes; and, notwithstanding all I could do to abate it, the Coats and Humors were so thickened by it, that the Eye which had the Suffusion in it became totally blind: And some Time after, that which I had Couch'd was in like manner entirely depriv'd of Sight' tho; the Cataract remained depress'd, and the pupilla perfectly clear"*

He also made a perfect description of an afferent pupil defect in a diseased eye:

> *"In this case it is remarkable that when both eyes are exposed to Light, the Pupil of the diseas'd Eye maintains the same Changes with regard to its Change of Diameter, ie to the Velocity of these Changes... as the pupil of the healthful Eye; and that on closing the well Eye, the Pupil of the diseased Eye... dilates slowly to near twice its Diameter, and continues immobile in that dilated State in all Degrees of Light, till the healthful Eye is again exposed to Light, when it contracts"*

There seems little doubt that had John Taylor chosen to establish himself in London or another European capital, contributing both in practice and in writing to the development of the specialty of ophthalmology, he would now be celebrated as one of the founders of ophthalmology as a science. As it is, he has merely remained the most disdained of the itinerant oculists of the eighteenth century. There were many others, of varying degrees of notoriety. All shared the requisite puffery and bombast essential to the plying of their trade, and all when required were able to show a clean pair of heels should the suspicion of clients become threatening. It was of course protective for the surgeon, not the patient, that the latter was required to keep an operated eye covered for several days afterwards. The result, good or bad, was a matter entirely for the subject, the operator having long gone.

Three examples of itinerants who visited Manchester to ply their trade, serve to illustrate the genre in the provinces; all graced the town with their presence in 1766. Announcing his arrival with a typically effusive advertisement in the *Manchester Mercury* in June 1766:

> SIGNIOR BELLOT's success in operating and treating all the Disorders of the Eye, being always attentive to the Public Good; the Dexterity with which he operates in the new Method of extracting the Cataract or the Glaucomatic Crystalline, and the Candour he shews, when consulted about Diseases of this noble Organ, has convinced the Publick how much superior Mr Bellot is to any oculist that has ever been here, and how much more to be confided in. The great Sums he has refused from those he judged incurable, and would not operate on, demonstrates his Probity.

Since Mr Bellot has practised the new Method of restoring Sight, of curing its Disorder, and of removing those Defects Known under the Name of Weakness of Sight Several Numbers of Persons of both Sexes, have happily pass'd through his Hands.

He continues as usual to assist the Poor; and it is with great Concern that he finds, that several People in the Past have been imposed on by Quacks: Whereas, his Custom is always to remain in a Place 'till he has perfected any Cure he undertakes.

NB Mr Bellot may be heard of at Mrs *Robinson's in Deansgate, Manchester.*

This advertisement was repeated one week later, and then predictably, the good doctor disappeared, doubtless heading for the next gullible township. Even more impressive was the advertisement heralding the arrival of the incredible polymath Dr Benvenuti in October of the same year:

For the Good of the PUBLIC, *This is to Give Notice*

THAT there is arriv'd from London, the famous Physician and Occulist, Dr. Benvenuti, who during his long stay in the Metropolis (*London*) has made himself renowned by his happy Operations, and many great Cures, as well as his House in *Great Suffolk Street, Charing Cross*, as in Public in Covent-Garden and Moorfields, unto so many Poor and Miserable Afflicted with different Disorders, as well of Inward and Outward Diseases, a great Part were given over by the most Eminent Doctors, Surgeons and Hospitals, and declared incurable, which is known by a great many Persons that were Eye-Witnesses of his surprising Cures.

This famous Doctor Cures the following Diseases, when left incurable, for he takes no Body in hand, unless he can make a perfect Cure.

1. Internally he cures all Disorders of the Head and Eyes, Deaf-ness, Hard Hearing, Head-Ach, weak Memory, the Vapours, Epilepsy, Palpitation of the Heart, the Asthma, Phthisick, Consumption, Dropsy, the Cholic, Hypochondriac and Hysteric disorders, broken Constitutions in Med &c. All Nephritic Pains, the gravel, Stranguary &c., and all Sorts of Fevers and Agues, the Rheumatism, Gout &c. Also all Degrees & Symptoms of the Venereal Disease. In other Diseases, not mentioned here, let the Patient send their Morning Urine, and he will let them know what Sickness they have, paying One Shilling.

2. External Disorders, which the Doctor must see and examine himself. He Cures all Wounds, Ulcers and Tumours, as the Fistulas, the Cancer, the Piles, Ruptures &c. He attends at his Lodgings the late Angel Inn, in Manchester, from Eight o'Clock 'till Twelve in the Morning, and from Two 'till Ten at Night. The Doctor Cures the Poor gratis every day, from Six 'till Eight in the Evening, at his Lodgings.

It is not known how long the people of Manchester benefitted from Dr Benvenuti's magnificent presence, but a piece from the *Manchester Mercury* in June 1767 indicates that his sense of timing may not always have been perfect:

COUNTRY NEWS: Norwich, June 6th. To detect impostors of any kind is deserving the Thanks of the Public, and is in no instance of greater Utility than to expose and suppress that Species of it, which, under pretence of extraordinary skill in Medicine, commit Merciless Depredations upon the Credulous and Necessitous. A foreigner, who calls himself Dr Fortunatus Benvenuti, who has several months Past, strolled about this Kingdom sumptuously dressed, in a handsome Chariot, with two Servants in Livery, after having been permitted with Impunity to continue many Weeks at Leicester, Birmingham, York, Liverpool, and other places, lately infested this City, to the additional Distress of many Diseased and indigent Persons. On Monday last he was summoned before the Mayor and two other Justices of the Peace, who demanded an Account of his Education abroad, as Well as the manner of passing his Time in this Country; by the Doctor's own Account, he acquired his amazing Erudition in an Apprenticeship to a Chymist at Turin; after producing many Certificates of importance abroad, he was called upon for his Authority for travelling in England, he said he had the King's Letter, which appeared to be a Foot Licence from the Commissioners of Hawkers and Pedlars: Upon the whole Examination he appeared to be destitute of Knowledge, Medicines and Instruments to perform the wondrous Cures he pretended to effect, except an Apparatus for Couching, and a tolerable Acquaintance with the Anatomical Structure of the Eye; he affected an Ignorance of the English Language, but betrayed himself to be too intelligent in it upon this Occasion, as he doubtless is to serve his own purposes: The Magistrates finding that himself, a Woman who passes for his Wife, and the Servants were Vagabonds, according to the Vagrant Act, acquainted them, that unless they quitted the City that afternoon, they should be Committed to the House of Correction for six Months: Accordingly, to the Relief of the Poor (whom he pretended to cure gratis, altho' each paid a shilling to the Servant before they were admitted to an Audience with the Doctor) and much to the credit of the Magistrates who exerted themselves in their favour, they decamped immediately.

Benvenuti did not advertise further and perhaps had returned to the continent, where he could ply his trade on virgin territory. In October 1766 there was competition: Dr Miller, also specialising in eye diseases, announced the following successful cures in the *Manchester Mercury*:

Sir, in gratitude to Doctor Miller, who is now in Manchester and for the benefit of the Public, request you insert the following Case in your paper -

The Wife of John Seddon, Whitster in Audenshaw, restored by Mr Miller, of a total Blindness, of 4 years, and may be seen at Mr Collier's, School master, in Tib

Lane. Since the Cure of Mrs Seddon, the following Patients have been operated and restored by Mr Miller, viz;

Mary Spencer, Old Quay, of a Psorophthalmia (of 27 years standing) or Sharp biting Humour in her Right Eye, with Tubercles or Puriginus Scab.

James Hague, of Hawley Hill, Near Ashton, cured of a long standing Tracoma, or burning and itching Humour in his Left Eye, with several Ulcers in the Eye Lids.

Jeremiah Tetterson, blind, (upwards of 50 years of age) was, at the *Eagle & Child*, in Hanging Ditch, operated by extraction the 23rd instant, and is now in a fair way of being restored to perfect Sight.

Bryon Morris, of Quay-Street, Blind of a Cataract, operated 26th instant, is without Pain and in a fair way, the above two patients were operated in less than two Seconds of a Minute.

Mary Kirby, near Spaw Style, Salford, Cured of a dry Lippitude, with a glutinous matter and itching in her Left Eye.

And two months later Dr (or Mr, it mattered not) Miller was still in Town, continuing to exhort potential clients in the December 23rd edition of the *Manchester Mercury*:

Mr MILLER, the Occulist, continues his Operations with Success, and invites all those who stand in need of his Skill, to apply as soon as possible.

Mr MILLER, a regular-bred occulist, whose Peculiar Method and Dexterity have met with the Particular Approbation of different Academies Abroad, (as is evident by Indisputable Attestations from those Societies) offers his assistance to all those who are any Ways afflicted in the Eyes, tho' the Disorder be of 20 years standing, and the Cure being attempted and missed by former unskilful Operators, all which may be evidenced by 126 Patients, who have been perfectly restored to Sight, when labouring under Divers Complaints in the Eyes, during his Residence in *Bristol, Birmingham, Leicester, Derby & Sheffield*, to whom he refers the Doubtful.

MR MILLER's daily practice convinces him of the Mal-Treatment many of the afflicted have suffered, by some Pretenders to this Art, who not staying sufficient Time in the same Place to Perfect their Undertakings, ignorantly and improperly Couching, have on that Account applied violent Remedies, in order to effect a sham Cure, the afflicted may be assured that his Method is contrary to theirs, being perform'd by an easy and safe Method of extracting the Cause of the Complaint, and that he will be ready at any time as desired by the Patient, to do the Operation under the Inspection of any Unprejudic'd Judges of the Faculty, and makes no Doubt of having the Honour of their Approbation, as he depend upon the Effects of his Operations to speak his Praise, better than a Multiplicity of Bombast and pompous Words without real Meaning, such as Pontifical, Imperial, Royal Ophthalmiator &c., expressions which tend rather to amuse and deceive the ignorant, than to convince the sensible of any particular skill in the Professor.

His Advice may be had every Morning, without Fee, whether their Case is curable by him or not, and will assist the Poor gratis, with the same Care and Tenderness, as those in a more exalted Station, at his apartments at the *Spread Eagle, in Salford, Manchester.*

For those less fortunate souls unable to obtain the Cure from these magicians, or perhaps for those requiring further treatment after the good doctors' departure, one could always rely upon a positive cornucopia of panaceas, offered with the same confidence as the skills of the itinerant. The *Manchester Mercury*, in July 1808, offered:

TO THE PUBLIC

The numberless accidents which are hourly liable to happen in families, from SCALDING-BURNING &c., loudly call for a Remedy, which every Mother might have constantly at hand, at once certain in its effects, simple in its mode of application, and cheap in its price, thereby to come within the reach of all – Parents are earnestly requested to make a trial of

Turner's Imperial Lotion

It comprehends very superior advantages to every other hitherto offered: it is not only an extraordinary Beautifier of the Skin, rendering it clean and smooth, but embraces the great and useful properties of removing every description of INFLAMMATION the Skin is liable to.

In OPHTHALMIA, or Weak Eyes, it will give a perfect Renovation, restoring to that delicate organ all its enchanting brilliancy, and even where it is constitutionally weak, this Application will, in most cases, make a perfect Cure.

Thirty years experience induces the proprietor to offer it to the world, and especially to those who have Medicine Chests, as an indispensable addition. To be had of *Mr Lynch*, Market-street-lane, Manchester in half pint bottles, price 4s 6d, or in pint bottles price only 6s 6d.

Mr Lynch's business was well-established and profitable, and he was clearly an effective publicist. We shall hear of him again.

During the seventeenth and eighteenth century the resident medical practitioners of a town were beginning to take identifiable forms: the physician dispensed the physick; the surgeon, initially barber-surgeon, performed dental procedures, amputations and whatever else he might turn his hand to; the apothecary dispensed medicines and to some extent provided medical advice; and the midwife delivered the children (before the man-midwives, later the obstetricians, began to invade their field in the later eighteenth century). There were bodies in existence which attested to qualification, at least in part. The Royal College of Physicians had been in existence since 1518, and did licence practitioners, but there were fewer than 100 Fellows before 1800, and licentiates were only slightly more numerous. Nevertheless, at least a medical degree was regarded as a requirement for Fellowship and there was therefore an element of control.

The Worshipful Society of Apothecaries was also well-established (being a London Livery Company since 1617) and there was considerable friction between it and the then College of Physicians about the latter's Royal right to monopoly. This was successfully challenged in the early eighteenth century such that apothecaries then became able to practice independently; in a sense they later evolved into the modern general practitioner. However, in practice, during the eighteenth century most apothecaries predominantly dispensed medicines as prescribed by the physicians. It was as late as 1815 that the first National regulatory function was introduced, giving the Worshipful Society the right to licence all apothecaries in the Kingdom, but only following formal teaching and apprenticeship.

The London Guild of Surgeons is the most ancient body of all, dating back to 1368. Prior to this the mediaeval barber-surgeon was essentially a military first-aider, but the creation of the Guild created a friction between barbers and surgeons which led to a number of professional treaties and reorganisations, the final schism occurring in 1745 with the formation of the Company of Surgeons. It was only in 1800 that this body became the Royal College of Surgeons. An essential difference between the surgeon and the physician (and one repeatedly portrayed by the latter as proof of the inferiority of the former) was the surgical tradition of training by apprenticeship, with no formal medical degree required. Manchester was graced by a Member of the College, as advertised in the *Manchester Mercury* in 1813:

> DOCTOR DUNN, *Oculist*, MEMBER of the Royal College of Surgeons, in London, may be consulted every day in the week, from ten in the morning till eight in the evening, at *Mr Burdett's*, No 7 *Oldham-Street, Manchester*, in all cases of blindness, deafness, ruptures, cancers &c. Dr. DUNN is particularly successful in extracting the cataract, and curing all disorders of the eyes, such as weakness and dimness of sight, pain swelling and inflammation; removes specks and films, by whatever cause occasioned.
>
> As a graduate of an Ancient and honourable University, and a Member of the Royal College of Surgeons, in London, he grounds his pretensions to regularity of education; and possessing the highest privilege of practice, he feels himself entitled to that confidence with which he has hitherto been so liberally honoured.

Prior to the introduction of forms of professional regulation, the public attitude to the medical profession in general was to say the least, mixed. The futility of so many contemporary treatments was perceived by many, and yet the doctors' services would

The Doctors' Consultation: Three such gentlemen converse sagely about the alternative treatments for the poor patient, who appears to be expiring in the background. A typical drawing of about 1800, by Thomas Rowlandson, the scourge of the medicine men and other professionals

continue to be sought by those who could afford them. The caricaturists had a field day, and none more so than Thomas Rowlandson, whose artistic skill was combined with both a deep perspicacity and a vicious sense of humour, the portrayal of which had its heyday (together with other cartoonists including Gillray and Nixon) at the end of the eighteenth century.

The turn of the nineteenth century brought with it new challenges to the oculists. One of the most provocative was the "Egyptian Ophthalmia". Following Nelson's defeat of the French at the Battle of the Nile in 1798, British troops landed at Aboukir Bay and by all accounts were rapidly afflicted in large numbers by a severe and chronic ocular inflammation (also affecting the French troops in Egypt). The eventual re-embarcation of the troops and their re-deployment in European theatres of war spread the disease widely, and up to 5,000 English troops were reported as being blinded by the disease. Of the 52nd Light Infantry alone, 636 men were affected, 40 blinded in one eye and 50 in both.

The exact nature of the ophthalmia remains a topic for argument; mainly presumed to be trachoma, but in the knowledge that the natural history of that disease today is rarely so aggressive, some have argued that it was either a different infection, or a combined bacterial infection. Whatever the cause, the disbandment of some regiments and the return home of blinded, useless but untreated soldiers served to spread the infection amongst the civilian population. The prevalence of eye disease was substantially increased by this single new infection, and the need for eye care became more pressing.

In this changing environment, John Cunningham Saunders in London had already shown a great interest in diseases of the eye and ear, and despite the potential risk to his reputation, had decided to specialise in the treatment of these. It was possibly Sir Astley Cooper, teacher and mentor of Saunders, who first suggested that he create an institution specifically to treat these diseases. The idea clearly attracted him, and the signed support of both physicians and surgeons from St. Thomas' and Guy's Hospitals must have persuaded him that the project was both feasible, and professionally not suicidal. It was on January 4th 1805 that a meeting was held at which a new institution was created, to be called "The London Dispensary for the Relief of the Poor Afflicted with Diseases of the Eye and the Ear"; Moorfields Eye Hospital was born.

It was also the Egyptian Ophthalmia that seemed to be the main impetus for the creation of eye hospitals elsewhere in England. The West of England Eye Infirmary dates from 1808; In Bristol in June 1810 began The Institution for the Cure of Diseases of the

Eye amongst the Poor; the Bath Eye Infirmary began in 1811 and was in operation for over 160 years. These four however were not by any means the first institutions in the world to advertise care for the eyes. That distinction goes to The St. John's Hospital for Diseases of the Eyes, Legs and Breasts, created in Holborn by William Rowley in 1773. One can only speculate as to his specific interests in these apparently disparate parts of the anatomy, but the hospital was to last only for a few years before disappearing. All other predecessors were also metropolitan: The Royal Infirmary for Diseases of the Eye had more hopeful beginnings, being given Royal patronage at its outset by George III in 1804. Clearly a small affair (address Cork Mews) it nevertheless persisted until 1872. There were others: The Ophthalmic Institution for the Cure of Cataract; The Western Ophthalmic Institution; The North London Ophthalmic Institution; The Metropolitan Institution for Diseases of the Eye and Ear; and so on with at least 6 others, all evanescent, existing for a few years and then disappearing to be replaced by others. For those in the provinces looking to the capital for their lead, a clear message had been sent: there was a market for specialist eye care.

In 1804 the Manchester Infirmary (founded 1752) appointed a new Honorary Surgeon, Benjamin Gibson MRCS. He was born in 1774, the son of a prosperous Newcastle linen draper. He was educated in Richmond, Yorkshire and then began an apprenticeship to William Ingham, a Newcastle surgeon. After several years with him, he went to London to study anatomy under the great Matthew Baillie FRS, at which time Gibson's high skills as

A blind and destitute soldier begs by the roadside, his army uniform in rags; a victim of the Egyptian Ophthalmia. A watercolour drawing by James Gillray

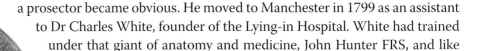

Benjamin Gibson MRCS,
Honorary Surgeon to the
Manchester Infirmary

a prosector became obvious. He moved to Manchester in 1799 as an assistant to Dr Charles White, founder of the Lying-in Hospital. White had trained under that giant of anatomy and medicine, John Hunter FRS, and like him had set up his own anatomy school at his house on Red Cross Street. He needed an assistant both in the school and in his practice, and he wrote to his colleagues in London and Edinburgh to ask for recommendations for an assistant. The name of Gibson came independently from both. He spent a time with White and then began in independent surgical practice at No.4 Portland Place, having undergone perhaps the most comprehensive surgical training possible at that time. He was then appointed to the Infirmary at the age of 30.

To a man of Gibson's outstanding manual skills, the appeal of eye surgery must have been evident. Although practising generally in surgery and midwifery, his interest in ophthalmology burgeoned and he became very well-known in Manchester as an oculist, the first resident surgeon genuinely to specialise in this area. He published specifically on the treatment of congenital cataract at an early age. Previously any attempt to operate upon this blinding disease in children was deferred until later childhood, at which time vision had been irreparably lost due to amblyopia. The condition was generally therefore, considered incurable. Gibson was courageous enough to attempt earlier intervention and was the first ophthalmologist in the world to publish on the subject. The circumstances of this surgery hardly bear thinking about today. Still considered amongst the most difficult forms of anterior segment eye surgery, and performed without any anaesthesia on infants, his efforts were almost certainly doomed to failure. His unrelated namesake Professor William Gibson of Philadelphia remarked in 1832:

> "I am inclined to recommend from experience the plan of Mr Gibson of Manchester, which is simply to enclose the body, arms and legs of the patient in a bag open at each end, and furnished with tapes or strings to secure the limbs. Thus situated, the child may be laid on a large pillow placed on a table, and firmly held by one or two assistants."

Notwithstanding the probable poor outcomes of Gibson's efforts, it is fitting that Manchester generated the world's first oculist to publish on paediatric cataract surgery; over two centuries later the Manchester Royal Eye Hospital has an international reputation for its results for this very type of surgery. Gibson also was the first to make clear the connection between inflamed eyes in babies (ophthalmia neonatorum) and vaginal discharge from the mother, a link much later found to be caused by gonorrhoea.

Gibson was described as being of "delicate constitution... with an agreeable and distinct, though somewhat weak voice"; to add to this asthenic appearance, in about 1810 he caught tuberculosis, which led to a prolonged deterioration in his health. He was

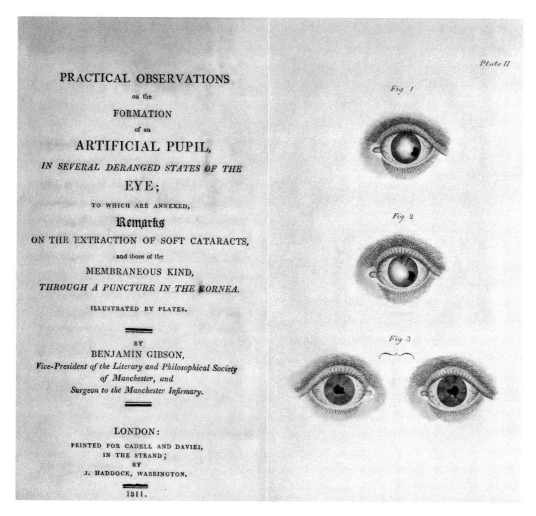

PRACTICAL OBSERVATIONS

on the

FORMATION

of an

ARTIFICIAL PUPIL,

IN SEVERAL DERANGED STATES OF THE

EYE;

TO WHICH ARE ANNEXED,

Remarks

ON THE EXTRACTION OF SOFT CATARACTS,

and those of the

MEMBRANEOUS KIND,

THROUGH A PUNCTURE IN THE CORNEA.

ILLUSTRATED BY PLATES.

BY

BENJAMIN GIBSON,

Vice-President of the Literary and Philosophical Society
of Manchester, and
Surgeon to the Manchester Infirmary.

LONDON:

PRINTED FOR CADELL AND DAVIES,
IN THE STRAND;
BY
J. HADDOCK, WARRINGTON.

1811.

Plate II

Fig 1

Fig 2

Fig 3

under the care of his colleague at the Infirmary, Dr John Ferriar. Despite his declining health he was able to write a detailed treatise on "Practical observations on the formation of an artificial pupil", advertised thus in the Manchester Mercury in February 2011:

Just Published, price 5s in Boards

PRACTICAL observations upon the formation of the *Artificial Pupil*. To which are annexed remarks upon the Extraction of soft and membraneous Cataracts, through a puncture in the CORNEA. Illustrated by plates, by BENJAMIN GIBSON, Vice President of the Literary and Philosophical Society of Manchester, and Surgeon to the Manchester Infirmary.

The pamphlet was dedicated emotionally to Ferriar, and proved to be his last work. He died in 1812, barely 37 years old. Following his death an unseemly argument developed between those who knew of his work in Manchester, and the publishers of Saunders' posthumous volume on ophthalmology, from London, the latter asserting that Gibson was merely practising the earlier "discovery" by Saunders of the technique of infantile cataract surgery. A vitriolic exchange was published in the *Lancet* in 1825, terminating with the comment of Robert Lyall, surgeon and oculist at Paisley, lately house surgeon at the Manchester Infirmary:

> "That there are living witnesses of Mr Gibson's operations… and myself besides… for congenital cataract in infants, which were performed *long before* the Mountain brought forth the Mouse, or rather before the FALSE CONCEPTION of the London Ophthalmic Institution. I rejoice to have this opportunity of rendering homage to the memory of so gifted and so distinguished a friend and patron as the late Benjamin Gibson."

Manchester was therefore, in 1812, in somewhat of an ophthalmological vacuum. An oculist of genuine talent had for the first time been serving the town for some years, before being prematurely taken. The remaining surgeons at the Infirmary, while couching the cataract occasionally, had not expressed any particular interest in diseases of the eye, and this included the replacement surgeon appointed after Gibson's death. The loss of his expertise was keenly felt. Ophthalmic institutions had begun to spring up in other parts of the country, and from these circumstances arose a clear opportunity for a medical entrepreneur.

CHAPTER ONE

Enter William Wilson: Oculist and Entrepreneur

İT WAS THE AUTUMN of 1814. Napoleon was (briefly) ensconced on Elba; the White House had recently been razed by the British in Washington; Beethoven had written eight of his nine symphonies; George III was in the final stages of his illness and the Regency had six years to run; Lord Liverpool was Prime Minister and was about to introduce the first of the hated Corn Laws; the Luddites had recently wreaked their revenge on the hated cotton machines. The scene was set: Manchester had exhibited the beginnings of an expert provision for ocular problems, but that expertise had recently been tragically lost; the pretext of the specialist eye hospital had already been set elsewhere; and Manchester was the epicentre of world industry, a burgeoning town with a wealth of opportunity.

William James Wilson was born in Leeds in 1792, the son of a prosperous solicitor. He was orphaned early in life, and brought up by his elder sister. There was clearly enough income for him to consider a career in medicine, and he gained experience in several towns. He was firstly apprenticed to Mr John Airey Braithwaite, a Quaker surgeon of Lancaster whose success emanated not so much from his medical career, as from the sale of his family's celebrated recipe for "The Black Drop". The Lancaster Gazette announced in 1802:

TO THE FACULTY

And those who take OPIUM, or its Preparations, is recommended *THE GENUINE* LANCASTER BLACK DROP Which many of the most eminent Physicians and Surgeons, in the United Kingdom of Great Britain and Ireland, employ and prescribe, in preference to any other preparation of Opium.

This medicine has long been known and esteemed in the North of England, by the name of THE QUAKERS GENUINE BLACK DROP, where it was first discovered by J.A. Braithwaite, in consequence of a laborious and attentive experimental investigation of the nature and properties of that invaluable drug.

It is well known, that in many constitutions the effects of common Opium or Laudanum, are extremely distressing, and that in all habits it produces one inconvenience; often creating restlessness and delirium, instead of producing sleep; and its use being generals succeeded by Head-achs, sickness and debility:- of these deleterious effects, the BLACK DROP is, by a chemical process, wholly deprived, whilst it retains, in the fullest degree, all the desirable powers of Opium, in relieving Pain, soothing Irritation, and procuring Repose.

William James Wilson Esq MRCS. A mezzotint from 1852 after a portrait by Willam Bonnar

MARKET STREET, FROM PICCADILLY, MANCHESTER.

The Black Drop was in fact a mixture of opium extract, vinegar, nutmeg and sugar, with effects no less potent than laudanum. It was manufactured by the Braithwaites in Kendal, hence its first sale as Kendal Black Drop. It claimed many victims; Samuel Taylor Coleridge, already using laudanum, moved to Keswick in 1800, where the Black Drop exacerbated his addiction and ensured his long decline.

In due course Wilson obtained further tuition from John Rowland, honorary surgeon at the Chester Infirmary. From there he moved to the capital, where he gained experience in surgery and midwifery, securing a post with Mr Spencer, a surgeon in Islington. With him he attended the Clerkenwell Workhouse, he gained experience at St. Bartholomew's Hospital, was a dresser at the London Hospital, and he had clearly begun to develop an interest in ophthalmology because he also secured tuition from Mr John Cunningham Saunders, founder surgeon of the London Infirmary for Curing Diseases of the Eye, at No. 40 Charterhouse Square (later to become Moorfields Eye Hospital). He became a Member of the (recently formed) Royal College of Surgeons in 1813.

The reasons for Wilson's decision to set up independent practice in Manchester are unknown, and unlike many others setting up in a new town, no newspaper advertisements emanated from him. He did not apply for the post of surgeon at the Manchester Infirmary following Benjamin Gibson's death in 1812. One interpretation is that Wilson was genuinely attempting (in contrast to many doctors of the time) to obtain a wealth of experience in order to secure his reputation and practice. It is clear that his professionalism and demeanour were very conducive to persuasion. Brockbank says that he was described thus: "In stature he was of middle size – well-formed, easy and graceful in all his movements. The countenance which was not particularly striking in repose, his features being rather small, was whenever he conversed, lighted up with intelligence and the most agreeable courtesy of expression, occasionally blended with rich humour, to which he had a natural propensity. This lent charm to his anecdotes, of which he had a large and original store". Wilson himself acknowledged his short stature, saying later in life "If the patient is tall I raise myself by standing on a book or two. I find old medical files serve the purpose very well."

It is clear from subsequent events that Wilson had spent time making known to some of Manchester society his wish to provide an ophthalmic service in Manchester. The preliminary discussions are only partly documented, but tacit approval of his scheme had already been obtained, to the extent that a local peer had already agreed to patronise the forthcoming institution, and a meeting on 12th October had already addressed the function and governance of the proposed institution. To achieve this at the age of 22 is not only a testament to his ambition and sociability, but also reminds us that maturity then was a somewhat earlier life event than now, and many doctors qualified in their teens in this era. The culmination of his efforts was a public meeting held on October 21st 1814, at the Bridgewater Arms in the centre of Manchester. This was one of three large and thriving Coaching Inns which provided services to all corners of the kingdom, and was situated at the corner of Market Street and Piccadilly. There were over 50 mail coach services from Manchester to London each week, the proprietor of the Bridgewater Arms, Alan Paterson, boasting the fastest London transport, the Royal Mail which, leaving the Inn at 1am, would reach London at 8pm the following day, a mere 43 hours. The Bridgewater Arms was a busy hub and a natural meeting

The first entry in the Minute Book of the Manchester Institution for Curing Diseases of the Eye, October 21st (Trafalgar Day) 1814

ENTER WILLIAM WILSON: OCULIST AND ENTREPRENEUR

place, and provided rooms for hire for that very purpose. It was auspicious that the venue should be chosen; it was in the same place in 1790 that a similar meeting had inaugurated the Manchester Lying-in Charity, now St. Mary's Hospital.

The date of the meeting is also worthy of comment. October 21st was Trafalgar Day, an anniversary even now officially celebrated in the Navy, but then, nine years after the famous victory, a public holiday, thus facilitating such gatherings. This author cannot fail to notice three other coincidences: firstly the hero himself had as one of his distinguishing features a rather obvious eye problem; secondly that for over 120 years of its existence, the future Royal Eye Hospital would have a busy entrance in Nelson Street; and thirdly that a significant part of its twentieth century work would be performed in a building originally named Nelson House.

The meeting, attended by prominent businessmen, clergy, lawyers and dignitaries, was not the first to be held; it is stated that "resolutions of a former meeting were read" but these have been lost. This meeting was chaired by William Fox, banker and Boroughreeve of Manchester (the Boroughreeve was the senior municipal post of the town, later to be designated Lord Mayor following the Municipal Corporations Act of 1835). William Wilson presented to the meeting his proposal for the creation of a new Institution. The communica-

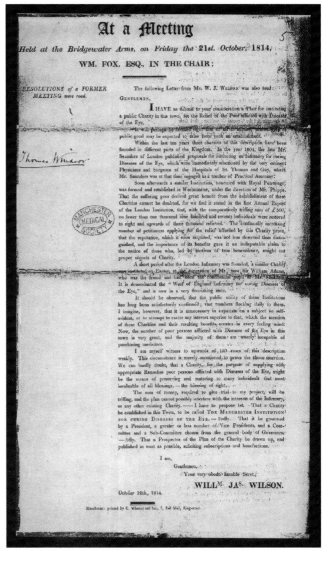

The Announcement of William James Wilson of the formation of the Manchester Institution for Curing Diseases of the Eye, published for the meeting of Trafalgar day, October 21st 1814. Reproduced with permission of John Rylands Library, University of Manchester

tion is recorded verbatim in the first minute book of the hospital, and was published for circulation by Wheelers of King Street. A copy is in the archives of the Manchester Medical Society, donated by Thomas Windsor, one of Wilson's successors as surgeon and an inveterate archivist. It reads:

Gentlemen

I have to submit to your consideration a plan for instituting a public Charity in this town for the Relief of the Poor afflicted, with Diseases of the Eyes. It will perhaps be deemed right first of all to inquire what degree of public good may be expected to arise from such an establishment. Within the last ten years three charities of this description have been founded in different parts of the Kingdom. In the year 1804 the late Mr Saunders of London published proposals for instituting an Infirmary for curing Diseases of the Eye, which were immediately sanctioned by the eminent Physicians and Surgeons of the Hospitals of St. Thomas and Guy where Mr Saunders was at that time engaged as a teacher of Practical Anatomy. Soon afterwards a similar institution honoured with Royal Patronage, was formed and established in Westminster under the direction of Mr Phipps. That the suffering poor derived great benefit from the establishment of these charities cannot be doubted, for we find it stated in the first Annual Report of the London Institution that with the comparatively trifling sum of £500 no fewer than one thousand nine hundred and seventy individuals were restored to sight and upwards of three thousand relieved. The continually increasing number of petitioners applying for the relief afforded by this Charity prove that the reputation which it soon acquired was not less deserved than distinguished and the importance of its benefits gave it an indisputable claim to the notice of those who led by motive of true benevolence, sought out proper objects of Charity.

A short period after the London Infirmary was founded, a similar Charity was instituted at Exeter at the suggestion of Mr William Adams who was the friend and had been the confidential pupil of Mr Saunders. It is denominated the "West of England Infirmary for Curing Diseases of the Eye" and is now in a flourishing state. It should be observed that the public utility of these institutions has long been satisfactorily confirmed: vast numbers flocking daily to them. I imagine however that it is unnecessary to expatiate on a subject so self evident or to attempt to excite any interest superior to that which the mention of these Charities and their resulting benefits creates in every feeling mind. Now the number of poor persons afflicted with Diseases of the Eye in this town is very great and the majority of them are utterly incapable of purchasing medicines. I am myself witness to upwards of 150 cases of this description and this circumstance is merely mentioned to prove the above aspects. We can hardly doubt that a charity for the purposes of supplying with appropriate remedies poor persons afflicted with Diseases of the Eye, might be the means of preserving and restoring to many individuals that most invaluable of all blessings, the blessing of sight. The sum of money required to give trial to my project will be trifling and the plan cannot possibly interfere with the interests of the Infirmary or any other existing Charity – I have to propose 1st that a Charity be established in this Town, to be called The Manchester Institution For Curing Diseases of the Eye. 2ndly – that it be governed by a President, a greater or lesser number of Vice Presidents and a Committee and a Sub-Committee chosen from the general body of Governors 3dly that a prospectus of the Plan of the Charity be drawn up and published as soon as possible soliciting Subscriptions and Benefactions

I am, Gentlemen, Your very Obed.t Humble Serv.t

WILL.M JA.S   WILSON

It was unanimously resolved that such an institution should be created and funded by subscription to governorships, and by donation. The Manchester Institution for Curing Diseases of the Eye was inaugurated. It was England and the world's fourth specialist eye hospital, of those which remain in existence today, and its first years are described in the next chapter.

Wilson remained a stalwart of the Eye Institution for 13 years, during which time it developed significantly. Nevertheless, to a surgeon aspiring to fame and fortune rather than mere social acceptability, an honorary post at the most prestigious charity in the Northwest of England, the Manchester Infirmary, was essential. That opportunity, the first in 15 years, arose in 1827 because the surgeon Mr Hamilton had resigned. It was clear that by this time Wilson's local reputation was high. Not only was he single-handedly responsible for the formation of the Eye Institution which was now embedded into the fabric of Manchester life, but he had been a leading light in medical education, as the Lecturer in Surgery at the newly formed School of Anatomy of Joseph Jordan. One of the joys of nineteenth century society was the immense public interest shown in such appointments; applications for posts were copied into the local press; much canvassing undoubtedly took place by the applicant and his seconds; and crucially, appointment was made not by the hospital boards of management or medicine, nor by committees set up specifically for the purpose (as today) but by election, the constituency being the trustees, or subscribers to the institution. In short, this was a popularity contest rather than a strict comparison of merits. The imperative for applicants to have achieved a place in local society was clear. Wilson had done so firstly by his well-known and respected association with the Manchester Eye Institution, secondly by his undoubtedly widening reputation as a surgeon amongst the stratum of society who paid for his services, and thirdly by himself being a subscriber and post-holder at charitable societies himself, thus demonstrating his probity, his high moral standing and his Christian values. The need for this combination of qualifications was to reach its zenith later, in the Victorian era.

The opening skirmishes preceding the election took place in the *Manchester Courier* and *Manchester Mercury* during March and April 1827. Preceding and during these official stages, doubtless a flurry of informal discussions over dinner, the exchange of sundry unprovenanced opinion, the calling-in of favours, insinuations against some applicants, and recommendations of ones own protégé, were exchanged with enthusiasm by the Trustees of the Infirmary, and doubtless gradual preparations for just such conversations had been made by prospective candidates over a number of years. Wilson made his application for the post (as did the other two Eye Institution Surgeons, John Windsor and Samuel Barton, the latter, rapidly perceiving a lack of support, withdrawing his application "in the hope of being more successful on a future vacancy"). Wilson had clearly been appraised of a move to prevent his appointment, and thus made a pre-emptive strike in the newspapers on April 7th:

> In the course of my canvass for the situation of Surgeon to your excellent establishment, it has been mentioned to me by several of the Trustees, that they consider the circumstance of my being at present one of the Surgeons of the Eye Institution is an objection to my appointment, as it would not be in my power to discharge the duties of both situations. I think it necessary therefore, to state most distinctly, that in the event of my election to the Infirmary, it is my intention immediately to resign the situation I hold in the Eye Institution.

During the thirteen years that I have discharged its duties, I have not held any situation in the Infirmary, no vacancy for the office of Surgeon having occurred since the year 1812, and I was anxious, in the meantime, to have an opportunity of obtaining further experience in one branch of my profession, and at the same time of rendering such service as it would be in my power to afford to this town and neighbourhood, as one of the Surgeons to the Eye Institution. I trust therefore, that the circumstance of my having for several years discharged the duties which that appointment called upon me to perform, will not operate to my disadvantage, now that I am seeking for the means of devoting my attention to a station of more extended usefulness.

I have the honour to be, with the greatest respect,

My Lords, Ladies and Gentlemen,

Your obliged, humble servant

WM. JAS. WILSON

In the meantime, an applicant who clearly perceived himself to be the Trustees' favourite also placed his application, in somewhat presumptive vein:

LADIES AND GENTLEMEN

The result of my Canvass, I am happy to say, has far exceeded my most sanguine expectations – and I feel very grateful for the kind consideration my humble claims have received from a large majority of the Trustees. I have yet to trespass further on your goodness by requesting your attendance on the day of Election, which is fixed for THURSDAY the 19th instant (at eleven o'clock in the forenoon) at the Large Room of the Exchange, when I trust my hopes will be realised, and I shall obtain the highest honour your munificent Institution can confer on its professional servant, by receiving at your hands the appointment I have so long and so ardently desired.

I have the honour to be, Ladies and Gentlemen,

Your most obedient humble servant

W.R.WHATTON F.A.S.

Member of the Royal College of Surgeons &c. &c.

In the *Manchester Mercury* an anonymous letter, from an "Old Trustee" of the Infirmary, accused Wilson of ingratitude towards the Eye Institution, declaring that he should in essence be tied to that institution for his whole professional life. In short order an anonymous rebuttal of these accusations appeared in the next *Courier*, penned by the anonymous, but clearly outraged "HUMANITAS", who declared the comments "a specious... unreasonable attack" and laid out his justification in a prolix letter ending "I should feel glad... to see him (Wilson) in a more exalted public station, for which I

deem him to be eminently suited". The verbal sparring undoubtedly continued outside the press, until the day of election arrived.

The blow-by-blow account of the subsequent election at the Cotton Exchange also occupies considerable space in the *Manchester Courier* of April 21st 1827, showing by the sheer numbers of Trustees voting in person, and the hours that they were prepared to devote to the process, the importance of such an event. Only part of this newspaper report is distilled below:

ELECTION OF A SURGEON TO THE INFIRMARY

On Thursday last, a meeting of the Trustees of the Infirmary took place in the Exchange dining-room, for the purpose of electing a Surgeon, in the Room of Mr Hamilton, who has resigned. The room was filled by a very numerous and highly respectable assemblage in gentlemen soon after eleven o'clock; but a delay of nearly half an hour took place, before the arrival of Mr Hibbert, the treasurer, for whom the meeting, in courtesy, reserved the Chair.

Considerable animated discussion followed about how best to vote; clearly the process was somewhat haphazard, and a few catcalls (including some requesting abandonment of the speeches, as everybody knew already for whom they intended to vote) were subdued by the chairman. The matter was descending into near-farce; a vote having already been informally commenced by sundry persons in the lobby, the gentlemen involved were politely but firmly recalled to the dining-room for further speeches:

After a great deal of confusion, it was finally arranged, on the motion of Mr CRIRIE, seconded by Mr HH BIRLEY, that the poll should be kept open until 4 o'clock, so that the trustees might have ample time to vote, *after* having heard the statements which might be urged in behalf of the different candidates.

A series of extraordinarily flowery speeches followed, nominating each candidate. It was a pretty strong field: they included Joseph Jordan, creator of the town's first anatomy school, and Thomas Turner who had similarly initiated a series of lectures on anatomy and pathology at the Manchester Literary & Philosophical Society. All had their proposers, but the two main protagonists were clear…

> Mr WILLIAM GARNET proposed MR WHATTON… In the course of his observations he would carefully abstain from disparaging any of the other candidates. No man entertained a greater respect for MR WILSON than he, but he spoke upon the authority of a high professional man, when he stated that the establishment of dispensaries, similar to that with which Mr WILSON was now connected, would afford a great relief to the Infirmary, and prove of infinite advantage to the public. It appeared, that during the 13 years the Eye Institution had been in existence, 16,000 patients had passed through the books of that institution, and it was highly desirable that no part of these patients should be removed to the Infirmary…

> Mr SAMUEL FLETCHER here called Mr GARNET to order – every mover and seconder had a right to state the merits of their own candidates, but not to disparage any of the others, in any manner whatever (*Hear Hear!*).

> Mr GARNET explained, that he did not intend to reflect, in the slightest degree, upon the character of Mr WILSON, than whom no man could do more for the benefit of the institution to which he belonged (*Hear!*).

In other words, Garnet and his cronies (of whom one no doubt was an "Old Trustee") wanted Wilson kept precisely where he was, at the Manchester Eye Institution. He was attempting to heighten the chances of his protégé, Whatton, by insinuating that Wilson might, if appointed to the Manchester Infirmary, simply bring his work with him, heightening their load). However, Wilson's main sponsor (possibly HUMANITAS?) also had his turn. The speaker had achieved some notoriety as the defender of the Peterloo magistrates in 1819, but Wilson was obviously happy for him to orate on his behalf:

> Mr FRANCIS PHILIPS proposed Mr WILSON. His services, in behalf of the Eye Institution, were so well known, that he would not dwell upon them. There was no mode of education so excellent, as that which was perfected by gradation. It was his decided opinion, and he knew it to be the opinion of several eminent professional men, that auxiliary institutions and dispensaries were the best nurseries for medical officers. Mr THOMAS MARKLAND briefly seconded the nomination.

> There being no other candidates, the CHAIRMAN stated, that the Trustees would now proceed to give their votes. After some little conversation, as to the right of voting, the polling commenced, and continued until 4 o'clock, when the numbers stood as follows:

Mr Wilson 321

Mr Turner............................ 222

Mr Whatton 100

Mr Boutflower........................ 23

Mr Brigham 18

Mr Jordan 13

Total number polled 697

The poll being closed, Mr Hibbert declared Mr Wilson to be duly elected. The announcement was received with a considerable degree of applause.

Wilson had achieved his ambition, but continued to grow in stature professionally. He was well-known for his long hours of work. Despite his continued interest in eye cases, he remained a general surgeon, and he was particularly highly regarded as a performer of surgery for bladder stones. He was considered generous to his apprentices and peers, lending surgical instruments willingly, from his extensive collection. His opinion was regularly sought in writing by those unable to attend Manchester, and "his opinions, written in a beautiful hand, were remarkable for fullness and perspicuity". In 1834 Wilson joined with a group of 76 Manchester doctors at the York Hotel, in King Street, to discuss the formation of "an association of members of the profession residing in the North of England" and under the chairmanship of Mr William Whatton (the very same) the Manchester Medical Society was inaugurated. The Council included Wilson and also John Windsor of the Manchester Eye Institution, and the first President was Dr John Hull, Honorary Physician to the Eye Institution. Wilson would go on to become President of the Manchester Medical Society from 1843–45, and the post would later be occupied by eight doctors who had served at the Eye Hospital. He was elected Honorary FRCS in 1843 and became President of the Provincial Medical Surgical Association in 1854. He published several papers, a notable early one being in the *London Medical Repository* in 1808 entitled "On certain morbid changes which take place in the eye-ball and on tumours situated in the orbit, with remarks", and in the *Edinburgh Medical and Surgical Journal* of 1814 "On purulent ophthalmia".

His widespread reputation as a cataract surgeon led to some patients making considerable journeys to Manchester. In 1846 he was consulted by one Rev. Patrick Brontë, curate of St. Michael & All Angels church in Haworth, a village near Bradford, who had been virtually blinded by cataract. He was accompanied to Manchester in August by his daughter Charlotte, after recommendation by Dr John Outhwaite, who had been trained in part by Wilson, and whose sister was godmother to Charlotte's sister Anne. Mr Wilson had arranged Manchester lodgings for them in the house of a former servant in Mount Pleasant, now near the Manchester Metropolitan University campus. On meeting him the Reverend noted that "Mr Wilson had the most agreeable courtesy of expression in conversation". His daughter wrote to a friend:

> *"Papa and I came here on Wednesday, we saw Mr Wilson the oculist the same day; he pronounces Papa's eyes quite ready for an operation and has fixed next Monday for the performance of it... we shall have to stay here for a month at least. One cheerful feature in the business is that Mr Wilson thinks most favourably of the case"*

The left cataract was removed, and he was assisted at this by Mr Charles Redfern, assistant surgeon to the Manchester Eye Hospital. No anaesthetic was used; cocaine anaesthesia would not appear for a further 40 years, and the recently discovered general anaesthetic agents would not be used for cataract surgery because of the danger of post-operative vomiting. The patient recorded his experience in the margins of a medical book that he carried with him:

> *"Belladonna – a virulent poison – was first applied, twice, in order to expand the pupil – this occasioned very acute pain for only about five seconds – The feeling, under the operation – which lasted fifteen minutes, was of a burning nature – but not intolerable – as I have read is generally the case, in surgical operation. My lens was extracted so that cataract can never return in that eye".*

Atropa belladonna, or Deadly nightshade. Extract of belladonna was used to dilate the pupil of the eye before cataract surgery on Patrick Brontë

The ability of extract of Belladonna (*Atropa belladonna*; deadly nightshade) to dilate the pupil had been known for millennia, and the resultant beautiful ladies gave it its common name (although they could no longer read the love letters their appearance may have generated). Used variously as poison (Livia probably killed Augustus with it in 14AD), cosmetic and then medicine in various forms, the ability to enlarge the pupil prior to cataract surgery improved the technique first introduced by Daviel in 1748, and this usage had begun about 50 years prior to Brontë's surgery. The more refined alkaloid, atropine, is still used today, though not for this purpose. Wilson charged him £10 for cataract surgery (about £1,000 today), even though Brontë noted approvingly: *"I believe he often charges £20 or £30".* Shortly afterwards Charlotte wrote again to the same friend:

> *"Papa is still lying in bed in a dark room with his eyes bandaged – No inflammation ensued but still it appears that the greatest care – perfect quiet and utter privation of light are necessary to ensure a good result from the operation – He was allowed to try his sight for the first time yesterday – he could see dimly – Mr Wilson seemed perfectly satisfied*

Brontë noted that he was bled with leeches on the temple twice, first with eight, and then six. He was attended night and day by a nurse; clearly she did not meet with the entire approval of his rather bored daughter. About one month after the operation:

> *"The nurse goes today – her departure will certainly be a relief though she is I daresay not the worst of her class"*

They escaped from Manchester, perhaps not entirely as intended by the surgeon. On 29th September Charlotte wrote:

> *"When I wrote to you last our return to Haworth was uncertain indeed – but Mr Wilson was called away to Scotland – his absence set us at liberty – I hastened our departure, and now we are at home"*

However, by December the results of the surgery were literally, clear:

> *"those were indeed mournful days, when Papa's vision was wholly obscured – when he could do nothing for himself and sat all day long in darkness and inertion – Now to see him walk about independently, read, write… is indeed a joyful change. He continues to see spots before the very eye which has been operated on… Mr Wilson… put it off as a matter of no consequence"*

Rev. Patrick Brontë following his cataract surgery, wearing his aphakic "pebble" glasses

Charlotte and her father spent just over one month in Manchester for her father to recuperate before he was allowed to travel. The stay, in unsalubrious lodgings, may have been tedious, but she did not entirely waste her time; she sat down to write a new book, and by the time they were ready to return to Haworth she had completed much of the manuscript of *Jane Eyre*.

Wilson remained on the honorary staff of the Manchester Royal Infirmary until April 1855, when he was forced to retire owing to declining health. He retired to Tickwood in Shropshire, but died in July of the same year. His obituary in the *Manchester Times* declared:

> His fame as an operative and a consulting surgeon knew no eclipse; above all his provincial brethren he stood eminent for the successful practice of the operation of lithotrity… There was one distinguishing feature of his attainments, and that was *breadth*. Let him be consulted in any case – ophthalmic, obstetric, surgical or medical – he was sure to be found equal to the emergency; self-possessed, cautious yet fertile in expedients… We will conclude by referring to the feeling excited amongst his medical brethren in Manchester by the announcement of his death. The remark elicited was generally in these or similar words: "Wilson is gone! We shall never have his equal amongst us again".

Perhaps William James Wilson, ironically for a doctor at the forefront of surgical specialisation, and chiefly remembered now as the creator of that venerable institution, the Manchester Royal Eye Hospital, would prefer to be remembered as stated in his epitaph, as a doctor of wide skills, known and respected in all branches of his profession. In short, not a specialist at all.

CHAPTER TWO

The Manchester Institution for Curing Diseases of the Eye

T HE MEN AT THE Bridgewater Arms meeting of October 21ˢᵗ 1814 were good to their word. There immediately followed discussion of a prospectus already prepared by William Wilson, in anticipation of a favourable response, setting out in detail the proposed governance structure and staffing of the new institution. It required a President, eight Vice-Presidents, and a Board of twelve Governors. It had already been decreed that a benefaction of five guineas would secure a governorship for life, and an annual subscription of 10s 6d (half a guinea) a governorship for one year.

It was necessary for the good standing of any charity that a patron of acceptable rank be found. It was understood on both sides that such a position was entirely inactive; the dignitary or member of the aristocracy was pleased to give his name to a charity he considered worthy, and undoubtedly many patrons collected a portfolio, which may have reflected their particular interests or concerns; but in practical terms their name may head the reports of the institution, but they would rarely take an active part, and often little interest, in its activities. Indeed, a future President, on being invited to the opening of a magnificent new building for the then Manchester Royal Eye Hospital in 1885, its most important day since its inception, could only plead a prior engagement. At the beginning however, a local dignitary was gracious enough to support this new charity, and he was Sir John Stanley Bt, later Lord Stanley of Alderley. His name as President headed the reports of the Manchester Eye Institution for its first 28 years.

The vice-presidents and committee were largely composed of the men who had shared the enthusiasm for the inaugural meeting. Among them were Robert Peel (a prominent Manchester businessman, and cousin of Sir Robert Peel, cotton magnate of Bury and father of the future Prime Minister; George Ramsden, a successful Manchester merchant, and Constable of Manchester (later one of the leading proponents of the creation of the Manchester & Salford Yeomanry, whose actions in 1819 at Peterloo were later vilified); John Taylor, of Robert Taylor & Son, Tailors & Drapers; Daniel Lynch, a highly successful purveyor of medicines, with his store on Market-Street Lane, and a prominent freemason; Rev. Moses Randall, a Chaplain of the Collegiate Church (later to become Manchester Cathedral); Rev. CW Ethelston, a Fellow of the Collegiate Church; the lawyers William Cririe, George Duckworth and Thomas

Hewitt; and of course the founder surgeon William Wilson. He had been fortunate also to persuade Dr John Hull, already one of Manchester's most prominent doctors, to become Honorary Physician, and he also served on the committee. William Fox, banker and one-time Boroughreeve of Manchester, was to remain Chairman for 34 years. In order to add medical kudos, Benjamin Travers, Honorary Surgeon to the London Eye Infirmary, was prevailed upon to be named as a member of the Board. Presumably he knew Wilson from the latter's time in London. His support was merely nominal and he was not known to have visited Manchester.

Daniel Lynch was clearly an astute businessman. He had been in business as a druggist since 1790, the oldest such firm in existence. In the transcript of the meeting of October 12th, he had generously offered to provide drugs free of charge to the new charity, for one year. For this he had been elected a Governor for life. However, most businessmen would write down the expense as a "loss-leader"; who else could now possibly be selected to provide drugs for the Manchester Eye Institution after its first year, than himself. While remaining an active member of the Board, the future quarterly bills for medicines payable to Lynch would often constitute the greatest sum owing, and would usually exceed £200 per annum.

The new charity was now created, overseen and medically staffed. A "Collector" was now appointed in the shape of Robert Smith, his function being to ensure the continuing receipt of the promised subscriptions, often doubtless requiring laborious travel around the region on horseback. It only remained to locate suitable premises for its first foray into healthcare, and a sub-committee was immediately appointed to find one. In fact that search was not difficult; one of the initial Governors, John Taylor, owned No. 60 King Street, and offered to lease part of it. On November 21st, exactly one month after the inaugural meeting, the minute book records:

> *Resolved, that the offer of the House near the top of King Street late in the possession of Mr Taylor is a proper situation to be rented for this Institution and that Mr B Wilson, Mr G Ramsden & Mr W J Wilson be authorised to treat for the same with Mr Booth the agent provided the rent does not exceed £50 per annum*

The exact address of this, the first house occupied by the Eye Institution, was never recorded in the minutes. However, the address is now clear following some investigation; John Taylor inherited No 60 King Street from his father, who had died in 1813, and he had taken over their tailors & drapers business. In fact it was decided that only a part of the house was required for the purpose, and a rent of £25 per annum was agreed. No. 60 was high on the East side of King Street; none of the houses of upper King Street still exist, but this one was sited just above the junction with Pall Mall. The higher part of the street (above its crossing with Red Cross Street [now Cross Street]) was at the turn of the century a prime residential street, incorporating the houses of several doctors. The most prominent of these was Charles White, founder of the Lying-in Hospital. However, during the first quarter of the nineteenth century

the area was to evolve into a financial and legal district. Not long after the opening of the Eye Institution Charles White's house would be demolished for the building of the Manchester Town Hall, which was opened in 1825 and occupied that site until 1919.

Those involved in creating the Eye Institution were undoubtedly delighted with progress. However, the Governors of the Manchester Infirmary were not amused. A newcomer to Manchester had had the temerity to canvass successfully in order to create a potential competitor to their dominance, albeit in one narrow field. There was of course a little "previous" here; Charles White himself, and a group of like-minded reactionary colleagues, had resigned *en bloc* from their honorary posts at the Infirmary 24 years previously in considerable bad blood, following a dispute over the number of honorary surgeons permitted (they had resisted an increase in number). He had created the Lying-in Hospital which had been successfully changing Manchester midwifery with a vigorous domiciliary service. Feelings still rankled, and the gentlemen of the Infirmary, having not appointed a surgeon oculist to replace Benjamin Gibson, were clearly feeling their charitable dominance to be somewhat pressurised. They were determined to maintain the pre-eminence of the Infirmary, and in particular to vilify the developing concept of specialism in surgery; its own surgeons were *proper* Surgeons – they amputated limbs, cut for the stone, prescribed blood-letting, and couched cataract, and would continue to do so. To have a new charity diverting donations away from them was intolerable. The minute from their meeting in November 1814 was published in the Manchester Mercury:

> The Weekly Board of the Manchester Infirmary and Dispensary feel it to be their duty to state for the information of the Trustees and public at large and in justice to the Surgeons of the Institution that 741 eye cases have been admitted from the 24th June 1813 to the present time and that the treatment of them has been attended with the greatest success. The Trustees may rest assured that the same attention and skill will continue to be devoted to diseases of the eye with advantage to the patients.

This response to the inauguration of the Eye Institution would typify relations between it and the Infirmary during succeeding decades; indeed it would take a century for the Infirmary finally to relinquish a claim on the management of ophthalmic problems, when it bartered land badly needed for an Eye Hospital extension, for the handing over of responsibility for the teaching of ophthalmology to undergraduates of the medical school.

Despite the Infirmary's appeal to the public, they began to vote with their feet; within six months of its creation, William Wilson was finding it too much work for one man, and in June 1815 three resolutions were passed:

> *Resolved 1st that from the representation of Mr Wilson, Surgeon to this institution made to the Committee this day it appears that the business of this Charity is too considerable to be transacted by one Surgeon*

> *Resolved 2ndly that an additional Surgeon be appointed and that the day of election be fixed for Thursday the 29th Inst at Eleven oClock in the forenoon in the Committee Room of the Institution*

> *Resolved 3rdly that no Surgeon be considered eligible unless he shall have obtained a Diploma from the Royal College of Surgeons in London and it is requested that each Candidate will send his testimonials to the Treasurer B Nelson Esq at least one week previous to the day of election*

> *Resolved, that the foregoing resolution be advertised in two of the Manchester newspapers*

Later that month, in competition with Mr John Windsor, Mr Samuel Barton was appointed the second Honorary Surgeon to the Eye Institution. The son of Benjamin Barton of Over Darwen, near Blackburn, he was born in 1790. He trained medically at St. Bartholomew's hospital under John Abernethy, and secured his MRCS in 1811, at which time he began his Manchester practice, which would later become established at 44 Mosley Street. He had unsuccessfully attempted to gain appointment as Honorary Surgeon to the Manchester Infirmary in 1812 following the death of Benjamin Gibson. He was to be elected FRCS in 1844. He would go on to become, after 41 years, one of the longest-serving honorary medical staff of the Eye Hospital, and perhaps the most prosperous. As for many surgeons at this time he would offer private tuition and apprenticeship. He did so for 7–8 years in the 1830s for his nephew, Samuel Crompton (grandson of another Samuel Crompton, the inventor of the spinning mule who transformed the productivity of the cotton industry and who therefore contributed so much to the industrial revolution in Manchester and the northwest). Samuel was a prizewinning graduate of St. Bartholomew's hospital who developed a close interest in diseases of the eye, but who never applied for a post at the Eye Hospital. In 1840 he was appointed Surgeon-in-Ordinary to Henshaw's Blind asylum in Manchester, a post which he would occupy for many years. He published in 1849 a treatise on *Results of an Investigation into the Causes of Blindness, with Practical Suggestions for the Preservation of the Eyesight.* He was very much a mentor for the blind community in Manchester.

Samuel Barton was an art-lover who could afford to buy very well, his residence was in Kersal Park. Pictures from his collection (his special interest was Dutch old masters)

The Art Treasures Exhibition, in the "Manchester Crystal Palace" 1857. Works from the collection of Samuel Barton Esq, Honorary Surgeon to the Manchester Eye Hospital, were lent for display

were lent for public display, including the famed Art Treasures Exhibition of 1857, which remains the largest (16,000 pictures on display) art exhibition ever shown in Great Britain, requiring a special construction which became known as "Manchester's Crystal Palace". His pictures loaned to the exhibition included works by Rembrandt, Jacob van Ruisdael, Phillips Wouwermans, Philip de Konig and Nicolaes Berchem. Barton moved to the well-to-do suburb of Whalley Range, and the sale particulars of his Kersal Park house, as appearing in the *Manchester Courier* of 23rd June 1855, give some flavour of the living standards of a successful medical man of the time:

> THAT MODERN, well-built Firebrick VILLA, known as Kensington Villa, situate in Kersal Park, with the gardens tastefully laid out, and now in the occupation of Samuel Barton Esq. The house contains large dining, drawing and morning rooms; store room, butler's and cook's pantries; large kitchen and scullery, servants' hall, commodious cellaring, seven bed rooms; hot, cold and shower baths, water closet &c. The stabling and coachman's dwelling are first class, having a three-stall stable and loose box, double coach-house, harness room &c. The house and stables are fitted up with gas, and have the town's water, and the whole plot contains 3,128 square yards, and is subject to the small chief rent of £29 6s 6d.

At his death in 1871 at the age of 81, his collection was widely advertised, and included works by Brueghel, Gainsborough, Rembrandt, Reynolds and Rubens. His estate was valued at £100,000 (about 14M today). There is no known portrait of him.

But I have digressed. We return to 1815: All aspects of medical charity provision were in the public domain, and this included at first the biannual, later the monthly publication of numbers of patients treated and admitted, followed by a more detailed annual report, presented at an open meeting, printed for dispersal amongst all subscribers, and published in the Manchester newspapers. There is therefore a wealth of information regarding the diseases treated and the relative numbers of each. The first, laconic report is inscribed into the minute book, covering the six months' activity up to September 1815. This entry, albeit simplistic and certainly overenthusiastic in terms of cure rate, was nevertheless an attempt at honest appraisal, and was essential to demonstrate to subscribers where their donations were spent.

Eye Institution Minute book entry September 28th 1815

The minute reads:	Discharged cured	702
	Relieved	97
	Incurable	18
	Remain on the books	188
	Total	1005

This, the first record of patient numbers treated at the Eye Institution, was in some ways perhaps a manifestation of the novelty of a new charity; by the end of the year, the

Admitted from the 1st of January, 1815, to the 1st of January, 1816.

Acute Inflammation	530
Ditto with Purulent Discharge *(Adults)*	41
Ditto Ditto *(Infants)*	98
Ditto with Pustules on the Cornea	129
Ditto with Ulcers	78
Protrusions of the Iris through Openings in the Cornea	11
Inflammation of the Iris	62
Ditto Venereal	9
Strumous Inflammation	634
Tinea	139
Inversion of the Eyelids	4
Eversion	4
Lippitudo	57
Wounds of the Eye-Ball	32
Diseases of the Lacrymal Passages	24
Restored to Sight by the Operation for Cataract *(Adults)*	31
Ditto Ditto Ditto Ditto *(Infants born Blind)*	5
Total	1885

The first Annual Medical Report of the Manchester Eye Institution, for 1815

number of patients treated would reach a total not achieved again for the next 40 years. Nevertheless the throughput of patients would be accompanied by constant efforts to generate enough revenue to support their care. At the end of 1815 a full annual report was published, showing that the newly founded Eye Institution had already treated 1,885 patients, more than three times the figure so ostentatiously advertised by the Infirmary in the previous year. The report incorporated a breakdown of the eye diseases treated, giving a fascinating insight both into the prevalence of various conditions at the time, and into the methods of diagnosis:

There are important general trends in this report: Firstly, the great majority of patients were treated for inflammations of the eye, mostly infections, in an era well over a century before antibiotics were discovered. The forms of description used to classify these inflammations are mainly obsolete. *Lippitudo* is an archaic term no longer used in ophthalmology. A person described as a *lippi* by the Romans was understood to have inflamed, swollen eyes, but not to be really ill. The *lippientes* therefore colloquially became those not working who had a variety of mild eye problems and were by inference, skivers. The term lippitudo was used to encompass this mixture of unimpressive eye inflammations, and at the time of this report the word may have been used as a form of "bucket diagnosis" for those forms of inflammation not falling readily into the other categories, and this probably included blepharitis. It fell into disuse later in the nineteenth century.

The term *strumous inflammation* is also no longer used. The word *struma*, confusingly, had two entirely different meanings in medicine. The first was goitre, and although thyroid disease could cause protrusion of the eyes, the numbers recorded here make it clear that the second meaning must be the relevant one; struma also meant swelling of the lymph nodes, and strumous inflammation almost inevitably meant scrofula, or discharging infection of the lymph glands, usually in the neck, from tuberculosis, a disease endemic in England at this time.

The term *tinea* is still used, and now means a fungal infection of the skin. However, in the early nineteenth century the term was used much more generally to mean any skin eruption, particularly those in the scalp and on the head. This would nevertheless include fungal infections such as ringworm and cattle ringworm, but also impetigo and erysipelas, probably herpes simplex and zoster, and possibly scabies, lice and other infestations. The similar term *porrigo* would later be used similarly to describe crusting skin eruptions of impetiginous type.

Venereal disease in a large town at this time was very common. Venereal iritis is separately mentioned, and although these diagnoses must have been speculative, they would almost certainly be presumed to be syphilitic. What however was faithfully recorded, without understanding the diagnosis, were the 98 babies with acute purulent inflammation. Most of these will have suffered from a blinding disease, now fortunately rare, known as ophthalmia neonatorum; that is, gonorrhoeal keratoconjunctivitis caught from the mother during birth.

The second feature of this report worthy of comment, is the surprisingly low number of "wounds of the eyeball". Considering the huge number of industrial injuries being sustained at this time, and the complete lack of protective wear, this number seems very small. However, some injuries will have presented later and be recorded as infections. Lastly, and perhaps in greatest contrast to modern ophthalmology, is the tiny number of cataract operations performed (less than one per week). There are probably three main reasons for this. Firstly, cataract is mainly a disease of the aged; in 1815, the average life expectancy was no more than 35 years. However, this calculation included the enormous death rates in infancy. The life expectancy for those surviving to adulthood was much higher, but here the prosperity of the individual had a significant effect. The well-off survived for longer, but of course paid privately for their cataract surgery which was carried out in their homes, and therefore did not figure in these hospital reports. The deserving poor died earlier. Secondly, the level of sophistication of cataract surgery at this stage was very low, with high rates of complication, and the operation was considered justifiable only in a minority completely handicapped by visual loss in both eyes. This leads inexorably to the third reason, which is that to facilitate extraction, cataract had to be very well-advanced, which often took many years; during this waiting period, a natural attrition occurred as patients died. It was only slowly during the nineteenth century that the frequency of cataract extraction increased in this population.

The remains of the first annual report are given over to a record of benefactions (totalling £195 and mainly consisting of subscriptions of one guinea, together with gifts ranging from ten guineas (Sir John Stanley, first President) to half a guinea from a large number. In contrast the expenditure of the hospital (not including the cost of medicines, which in this first year were donated by Mr Lynch) totalled £202.9s 11d. As Mr Micawber might have said (when speaking through Dickens some 35 years later): "Annual income 195 pounds, annual expenditure 202 pounds nine shilling and elevenpence, result misery". The annual report therefore includes a very necessary appeal to the public for funds, itself an exquisite composition:

The species of philanthropy, manifesting itself by a desire of ameliorating the condition of the Poor, which at present prevails so generally amongst the higher and middle classes of society, might lead us to indulge the most sanguine hopes as to the success of our application, and we can scarcely suffer ourselves to believe, that a Charity characterised by such extensive utility can ever be suffered to languish for want of pecuniary support, in a town so eminently distinguished as Manchester is for the benevolence and generosity of its inhabitants. Heaven has blessed our country with prosperity, and Heaven has taught us how to use it…

Etcetera. How could the good folk of Manchester fail to contribute generously? Unfortunately the calls upon their goodwill from any number of charities meant that donations to the Eye Institution actually reduced in 1816, requiring continued efforts from the committee, and the statement in the minutes of December 18th 1817 that:

From the present distressed state of the funds of this Charity as well as from the increasing demands upon it by the poor it becomes absolutely necessary immediately to solicit further subscriptions from the public

By that same month, it was felt that even two surgeons were inadequate to provide the necessary services, and applications were invited for a third. Three candidates advertised their interest in the Manchester Mercury, including John Windsor, who was applying for a second time:

TO THE TRUSTEES OF THE
MANCHESTER EYE INSTITUTION

A VACANCY for a surgeon to the Manchester Eye Institution having occurred, I beg leave to offer myself as Candidate for that Office, and to request the favour of your VOTES on the 22nd of the next month, the day of election. Permit me to add, that on a former occasion, my Testimonials were produced, and a Resolution was then passed deeming me eligible. Should I be favoured with your support, it will be my earnest endeavour to merit your approbation, by faithfully discharging the duties of the appointment.

I am, very respectfully, &c,

John Windsor FLS, Member of the Royal College of Surgeons, &c

Windsor was a Yorkshireman and a Quaker, born in Settle in 1787, the son of Thomas Windsor, cordwainer. After an apprenticeship to a local surgeon, William Sutcliff, he then moved to London where he became MRCS in 1812. After a brief time in Edinburgh he returned to London to work under the great Sir Astley Paston Cooper Bt. FRS of Guy's Hospital, then moving to Manchester in 1815 to set up practice at 29 Piccadilly, his home for more than 50 years thereafter. He was elected Honorary Surgeon to the Manchester Eye Institution in early 1818, but unfortunately the details of his appointment are unknown as the relevant Board minutes have been lost. The election day was set for January 22nd, but the minutes of that day's meeting, having been commenced in the presence of 59 Trustees, abruptly end with no business conducted. Was there a fire on the premises?; did one of those present collapse and interrupt proceedings; was there a riot passing, or some other event necessitating immediate evacuation? It may never be known. Not only were this meeting's minutes never completed, but there was no further entry until October 8th of that year, when mundane business was recorded as usual. Perhaps this was something as prosaic as a purloined, but then returned minute book. Or perhaps not – the Annual Meeting of March 26th 1818 was advertised in the *Manchester Mercury* as usual for "eleven o'clock in the forenoon", at the Institution, but no report of the meeting appeared in the press, nor did any published words about it appear for the rest of 1818. Had some crisis overtaken matters?

Windsor was a hard-working genial man who was also an expert botanist, being mentioned as such in botanical textbooks of the time. He published on the local flora from his home town, in a book entitled *Flora Cravoniensis*. In 1822 he made a visit to Paris where he spent time following Laennec at Hôpital Necker. Laennec had invented the first stethoscope in 1816, and Windsor brought two back to Manchester with him, keeping one and giving the other to Dr Hull, also associated with the Eye Hospital. He was the first to use and describe the use of the stethoscope in the North, and one of the first in England. Windsor became a very long-serving member of the honorary medical staff, being Surgeon until 1857, when he took up the "emeritus" position of Consulting Surgeon, until his death in 1867, having been on the staff for 49 years. He was President of the Manchester Medical Society in 1859. He published on many medical subjects, but most prominently on tumours of the eye. Many years later in 1920, his grandson Lt. Col. Frank Windsor donated the portrait of him (illustrated here) for the hospital boardroom.

Any new organisation finds teething problems in its infancy, and the Manchester Eye Institution was no exception. The Board of October 18th 1818 had a wide-ranging discussion on certain problems, and made several disparate decisions which characterise beautifully the issues encountered. The first was the chronic lack of space, so that at each successive building occupied thereafter, there was initial enthusiasm, followed by attempts to maximise or enlarge current space, and then finally a decision that the current building was inadequate. On this day:

> *2ndly that Mr Taylor and Mr W Wilson be requested to wait upon Mr B Booth with a view to obtain permission to make certain alterations relative to forming a road to communicate with the Back Street – also to procure an estimate of the expenses attendant thereupon*

The second decision dealt with the perennial problem of which patients were to be allowed treatment without charge at this charitable institution. Those who could pay should be required to pay, and the "deserving poor" were required to prove their status. Thus:

> *That no person be admitted a patient without a recommendation from a Subscriber or Benefactor as before named except in cases of Accident or emergency which are admitted at once. That no person be admitted who is able of him or herself to subsist and Pay for medical treatment*

A Laennec stethoscope, of the type brought back to England by John Windsor

John Windsor FRCS, Honorary Surgeon to the Manchester Eye Institution

At times there appeared to be patients whose accommodation in the hospital provided rather more in the way of home comforts than those to which they were accustomed, and perhaps feigned illness was sometimes experienced in these circumstances. A firm but fair approach was clearly required:

> *That no person be admitted or suffered to remain an Inpatient except his or her case requires an operation or in other instances of Great distress and emergency*

And perhaps an unwise surgical decision with a grave outcome, or even an incorrect operation, provoked the following rather obvious requirement of the medical staff:

> *That no operation be performed without a previous Consultation being held*

The below expression of frustration emanated no doubt from an occasion or two when the queue for treatment stretched far out into the street, the patients waiting patiently for the expected doctor who never arrived:

> *That each Surgeon whom private engagements, indisposition or other Cause shall oblige to be absent shall engage one of the other Surgeons to attend for him*

In the following year, the Board reflected, in their appeal below, the last and perennially the greatest of the problems of the Institution, and of every similar small charity at this time; the chronic difficulty in obtaining enough funds to support their work:

2ndly that the following gentlemen shall be requested to call upon the subscribers at large with the view of inducing them to double their subscriptions

For reasons unknown, the property in King Street became unsuitable at some stage. The Manchester Gazetteer of 1825 records that the Manchester Eye Institution moved to 35 Faulkner Street in 1822, but there is no mention of such a move in the hospital minutes which run up to December 13th of that year. Frustratingly, a yawning gap in the minute book runs from this meeting until April 1827. It is difficult to believe that records of such previous diligence, were not continued during the missing period, and since the records of this period were later rebound, it must be assumed that the records were simply lost. However, when re-established, only 906 patients were recorded as having been treated in 1827, fewer than half the number seen in the inaugural year, 1815. One wonders whether the very existence of the Institution had been under threat. In 1824, William Swire created an up-to-date map of the centre of Manchester, listing the locations of important buildings. This is the first recorded location of the Eye Institution, and confirms it at No. 35 Faulkner Street, although it is described as the "Opthalmic Infirmary" (confirming that an inadequate background in classical Greek is not merely the preserve of modern-day medical administrators, but also of contemporary cartographers or typesetters).

The address had a previous resident of some fame: In1794, one John Dalton, son of a Quaker from Cockermouth, and lately teaching at a school in Kendal, moved to Manchester. Already gaining a reputation as an inquisitive scientist and polymath, he had been appointed a teacher of mathematics and natural philosophy at the New College, a nonconformist educational establishment (later to become nomadic, eventually settling as Harris Manchester College, Oxford). Dalton, on moving to Manchester, took up lodgings at 35 Faulkner Street, now the address of the Manchester

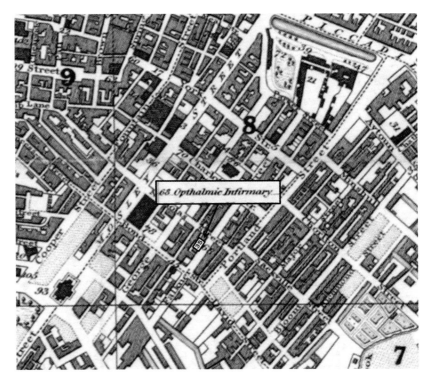

The position of the Eye Institution at No. 35 Faulkner Street on the 1824 map of Manchester by William Swire, has been highlighted. Above it on the map is the Manchester Infirmary situated in Piccadilly. (Reproduced courtesy of Manchester Libraries Information & Archives, Manchester City Council)

John Dalton FRS, previous resident of 35 Faulkner Street. A mezzotint of 1834 from the collection of the US Library of Congress

Eye Institution. He stayed there until 1800. One of Manchester's greatest scientists (elected FRS in this year, 1822, following his earlier refusal to accept nomination), the father of Atomic Theory and the teacher of James Joule, he had presented his treatise on colour-blindness (based in part on his personal experience of this condition), namely "Extraordinary Facts relating to the Vision of Colours" to the Manchester Literary & Philosophical Society in 1794, while living at No. 35. His presentation, the first formally to recognise the existence of colour-blindness, identified the hereditary nature of the condition (his brother was also colour-blind) but unfortunately was completely wrong on his hypothesis of a cause; he thought that the humours inside his eye were blue-coloured, causing the light to be filtered. Notwithstanding his mistaken hypothesis on the cause of his defective colour vision, the various types of colour-blindness are still sometimes referred to as "Daltonism".

Upon his death in 1844, his eyeballs, at his own request, were removed by Dr Joseph Ransome, his physician, who was able quickly to disprove Dalton's hypothesis (his humours were of course colourless, or as described rather more elegantly at the time by Ransome, "perfectly pellucid") but Ransome also preserved the remains, which passed into the custodianship of the Manchester Literary and Philosophical Society. This permitted a DNA examination of residual retina in 1995 by Hunt and others, confirming that he actually suffered from the very uncommon deuteranopia (complete red-green colour blindness). He had remarked about his own vision:

> *"That part of the image which others call red appears to me little more than a shade or defect of light. After that the orange, yellow and green seem one colour which descends pretty uniformly from an intense to a rare yellow, making what I should call different shades of yellow"*

The financial state of the Eye Institution continued in a state of uncertainty for several years, despite the regular exhortations for public donation. In 1822 however, matters were clearly worse than usual. Notwithstanding the Board's regular vote of thanks to the Honorary Surgeons for their voluntary support of the institution, it was clearly felt that financially, they might be able to produce more funds themselves; there was a feeling that the status of Honorary Surgeon, facilitating as it did a successful private practice, might lead to more direct financial support. It is worthy of note that the Manchester Gazetteer of 1825 showed that there were precisely 100 gentlemen practising as surgeons in Manchester (not including dental surgeons), a huge number even for the population of this growing town, and comparing to only 19 physicians. Only a few of these surgeons could claim the attribute of honorary status at one of the hospitals or dispensaries. It was payback time. At the Board meeting of December 13th 1822, the following resolutions were passed:

Resolved that Mr Wilson be respectfully requested to deliver during the early part of next year a course of lectures on the structure, function and diseases of the Eye, and that the profits of such lectures be applied in aid of the funds of the Charity

That the Medical Officers be severally solicited to give a course of clinical lectures during the ensuing summer to the pupils of the Institute.

That in consequence of the present very repressed state of the funds all Gentlemen wishing to see the practice followed in this Institution for the relief of diseases of the Eye and who are not apprentices to the Medical Officers of the Charity be considered General pupils and that the fees of each pupil be applied for the benefit of the Charity

That the fees of admission for such General pupils be regulated according to the following table

> *for 12 months 7 guineas*
>
> *for 6 months 5 guineas*
>
> *for 3 months 3 guineas*

William Wilson immediately gave his consent to these requests. Pupillage was previously arranged by application to the individual surgeon, who himself was paid, and who undoubtedly brought his pupil to the Eye Institution. This was undoubtedly a much-appreciated response from Wilson; contemporaries and predecessors at major hospitals sometimes supplemented income significantly from teaching; in London some 50 years previously a furious argument between John Hunter and his despised colleagues at St George's, on precisely this subject, produced a permanent schism.

In May 1827, after creating and serving the Manchester Eye Institution for 13 years, William Wilson achieved his true ambition – to be appointed Honorary Surgeon to the Manchester Infirmary. He resigned his position, and the thanks of the Board were given for his long and important services. It was rapidly proposed that the vacancy needed to be filled, but that proposal was rejected at the Board of 25th May. There are hints of politicking around this time, and an amendment to the Institution rules was unanimously passed, preventing any from voting until they had been Trustees for three months or more. One suspects that a degree of canvassing had been going on behind the scenes, and one wonders whether Messrs Barton and Windsor had been working to prevent the third Honorary Surgeon post from being filled. If so, they were successful – instead the post of Assistant Surgeon was created, and two were to be appointed to replace the gap left by Mr Wilson. The duties of these doctors, clearly subordinate to the two Honorary Surgeons, were delineated at the June meeting, during an opportunity taken to re-write all the rules of the Institution:

That the duties of the assistant Surgeons shall be to attend with the Surgeons on their respective days, and to operate and prescribe for such cases as the Surgeon when present shall assign to him,

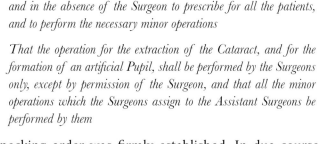

THE

OCULIST'S VADE-MECUM:

A

COMPLETE PRACTICAL SYSTEM

OF

OPHTHALMIC SURGERY.

WITH NUMEROUS WOOD-CUTS AND COLOURED ENGRAVINGS OF THE
DISEASES AND OPERATIONS ON THE EYE.

BY

JOHN WALKER,

Surgeon to the Manchester Eye Hospital, formerly Lecturer on the Eye in the Manchester
Royal School of Anatomy and Medicine, &c.

LONDON:
LONGMAN, BROWN, GREEN, AND LONGMANS.
MANCHESTER: SIMMS AND DINHAM.
1843.

and in the absence of the Surgeon to prescribe for all the patients, and to perform the necessary minor operations

That the operation for the extraction of the Cataract, and for the formation of an artificial Pupil, shall be performed by the Surgeons only, except by permission of the Surgeon, and that all the minor operations which the Surgeons assign to the Assistant Surgeons be performed by them

The pecking order was firmly established. In due course after advertisement, three applications were made, and at an election meeting attended by 88 Trustees, Messrs RT Hunt and JE Gordon were appointed. Mr Hunt would rise to become one of the eminent surgeons of the Manchester Eye Hospital. Unfortunately Mr Gordon, in contrast, was not long for this world. After what was described as a long and painful illness, he died in 1829, aged 25 years, his place being taken by Mr John Walker.

John Walker was a third-generation Manchester doctor. He was a prolific writer and after several monographs produced *The Principles of Ophthalmic Surgery* in 1834, *The Physiology of the Eye* in 1837 (300pp) and then his magnum opus, *The Oculist's Vade-mecum: a Complete Practical System of Ophthalmic Surgery* in 1843 (which, with 420 pages seems rather heavy for

The frontispiece of *The Oculist's Vade-mecum,* by John Walker, Honorary Surgeon to the Manchester Eye Institution

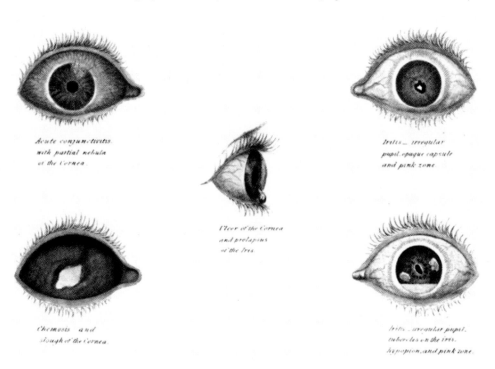

Acute conjunctivitis
with partial nebula
of the Cornea

Ulcer of the Cornea
and prolapsus
of the Iris

Iritis — irregular
pupil opaque capsule
and pink zone

Chemosis and
slough of the Cornea

Iritis — irregular pupil,
tubercles on the iris,
hypopion and pink zone.

a *Vade-mecum*). His work was entirely of its time, much favouring blood-letting, the application of mercury, astringents, nauseants and compresses, with strictly controlled diets. He wrote at length on the operation for cataract, and his book was illustrated by woodcuts. He was clearly a keen teacher, lecturing on ophthalmology at the Royal Pine Street School of Anatomy & Medicine in Manchester. He is however most well-known in the town for being almost single-handedly the driving force behind the Manchester Medical Society. Since 1781 the Manchester Literary & Philosophical Society had been the main forum for the discussion of medicine, science and literature (and for many years its President had been John Dalton FRS). However, several amongst the increasing number of Manchester doctors felt that their profession should form a learned society of its own in the town. Preliminary enthusiasm was followed by apathy until Walker and a colleague, Joseph Catlow, took it upon themselves to make 230 house-calls in two weeks to Manchester doctors, in an attempt to persuade them of the need for such a society. They were successful, and in due course the first meeting of the Manchester Medical Society took place in 1834, the first President being the Honorary Physician to the Royal Eye Hospital, Dr John Hull. The society remains active today in its 180th year, and eight surgeons from this hospital have been presidents.

Although an oculist surgeon, Walker remained a generalist and his work took him to the homes of many patients. In 1847 he caught a fever, most likely typhus, from a patient in a Manchester slum, and died. He did not seem particularly well-off, for after his death the Manchester Board of Guardians arranged a petition to the Poor Law Commissioners soliciting subscriptions to help his surviving family. The matter of a doctor succumbing from a disease caught during the course of his duties was emotive, but often an occupational hazard at this time. The matter actually reached the ear of Sir George Grey, the Home Secretary, who provided his support in requesting that the Lords of the Treasury make donations in this and similar circumstances. The outcome of this for his family is not known, and unfortunately no portrait of him ever appears to have been painted.

In the summer of 1827, the Eye Institution made its second move of premises. The Manchester Courier has it at 35 Faulkner Street in June, but at 7 Princess Street by 3rd August. Surprisingly there is no mention whatever of the proposed move in the minute book, nor any allusion to the need for new premises. Perhaps this was something as prosaic as an expired lease, but the absence of commentary is mysterious. The Board of July 6th recorded the need for new furnishings, presumably just before or just after the move:

> *Resolved that the following articles be provided for the use of the Institution*
>
> *3 iron bedsteads*
>
> *3 flock beds and bolsters and 5 pillows*
>
> *4 pairs of blankets*

5 single blankets

9 pairs of sheets 10 bolster and 10 pillowcases

3 cotton coverlids

3 blinds green… with rings and hooks for front room (for male ward)

1 large blind for back room (for female ward)

2 night chairs

Bell pulls for upper room and a bell to each ward

Old sign board to be made into a table for the Board Room

Book to be provided for the Insertion of the Resolutions

Sheets 2 1/2 yds

Beds 3 ft 4 wide

To Furnish an inventory of all the furniture and fixtures – and the surgical instruments

Contemporary maps indicate that 7 Princess Street was a small property at its very Western end, almost at the junction with Cross Street, and on the edge of the area subsequently cleared to become Albert Square. The conversion of the (presumably large) Eye Institution sign from outside the Faulkner Street premises, into a Boardroom table, signified perhaps the first opportunity to reserve a room within the hospital for such purposes. All previous minutes refer merely to a "Committee Room" and since such rooms were available for hire at several public houses one wonders whether this was the first in-house meeting. Subsequent meetings were severally recorded as being held at the Eye Institution.

The day-to-day expenses of keeping an establishment such as the Manchester Eye Institution are illustrated by the invoices recorded in the hospital minute book. One regular payee was Mrs Ann Parry, purveyor of leeches. She was to be found at 35 Faulkner Street, until recently the same address as the Eye Institution. A John Parry, probably her husband, is recorded at that address in the Manchester Gazetteer of 1825, as a "cupper & bleeder", one of seven in Manchester at that time. Clearly the partnership thrived; Mrs Parry collected the leeches; Mr Parry applied them, and also used the "artificial leech" (a sort of human fleam) followed by "wet cupping" (suction to encourage bloodflow). In December 1829 Mrs Parry submitted a bill to the Institution for 228 leeches at a penny ha'penny each, total £1.8s 6d.

The number of leeches used at the Eye Institution

The account of Mrs Parry, purveyor of leeches at a penny-ha'penny each to the Eye Institution, for the fourth quarter of 1829 was to burgeon over the succeeding years, with up to 600 supplied per quarter, the cost rising to twopence ha'penny each in the eighteen-thirties, and later threepence. Even allowing for a rate of attrition and escape from the hospital leech-jar, this number purchased demonstrates how commonplace they were in medical practice at this time, and how important they were believed to be (the outlay was significant). The early and mid-nineteenth century was the period during which the application of leeches was most frequently ordered by doctors. Most such leeches were the native medicinal leech, *Hirudo medicinalis*, but several others could be used with similar effect, and at the peak of their medical popularity suppliers were in great demand, large quantities being harvested for local usage, and they were even exported from Europe to the United States, where Swedish leeches were regarded as particularly desirable.

Mrs Parry was clearly well-established in this business. Whether she merely traded leeches from collectors, or collected herself, is not known. The leeches were common natural inhabitants of boggy and marshy ground, with which the surroundings of Manchester (and probably the shallows of the Irk and Irwell themselves) were well-provided, and their preferred natural targets were the legs of grazing animals, particularly horses which were of course kept in enormous numbers during this period. Leeches could be harvested from the legs of domestic animals, but the entrepreneurial collector offered a more tempting delicacy – her own legs, which were proffered on a regular and prolonged basis, cumulatively risking chronic anaemia, infection, trench foot, disfigurement, and possibly hypothermia, though apparently collection was very much a seasonal occupation. The vast array of leech storage jars now collected by antiquarians testifies to the importance of keeping (and of course at that time, re-using) leeches, which were usually applied either via a small glass leech-cup, or through a two-ended glass "leech tube" which permitted a more accurate bite. Applications to eye patients were undertaken for two reasons; firstly, as by physicians, as a controlled method of bleeding to "balance the humours", and secondly, usually to the temples, as an "anti-phlogistic" treatment of post-operative inflammation or swelling.

The medicinal usage of leeches declined sharply in the latter part of the nineteenth century, firstly as the medical profession began to realise the futility of their general application, and secondly as supplies dwindled owing to widespread over-harvesting. In due course the decline of the domestic horse in the early twentieth century removed a natural host, and *Hirudo medicinalis* actually became quite rare in Northern Europe. Nevertheless, while it lasted, Mrs Parry carried on a roaring trade. It is fascinating to record the re-emergence of the medicinal leech during the late twentieth century, where controlled application, especially to haematomas, can be of proven value, and they have been used in the twenty-first century in the Manchester Royal Eye Hospital. Their production is now however rather more controlled, in leech farms, and they are supplied and used worldwide.

In 1831 it became apparent that more space was needed than that provided at No. 7 Princess Street. It was resolved:

*That the following Gentlm be appointed a Committee to inspect such of the rooms as Mr Foster
can spare, and report the terms upon which the rooms can be obtained, and also to report to the
next Monthly Board the suitability of the said rooms for the use of this Institution:*

> *Mr Barton Dr Hull   Mr Lynch Mr Windsor*

And soon afterwards:

*Resolved that as the Front Room of Mr Foster's house is considered most suitable for the
purposes of the Institution, it is determined to rent it at the sum of £8.8s annually and that
Mr Thomason be hereby authorised to order the necessary alterations*

The location of these premises is not stated, but it seems unlikely that any useful rooms
would be distant from No. 7 Princess Street. There is no Mr Foster recorded as resident
in this part of town in the 1825 gazetteer; perhaps he had moved in after this census
was taken. It is probable that the rented room was at No. 13 Princess Street and that
the property was more to the liking of the board; the monthly newspaper reports have
the Eye Institution moving to that address by October of the same year.

The history of ophthalmic hospitals in England during the late eighteenth and nineteenth centuries is littered with institutions that were set up with the best of intentions,
but for one reason or another failed to survive to the present, or in some cases for even
a few years. The only example of another such hospital in Lancashire had recently been
created in Wigan, as described by the *Manchester Courier* in 1830:

WIGAN – We perceive, by a report of the Institution for curing diseases of the Eye and Ear, at Wigan, which has just been published, that the Institution has been of considerable benefit in the first year of its operation. It seems that 453 patients have been admitted during the twelve months, and that the greater part have been either cured or relieved. The receipts of the year amounted to £52 9s 6d., and the expenditure £61 18s 1d.

It is not known how long the Wigan hospital was in existence – no further newspaper references could be located, and the institution was not known to Arnold Sorsby, whose 1946 dissertation on closed provincial eye hospitals, was thought to be comprehensive.

At this time a key employee of the Eye Institution was the House Steward and Collector. The post had been occupied for eleven years by one Nicholas Thomason, during which time his salary had been increased from £29 to £40 per annum, but his death in 1838 led to an advertisement for the post, the content of which makes it clear the degree to which his life had been subordinated to the hospital, and possibly the extent to which the Board realised he had been underpaid:

MANCHESTER EYE INSTITUTION

In consequence of the death of Mr N Thomason a HOUSE STEWARD is WANTED for the above Institution. His duties will be to collect the annual subscriptions, to administer medicine, to prepare food for the in-patients, to take care of the house generally, and to devote his whole time to the Institution. A married man, without family, would be preferred. Salary £50, with the usual commission on subscriptions. House rent and coals free of expense.

R BASNETT MA, Honorary Secretary

Thomason had a daughter and son, the latter apparently acting as his assistant. They had now lost their home and livelihood, but it seems were not evicted summarily, the following entry being found in the Board minutes:

Resolved that Henry Thomason be paid 10£ being a quarters salary due to his father & himself as his father's assistant 25th March last, & a proportionate sum for such period as he may remain in his present situation from that time. Resolved that £2 10s be paid to Miss Thomason as a quarters salary due to her 25th March last. Resolved that five pounds be given to Miss Thomason on her leaving the institution as a mark of approbation by the committee for her past services.

It is hoped that they found alternative accommodation and employment. Clearly it was considered necessary for the incumbent House Steward to be a man, notwithstanding the undoubted domestic work, and possibly nursing, provided by his daughter. In due course Thomas Bradbury was appointed to replace Thomason. He was required to find the very large sum of £200 as security, because of his regular handling of the subscriptions to the Institution; he was not to prove the Board's best appointee (see later).

In 1838 a stalwart of the Manchester Eye Institution departed. Dr John Hull MD

Dr John Hull MD,
Honorary Physician to
the Manchester Eye
Institution

LRCP had been honorary physician since its creation, but had chosen to retire to his roots in Poulton-le-Fylde. Born in 1761, his father had been an apothecary, but he was orphaned at six years of age. He was apprenticed at 16 to a Mr Lancaster, surgeon of Blackburn, for 4 years, then studied in London at the Corporation of Surgeons, returning north in 1785 to work in partnership with Lancaster. He was appointed MD in 1792 at the University of Leyden. He initially specialised in midwifery, and moved to Manchester in 1796. In 1809 he had built a house at 37 Mosley Street, and its prominence became such that many advertising their wares or services locally would state in the newspapers "near to Dr Hull's". In addition to his work at the Eye Hospital he was President of the Manchester & Salford Institution for the Treatment of Diseases of the Skin (The Salford Lock Hospital, set up initially to treat venereal disease because the Manchester Royal Infirmary staff refused to treat such degenerates). He was also physician at the Lying-in Hospital, physician at the General Dispensary for Children, an officer at the Salford Hundred Humane Society, and a subscriber to numerous charitable institutions. He was the inaugural President of the Manchester Medical Society in 1834, being re-elected a further three times before his retirement. His energy was renowned, and one of his pupils stated that he always rose at 6am, breakfasted on bread and milk, and then visited patients on horseback until midday. He consulted in his rooms from 1–3pm, and then visited patients in his carriage. This of course was a private practice day; he consulted gratis on other days at the four hospitals of which he was honorary physician. He wrote in 1838 to the Board:

Mr Dear Sir

Having now relinquished the Practice of my Profession I will thank you to inform the board of the Eye Institution that I beg to resign to office of Consulting Physician to this excellent Charity and will thank you to forward at your earliest convenience to select my successor With all good wishes for the flourishing state of the Charity

I remain, Dear Sir, Your very obed'. Servant

John Hull

In addition to his medical career Hull was a true polymath. He was an avid book collector, and most especially an amateur botanist, publishing a definitive book on British Flora in 1799, and in 1800, *Elements of Botany*. He prepared for his departure by the sale of his house on Mosley Street, incorporating stabling for 4 and a fine coach-house. His very fine library of 10,000 books was widely advertised, and auctioned off over several days in May 1838, as was his 2-horse phaeton, and shares in prestigious institutions including the Portico Library and the Exchange Library. He clearly intended a clean sweep of his working life (after finally stopping at 77 years of age), but enjoyed only five years of retirement before dying of bronchitis in 1843.

To replace Dr Hull, in May 1838 Dr RW Robinson was appointed Honorary Physician. He would be the last to hold this post in the nineteenth century, resigning in 1855. Honorary Physicians would be briefly reinstated in the early twentieth century.

Since 1814, the Institution had a virtually continuous record of difficult financial circumstances. However, matters had changed somewhat for the better, and there had presumably been some insecurity about No. 13 Princess Street. In the minutes of May 1838:

> *Moved by the Rev Basnett seconded by Mr Norris-*
>
> *That in consequence of the uncertain tenure which the Committee hold these premises, it is desirable that steps be taken as soon as may be to build or purchase or provide a permanent Institution. As the Treasurer now holds £500 in the Manchester Bank, it is expedient that a building Committee be formed, & that £400 be set apart for fresh premises, & invested in Government Securities, which sum it is not intended shall be sold out & applied to any other purpose except in some case of financial difficulty otherwise absolutely insurmountable*

The diligence of Mr Thomason over many years as a collector of subscriptions, and the persistence of the Board in advertising for, and securing new donations, benefactions and subscriptions, was clearly paying off. For the first time, with money to set aside and to invest, a development strategy was conceivable, and it was predictable that more appropriate premises would be the first priority. In the minutes of June 1838:

> *Resolved that the following advertisement be published in the Guardian & the Courier of Saturday next: Wanted to purchase for the Eye Institution, land or premises in a central & airy situation. Full particulars to be with Mr Bradbury at the Institution, Princess St.*

This newly favourable state of the finances was given a further boost soon afterwards by a bequest of £300 from Miss Eleanor Byrom, wealthy and unmarried daughter of Edward Byrom, a wealthy banker (the founder of St. John's Church [in Byrom Street], with which the staff and patients of the Manchester Eye Hospital would become much more familiar in due course) and descendant of John Byrom FRS, famed Manchester poet and shorthand-inventor. It was said that "with a large fortune she inherited a generous and loving heart", so leaving about £4,000 to various charitable institutions in Manchester. The additional sum made even more secure the desire to move to better premises. It also gave a greater sense of confidence, and the Board felt that the time was now right to change the name of the Institution.

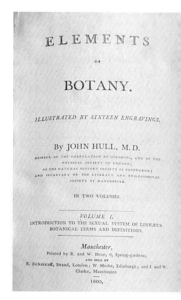

The frontispiece of *Elements of Botany*, the magnum opus of Dr John Hull

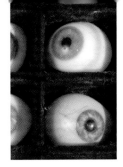

CHAPTER THREE

The Manchester Eye Hospital

Sᴵɴᴄᴇ ɪᴛs ʙᴇɢɪɴɴɪɴɢ ɪɴ 1814, the charity had been given the typically prolix Regency title of "The Manchester Institution for Curing Diseases of the Eye". The word "institution" gave respectability but not definition. Several contemporary charities were named "dispensaries", implying that their main function was the treatment of outpatients either at the charity premises, or at home. In contrast, the word "hospital" implied not only status but particular function. The word had evolved from the original Latin *hospes* meaning "stranger", firstly into a place which offered rest for strangers, or travellers (that is, a guest-house of sorts); then, especially when used by religious orders, as a school or alms-house; and lastly in its various guises (hostel, hotel, spital) as a place where the *host* provides succour. The greatest Manchester hospital, the Infirmary, stood magnificent in Piccadilly with many beds with which to host patients. However, the Manchester Eye Institution had now been in existence for approaching one quarter of a century, had become well-respected and admired by the citizens of Manchester, and now felt that a change in designation was deserved. Thus at the meeting of the Board on September 27th 1838:

> *Resolved that it is desirable that the designation of the Institution be changed to that of the* ***"Manchester Eye Hospital"*** *and that the resolution be submitted, with the revised rules, to the next General Board*

However, the newly defined importance of the Hospital did not prevent the need for continued mundane tasks. The facilities provided for those waiting for appointments clearly remained substandard, and in a Board meeting of October the desire to provide somewhat more salubrious waiting facilities for outpatients was expressed:

> *Resolved that it is expedient to provide a temporary shed or some shelter in the yard for the patients who have to wait there*

And a note the following month recorded the perennially recurring theme of capital schemes in the provision of healthcare; the initial under-estimate of cost, followed by a dose of reality:

Resolved that as the subcommittee appointed for the purpose of erecting a shed, found that they could do nothing with the small sum mentioned in the resolution of last meeting, the treasurer be empowered to defray the expense incurred

In 1839 the current Committee Members of the Eye Hospital were recorded in the minutes. Who were they, these names on paper? Most of them were self-made men of Cottonopolis; factory-owners and businessmen; important men; men with portraits. They were the very wealthy, who sometimes gave a considerable amount of time, and a little money, to the charitable institutions of the town. In addition there was a figure-head or two from the peerage, and a sprinkling of clergy:

The President was Sir John Thomas Stanley Bt. FRS, 7th Baronet of Alderley; born in 1766, the family seat was Alderley Park, south of Manchester, which for many years recently has been used as a pharmaceutical research centre for Astra Zeneca. The Stanley family were traditionally High Sheriffs of Cheshire. A gentleman of leisure, he was a traveller and writer (and for the latter, had been elected a Fellow of the Royal Society). He had previously occupied the sinecure of MP for Wootton Basset, one of the rotten boroughs abolished in the Reform Act of 1832, and had been High Sheriff of Anglesey. In this year of 1839 he was to be elevated to the peerage, becoming first Baron Stanley of Alderley.

Lord Francis Egerton, Vice-President of the Eye Hospital (Reproduced with permission of the National Portrait Gallery)

The first Vice-President was Lord Francis Egerton, 1st Earl of Ellesmere, son of the Duke of Sutherland, who was born in London in 1800. After a traditional education for one of the nobility; Eton and Oxford (Christ Church, naturally) he was MP for a pocket borough by 22, but then later became MP for South Lancashire, a seat which he occupied at this time. A natural linguist, poet and translator, his first volume of poetry was published before the age of 20. He found time in this year, 1839, to spend several months touring the Mediterranean and Levant, from which flowed further publications. He was also a prominent patron of the arts, being a trustee of the National Gallery and an inaugural donor of art to the newly formed National Portrait Gallery. He later became President of the Royal Geographical Society.

Sir Benjamin Heywood Bt. FRS, Vice-President, was born in Manchester in 1793, the scion of a banking family. At 21 he became a partner in his father's bank, Heywood Brothers & Co.in St. Anne Street, and took over on his father's death in 1828. In 1824 he was one of the founders of the Manchester Mechanics' Institute, and currently its President. He had been MP for Lancashire, and had been rewarded with his baronetcy by Prime Minister Lord Gray (as had several others) for supporting the Reform Bill in 1832.

Sir Benjamin Heywood, Vice-President of the Eye Hospital (Reproduced with permission of the Royal Bank of Scotland Group © 2014)

Thomas Joseph Trafford was born in Chorley in 1778, the son of a wealthy landowner. The family seat was at Trafford Park. His responsibility as absentee Major-Commandant of the Manchester and Salford Yeomanry, during the massacre of Peterloo in 1819, was much debated, and he resigned his commission in the following year. Trafford and his family were Catholic, and until the Catholic Relief Act of 1829 were not allowed to take up any positions of public office. Thereafter he became High Sheriff of Lancashire and

Thomas (later Sir Thomas, Bt) de Trafford, Board member of the Eye Hospital

Daniel and William Grant, Board members of the Eye Hospital (Reproduced with permission of Ramsbottom Heritage Society)

was still incumbent at this date. He was to be made baronet by Queen Victoria in 1841, also reclaiming the old Norman family name as Sir Joseph de Trafford.

The Grants, William and Daniel (with brother Charles) ran the family business in Manchester, William Grant & Brothers. William was born in 1769 and Daniel in 1780, the sons of a Scottish cattle-dealer, but the family migrated to Lancashire in 1783 to find better work. From mundane employment as a calico printer, in 1800 William managed to set up his own business, later buying the Ramsbottom print works from Sir Robert Peel. At a time of cheap hard labour, the brothers were known for their relatively good care of employees, and for their various benevolent contributions. They were acquainted with Charles Dickens, who had clearly been impressed with their personalities, and as ideal employers they became the models for the Cheeryble brothers in Nicholas Nickleby.

Wilson Crewdson was one of several family members in the cotton trade. Born in Kendal in 1790 and a member of the Crewdsons banking family, he moved with his family to Manchester and lived on Plymouth Grove.

Elkanah Armitage was born in 1794 in Failsworth. He worked in cotton mills from the age of 8 but progressed into administration, leaving to set up his own weaving and drapery business. He built Pembleton New Mill and by 1848 he employed 600 and was a wealthy man. He had been Mayor of Manchester, High Sheriff of Lancashire, and became a radical liberal politician. He had also served as a governor of the Manchester Infirmary.

Alexander Bannerman was the son of Henry Bannerman, a Scottish farmer who sold up in 1808 and moved his family to Manchester, determined to make his fortune in the cotton market. He succeeded. By 1839 Henry Bannerman & Sons were successful traders in calico, muslin and other fabrics, with a huge warehouse on York Street, and owning 4 cotton mills.

The Reverend Richard Basnett MA was Rector of St. James's Chapel in Gorton, and was an indefatigable worker for the Hospital, serving at this time as its Honorary Secretary. Reverend H Fielding MA was a Chaplain of the Collegiate Church (later Manchester Cathedral). Reverend Hugh Stowell MA, at this time Rector of Christ Church, was a popular preacher and a prolific publisher of sermons and tracts including *"A Model for Men of Business"* (1834). Samuel Fletcher was a merchant banker and a magistrate for the Salford Hundred. He would later be involved in the inauguration of Owens College. George Grundy was a manufacturer of oil of vitriol (sulphuric acid), at that time necessary in the brass foundries for tin plating, but mainly used for tanning leather. James Collier Harter began in business as a drysalter, his fortune followed and his home was at Broughton New Hall. He was reputed to be particularly generous in his contributions to charitable organisations, and was also Treasurer of the Manchester Infirmary for many years. He was a senior churchwarden of Manchester. John Josiah Ollivant, born 1798, was from a line of Ollivant silversmiths, and Thomas & John Ollivant were purveyors of crockery and cutlery, and sellers of silver, watches, clocks and tableware.

These then were the wealthy, worthy and well-to-do of Manchester who gave their time to run institutions such as the Manchester Eye Hospital. All hospitals and other charities had similar members of their Boards, and several of the above would serve on two or even three such charities. Their contributions of time and expertise, and those of the honorary medical staff and trustees, were regarded very differently by their supporters and sympathisers (including the newspapers), when compared to some social commentators of the time:

A large number of annual reports of the Eye Hospital remain in existence, and each was published in all Manchester newspapers during this period. There is a degree of repetition involved from year to year, though the constant search for new funds can excuse a degree of hyperbole when describing the benefit of the charity. The report of 1848, as reproduced in the *Manchester Times*, contained the following passages from a flowery speech by the Reverend Charles Richson, committee member:

> If they found an institution conferring such great benefits on the poorer classes as the Eye Institution, at so small a cost, they must certainly feel they were not actuated by the spirit of Christianity, nay, he would not say of Christianity, but of the commonest philanthropy, if they refused to render it assistance (Hear hear!)…
>
> He did not know any class of the community to which we were more deeply indebted… than we are to our Medical Advisers (Hear hear!). There was sometimes hard measure dealt to them: it was forgotten that their services in Public Institutions were altogether gratuitous; and sometimes the poor themselves expected more than they ought fairly to expect… and yet, notwithstanding, he did not know any body of men who gave their labours more freely to the poor… There was no class of the community more to be pitied, than the poor blind… (if) you preserve his eye-sight; he is able to provide for himself an honest independence, which every right-minded English working man loved to gain (Hear hear!)… Surely of these benefactors of the poor it might be said, in the touching language of the Patriarch, "when the eye saw them, then it blessed them".

Friedrich Engels held a rather different view of the benefaction of the governors and trustees of, and the subscribers to, such charities. Writing in *The Condition of the Working Class in England* in 1844 (for which of course Manchester was his laboratory, and its institutions his specimens) his opinion was:

> Let no one believe, however, that the "cultivated" Englishman openly brags with his egotism. On the contrary, he conceals it under the vilest hypocrisy. What? The wealthy English fail to remember the poor? They who have founded philanthropic

Elkanah Armitage, Board member of the Eye Hospital (Reproduced with permission of Manchester Town Hall)

Reverend Richard Basnett, Honorary Secretary of the Eye Hospital

Reverend Hugh Stowell, Board member of the Eye Hospital

institutions, such as no other country can boast of? Philanthropic institutions forsooth! As though you rendered the proletarians a service in first sucking out their very life-blood and then practising your self-complacent, Pharisaic philanthropy upon them, placing yourselves before the world as mighty benefactors of humanity when you give back the plundered victims the hundredth part of what belongs to them! Charity which degrades him who gives more than him who takes; charity which treads the downtrodden still deeper in the dust, which demands that the degraded, the pariah cast out by society, shall first surrender the last that remains to him, his very claim to manhood, shall first beg for mercy before your mercy deigns to press, in the shape of an alms, the brand of degradation upon his brow.

When interpreting Engels' apoplectic condemnation of English society, it is interesting to note that while in Manchester this son of a rich middle-class family lived in a large suite of rooms, was a member of the luxurious Albert Club in town, and rode regularly with the Cheshire Hunt. The selection of these two contrasting interpretations of charitable medicine is not an essay upon Victorian inequalities and social structure, nor is it a polemic on behalf of the downtrodden poor. Whatever their motives, whatever their relative wealth acquired elsewhere, and notwithstanding their lack of scientific knowledge upon which to base their practices (a comment made with the powerful tool of retrospect, and made all too readily sometimes by those who fail to acknowledge its power), the doctors of the nineteenth century undoubtedly spent a considerable part of their week in unpaid work. There is evidence that they worked very hard, and there is no evidence that they failed to work in the hospitals to the best of their ability, as they did for their private patients. The records of the Manchester Eye Hospital certainly suggest nothing else. However, the deserving poor were indeed expected to show due gratitude for the charity bestowed upon them, to the board of the charity from which they had benefitted. The numbers, and sometimes the names, of individuals attending monthly Board meetings of the Manchester Eye Hospital, to give verbal thanks, cap in hand, to those dispensing such charity, were diligently recorded in the minutes, and these were clearly regarded firstly as entirely necessary and appropriate, and secondly somewhat of a feather in the cap of the Charity. It may be that the Board, while appreciating these thanks, considered them, when delivered personally, somewhat burdensome on their time, and had resolved at one stage that it would be appropriate for patients to be encouraged to give thanks instead to God at their normal place of worship. Nevertheless patients continued to attend and give thanks directly, for many years. Occasionally children who had been treated at the Hospital later presented samplers in thanks, and one example is shown here:

The spiritual, as well as the physical well-being of inpatients, was felt to be the duty of the Board of the Manchester Eye Hospital. It was resolved that the House Steward should read prayers morning and evening to the patients, and also that a prayer book, bibles and a copy of The Whole Duty of Man (published anonymously in 1658 and defining the religious and moral strictures of a true Protestant) be provided for each ward, the books being obtained from the Society for Promoting Christian Knowledge. The books were each gilded "Eye Hospital" on the back, presumably so that they could be identified later if inadvertently removed by inpatients. Their behaviour was expected to adhere to proper Christian standards of probity, quietude and humility. Conversation was not encouraged. Occasionally an inpatient was found to be breaching curfew, drunk or generally of unsatisfactory deportment. Such behaviour was not considered acceptable and was often dealt with summarily. On one occasion:

Resolved, that Geo. Ward be discharged from the Hospital in consequence of his bad behaviour, and that no further relief be afforded to him

Resolved, that in future any patient misconducting himself in any way or not conforming to the rules of the Hospital, be immediately discharged by the House Steward; and that such patient be not again admitted, except after an appeal to the Board

A sampler giving thanks, by the young J Burgess, who rhymes "I've importund, I've Heaven implord; My prayers are heard, my eyes restored"

The staff of course, were expected to set fine examples of such standards. However, in 1839 concerns were expressed as to the financial probity of Mr Bradbury, the Collector. The minutes recorded:

Resolved that Th. Bradbury be required to make up his accounts with the treasurer immediately, & that the Rev. R Basnett be requested to assist the treasurer in the examination of them.

Within days, "repeated irregularities" having been discovered, Bradbury was sacked, and it was felt necessary to advertise in the Manchester Courier of 8th June 1839 to limit the presumed losses:

NOTICE TO THE SUBSCRIBERS OF THE MANCHESTER EYE HOSPITAL

As Mr THOMAS BRADBURY, the present collector, is LEAVING HIS SITUATION, subscribers are respectfully requested to WITHHOLD THEIR SUBSCRIPTIONS until a new collector is appointed.

R BASSNETT MA   Hon Secretary   13 Princess-street

It is not entirely clear what Bradbury's misdemeanours were actually found to be; any evidence of embezzlement would have been extremely serious (at this time, petty thieves and pickpockets were still sometimes hanged). There was no record of a prosecution, and his salary continued to be paid until July. Perhaps it transpired that he was merely an inadequate book-keeper. A replacement as House Steward, in the form of Mr William Atkinson from Frodsham, was rapidly obtained. His appointment as Collector was deferred until he could produce security, now elevated to £300 because of recent experiences. His wife Frances was also employed, specifically as "Matron". She was the first of a long line to be so designated. At this time the title did not necessarily denote any nursing experience. The term was simply an adaptation of the French *maître*, and the title had been used, perhaps rather hopefully, to describe the wives of the Masters of workhouses. She almost certainly had no nursing experience, but became the housekeeper and doubtless took on some nursing tasks.

On September 26th 1839, a Special General Meeting of Trustees was called to discuss the successful location of new premises:

Resolved,

1st that, it having been for some time in contemplation to remove the present Eye Hospital to more commodious premises and a better situation, a house no 3 South Parade, St Mary's, having been examined by several gentlemen of this Committee and recommended as offering these advantages, the same be approved

2[d] That Mess[rs] Crewdson, Fleming, Grundy & Basnett be appointed a sub-committee and be empowered to purchase the same for a sum not exceeding £1333, and that such sum as may be required beyond the amount now in the funds, if not raised by private subscriptions, be borrowed on security of the Building. Two of the above members to form a Quorum. The proposals to be vested in Trustees

And subsequently:

Resolved that Mr Newall be requested to procured 800£ on mortgage of the premises, in case the money cannot be raised by the Bank of Manchester & that Mr Crewdson Mr Ollivant & Mr Grundy be requested to apply to the Bank of Manchester for the same loan

Negotiations now accelerated; the mortgage was offered, withdrawn and rearranged elsewhere, and the purchase of existing fittings in No. 3 South Parade was negotiated for the princely sum of £39.13s 0d, including kitchen range, iron boiler, iron safe, chairs, cushions, blinds and coffee mill. Land adjacent to the back of the premises, on Back South Parade, was rented from the Collegiate Church, and an adjacent warehouse was modified at a cost of £101. The property was insured for £600 with the Manchester Fire Insurance Office. A flurry of activity made the property ready in early 1840, the official mark of the change being a new brass plate for the front door, proudly stating "Eye Hospital". The building was occupied in March with the first committee meeting on 26th.

South Parade was clearly perceived to be a good location for a hospital. The Eye Hospital had only been in situ for 3 months before it was joined, right next door at No. 2, by the Lying-In Hospital, which had moved from Stanley Street in the 50th year of its existence.

There are several contemporary drawings of St. Mary's church in existence (the drawing of churches was considered an admirable hobby for the amateur artist at this time) but unfortunately there appeared to be only one position from which it could be viewed with anything approaching an attractive aspect, and that was on the corner of South Parade and College Street, with the artist's back to the Eye Hospital, so that unfortunately neither hospital has been included in any illustrations.

The church was of ersatz Doric neo-classical styling with an extraordinarily disproportionate tower (the tallest in Manchester). Though contemporaneously described by Aston as "universally and deservedly admired"; the tower later had to be decapitated because of structural problems; for a while beforehand the large cross-on-orb finial had leaned precariously over the nave, threatening to plunge through onto the congregation at any time. The apse bulged ostentatiously to the East. The Lying-In Hospital "at St. Mary's" became colloquially referred to by its location after a while, and in due course it officially took the name of the church, becoming "St. Mary's Hospital and Dispensary for the Diseases peculiar to Women and also for the Diseases of Children under Six Years of Age". Clearly it had ample funds to spend on headed notepaper and sign-writing. The Eye Hospital however, retained its resolutely

The Eye Hospital and Lying-in Hospital, next door to each other on South Parade

simple and descriptive title at this and future addresses.

The Honorary Secretary of the Eye Hospital for the previous three years was Rev Richard Basnett, of St. James's Chapel, Gorton. Not only had he been a very active member of the Eye Hospital Board, but he was also involved in several other charitable institutions including the Salford Lock Hospital. He clearly felt that having helped to steer the hospital into its new premises, the time was appropriate to leave. Ironically he had long ago been curate at St. Mary's church, but his explanation now, in December 1840, would be entirely understandable to anyone of his advancing years who had to walk from Gorton to town and back (about 7 miles), on many occasions:

Sir

Being frequently much engaged in delivering religious tracts from house to house & in other parochial duties, I am under the necessity of diminishing my journey to Manchester as much as possible. I have now no horse & find the unavoidable walks that I have to take in this township quite sufficient. After a connection of about 13 years, it is with regret that I say I have made up my mind to resign the secretaryship of your valuable institution

I have the honor to be, Sir

Your very obedient humble servant

R Basnett

St. Mary's Church, drawn in abut 1820 from the corner of South Parade and College Street

It was not long before the financial optimism preceding the occupation of South Parade evaporated. In early 1841 "in consequence of the low estates of the funds", inpatients were now required to pay 3s 6d weekly board, in advance. The on-going cost of drugs continued to be a strain on the hospital, the most recent quarterly invoice from Lynch's being for £48.16s 4d. In March, competitive tender was introduced:

The following report having been forwarded to the Committee by the Medical Board

The Medical Officers beg leave to recommend to the Committee the adoption of the following regulations relating to the compounding of the medicines used at the Eye Hospital. That as Mr Simpson has agreed to send a person to dispense the medicines he shall supply the Hospital with such medicines as may be required during the next year, and that Mr Lynch shall have the option of supplying the Hospital during the following year in order that the scales of prices may be compared

And rather more controversially for a charitable institution supposedly providing free care, in October 1841:

In consequence of the low state of the funds of the Institution the Committee resolve that each parties as are able to do so shall pay for the medicine furnished to them as in the opinion of the medical men shall be right and proper

The hospital funds gradually stabilised, and later in the same year, a gas supply was first brought into the hospital. In 1844 Mr Samuel Barton resigned from being an Honorary Surgeon-in-Ordinary and at his request became a Consulting Surgeon (with a retained commitment if requested, but without fixed days for consultation); and Mr Richard Hunt MRCS was promoted from Assistant Surgeon to Honorary Surgeon in his place. Mr John Walker, Assistant Surgeon since 1829 was similarly promoted, but was only to live for another three years. Hunt had been Assistant Surgeon since the retirement of William Wilson in 1827, and would remain Honorary Surgeon until 1867. He was also Honorary Surgeon to the Lying-in Hospital and was to become a busy teacher at the Manchester Medical School. As a result of these appointments, two replacement Assistant Surgeons were required, and from a field of 4, two were appointed in September:

The Chairman announced to the meeting that they had been convened for the purpose of electing two assistant surgeons and that there were four candidates who had offered themselves and who were eligible to be appointed

Mr Redfern was proposed by Edw[d] Norris & seconded by E M Cooper Esq

Mr Peter Royle was proposed by James Aspinall Turner Esq seconded by Mr Blackett of the Stockport OddFellows

Mr Bent was proposed by the Rev[d] R Bassnett & seconded by Mr Newall Esq

Mr Lynch proposed by Geo Mellon Esq & seconded by Thos Labrey Esq

The number of the votes for each candidate were then counted, when the Chairman announced the numbers as follows

For Mr Redfern	*77*
Mr Bent	*66*
Mr Royle	*38*
Mr Lynch	*28*

Mr Redfern & Mr Bent were therefore declared duly elected

The Annual Report of 1848 interestingly shows a total number of patients treated hardly greater than that in the very first annual report, in 1815. However, the diagnostic classification was far more comprehensive, and as usual this was published:

This list of "Diseases" is difficult for a modern ophthalmologist, let alone a layman, to understand, and even a direct comparison with the 1815 report is not possible as categorisation was changing, and diagnostic methods were gradually evolving. There

Richard Hunt MRCS, Honorary Surgeon to the Eye Hospital 1844–1867

are two very obvious features of this report: Firstly, there seem to be very few injuries dealt with in a town famed for its tens of thousands of workers in hundreds of factories in an era devoid of eye protection; perhaps only the most severe came to the Hospital; perhaps the corneal opacities and ulcers attest to late presentation. Secondly, virtually all of these diseases are of the outer or anterior part of the eye. At this date, it was virtually impossible to examine the back of the eye, and although one case of choroiditis was mentioned, one wonders how it was diagnosed. There is no glaucoma here, and no detached retina. It is essentially a list of what could be seen with available technology and lighting, and what was thought then to be diagnosable, and that amounts overwhelmingly to infective conditions; the ophthalmoscope had yet to appear.

In the eighteenth and nineteenth centuries, many treatises appeared on *The Operation for Artificial Pupil* and this reflects the problematic and common end-results of iritis, infected corneal and penetrating injuries, and "ophthalmia" in general; the adhesion of the iris to lens and/or cornea, often obliterating the pupil and preventing vision. In such eyes the causes of lost vision were often not so simple, but nevertheless, operating to recreate a pupil, to permit light back into the eye, was sometimes performed, with as many techniques as there were pupil abnormalities. In the absence of effective anti-inflammatory treatments, many such operations were doomed to failure.

For many years, part of the regular income of the Manchester Eye Hospital had been provided by a range of co-operative societies, workhouses and other institutions whose members, occupants or dependents regularly called upon the services of the Hospital. Significant contributors to the Eye Hospital revenue were the Overseers of the Poor of the Township of Manchester, those responsible for distributing finance according to the Poor Laws. In 1839 they contributed 10 guineas, the same sum to the Lying-in Hospital, £150 to the Infirmary, and to several others totalling £362. This was a considerable expense on healthcare at this time, but to place this into perspective, in the same year £1221 was spent by the Bastardy Department, £169 was paid to the Poor for stone-breaking, £27 in imprisoning vagrants, and £2568 on the salaries of the Comptroller, Workhouse Overseers, Assistants and Clerks. In recognition of the predictable services provided by the Eye Hospital, regular subscriptions, partly in lieu of ad hoc payments, were tendered. There was therefore a contractual relationship between the Hospital and such institutions, which on occasion was strained by anecdotes such as that following. At the monthly Committee meeting of July 25th 1850:

The following letter from the Workhouse Committee of the Ashton Union was read

Ashton Under Lyne 5th July 1850 Dear Sir

The Workhouse Committee of this Union have directed me to write to you as Honorary Secretary of the Manchester Eye Hospital and request you to give them some information so far as you can respecting the admission of one Mary N... sent from this Union on the 1st of June last, labouring under disease of the eyes. Mr Charles Ellis the Superintendent of the Fever Hospital was directed to take the woman, which he did, and after he had left her he had occasion to call again, where the Matron gave him a note from the Surgeon Mr Windsor, copy as follows

"This female will be admitted into the Eye Hospital as soon as she has had a thorough washing and cleaning from head to foot (so as to be quite free from vermine) and supplied with change of linen"

> *John Windsor, Surgeon*

upon which Ellis desired to see the woman as he said her clothing was old but clean and requested to be shewn in what respects it was filthy. This the Matron could not do and immediately commenced laying the blame upon a servant an Irishwoman then present and wished the Note of Mr Windsor's to be destroyed but Ellis refused saying "No I shall shew this to the Guardians". Will you be kind enough to enquire wether Mr Windsor really did see the woman previous to giving the Note? or he gave it through the representation of other parties, because the Committee considers there is a great imputation cast upon them in alleging that the woman was sent from here in such a filthy state as his note implies. They cannot at present but be of opinion that this note was given thro' misrepresentation especially as the Matron wished it destroyed and the woman was allowed to remain because if it could be substantiated why keep the woman In until the 29th June, and waive her cleansing and then only removed, because she was not strong enough to undergo an operation on the Eye and Mr Windsor said he would be glad to have her again when she gained a little strength. They also request to be informed wether any more patients will be received from this Union? as Mr Atkinson said to Ellis upon a late occasion "We will not have any more from Ashton I have put a stop to that". Ellis has complained several times of the rough and rude manner in which he has been received by Mr Atkinson. The Committee are anxious to know the reasons and why Mr Atkinson should make use of the above observation for it must be remembered that this Union have subscribed £10..10..0 per Annum for the last four or five years, and has never sent any excessive N^o of patients and I do think only 3 Indoor patients

> *I am Dear Sir*

> > *Your Most Obt Servt*

> > *Joseph Higginbottom*

This was clearly a sensitive situation. The Honorary Secretary replied:

Dear Sir

I am directed to inform you that the Committee of the Manchester Eye Hospital have had under consideration your letter to them of the 5th inst. Mr Windsor Surgeon was present and gave his report upon the case. The Committee moreover summoned before them and examined

> *1st Atkinson the Steward*

> *2nd His Wife the Matron*

> *3rd The woman who had examined Mary N… when she was brought to the Hospital thus subjecting to examination every person under their control who could give information upon the matter:- Mr Windsor states that he did not see the woman but reported upon*

The Statement of the
Medical Officers for the
Eye Hospital Annual
Report 1848

The STATEMENT of the MEDICAL OFFICERS was as follows :—

MEDICAL REPORT FOR 1848.

Patients admitted from 1st of January, 1847, to 1st January, 1848... 1484
Remaining on the Books upon making up last Report 445

1929

Discharged Cured and Relieved 1375
Incurable.. 51
Absented themselves 79
Remain on the Books.. 424

1929

DISEASES.

Ophthalmia, Acute and Chronic	254
,, ,, Catarrhal	26
,, ,, Purulent	61
,, ,, Pustular	49
,, ,, Strumous	46
,, ,, Traumatic	10
Cornea, Conical	2
,, Vascular	3
,, Inflammation of	25
,, Abscess of	6
,, Opacities of	162
,, Ulcers of	178
,, Sloughy	3
Staphyloma	15
Hypopion	1
Sclerotitis	24
Choroiditis	1
Iritis, Acute, Chronic, and Syphilitic	42
Myosis	3
Closed Pupils	3
Iris, Paralysis of	1
Amaurosis	61
Amblyopia	41
Asthenopia	18
Myopia	3
Presbyopia	1
Eye Ball, Suppuration of	1
Eye Ball, Tumour of	3
Fistula Lachrymalis	14
Lachrymal Sac, Inflammation of	3
,, Suppuration of	7
Pterygium	1
Tinea Tarsi	54
Lippitudo	10
Eye Lids, Abscess of	5
,, Granular	4
,, Tumours of	31
,, Ulcers of	2
,, Adhesion of	2
,, Erysipelas of	3
Epiphora	4
Trichiasis	6
Entropion	6
Ectropion	2
Ptosis	5
Porrigo	3
Strabismus	8
Fungus Oculi	2
Ecchymosis	2
Accidents	187
Restored to sight by operations for Cataract and Artificial Pupil	38
Total	1442

her filthy condition in consequence of what was stated to him by the Matron and servants, but of the correctness of the statement, the Committee feel very little doubt after the examination of the female servant in the Hospital. When Mary N… was brought to the Hospital complaint was made immediately about her filthy apparel, and Ellis, at least by an irresistible inference admitted it, inasmuch as he sent other clothes on the following day. The Matron denies (in the most unqualified and emphatic manner) that she sought the destruction of the note or certificate given by Mr Windsor, asserting that she was ignorant any such had been given and therefore could not make such a request. The clean clothing having been supplied, Mr Windsor then attended the case for several weeks, but found other illness about her which rendered it highly inexpedient that she should have the operation performed upon her, which in his judgement was necessary, and therefore she was dismissed until she could gain strength sufficient to undergo such operation with reasonable safety.

In reply to the question touching the future admission of patients from your Union, I am requested to state that Atkinson denies that he ever used any threat of this description named in your letter, but that he did state that none would be received which came direct from a Fever Hospital, and therefore must be considered as fever cases, and the reason assigned for his so doing is that a former case from Ashton which turned out to be a case of fever, and death ensuing some three days after.

The Eye Hospital Committee assure the Board of Guardians that every attention will be given to the cases committed to their care by the Guardians, and as it is almost an isolated complaint against Atkinson after seven years servitude they are of opinion that blame may rest elsewhere

I am Dear Sir

Your Most Obt Svt

H Blair, Honorary Secretary

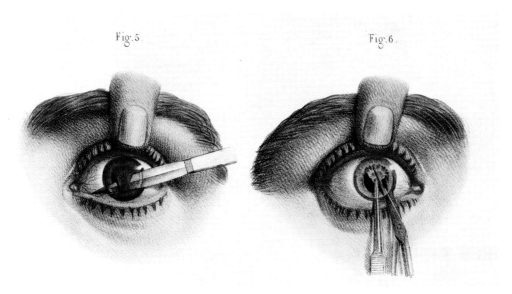

Two diagrams illustrating methods of *Operation for the Artificial Pupil*, from a contemporary treatise

Atkinson the steward was paid a salary of £70 per annum at this time (which also supported his wife who worked as stewardess), and shortly after the above events, two servants were appointed to assist him, with a pay of £8.10s 0d per annum each, and board and lodging (for which the Hospital provided 6s 0d per week). One wonders whether the Board were aware of his declining health, as he resigned his position very soon afterwards, being replaced by Mr & Mrs Morris, at the same salary. An entry in the minutes of October 31st gives some flavour of the popularity of the outpatient service at the Eye Hospital:

> *Moved by the Revd Basnett, seconded by Mr Railton and resolved, that an Iron Railing be fixed in the receiving room, to prevent the patients pressing upon the Medical Officers tables, also that the Revd C Richson be requested to kindly superintend the fixing of the same and other arrangements for the convenience of the Medical Officers*

The removal of eyes by operation, when too badly injured to save, or painfully blind, was a fairly common occurrence in this era. There was however a cosmetic solution, in the form of handcrafted artificial eyes, and in 1852 a commercial liaison was formed with a Monsieur Boissonneau, who had offered his services:

> *Moved by Mr Windsor Seconded by Mr Nathan and Resolved unanimously that the best thanks of the Committee of the Manchester Eye Hospital be presented to M. Boissonneau for his very kind and liberal offer to supply gratuitously with artificial eyes such poor patients as are considered suitable objects for that purpose by the Medical Officers. Moved by Mr Hunt seconded by the Revd F B Wright and Resolved unanimously that M. Boissonneau be appointed adapter of artificial eyes to this Hospital*

In fact M. Boissonneau was a prolific author on his subject in both French and English, one example being *Methode of Complete and Individual Appropriation of Artificial Eyes Comprising the Different Kinds of Advertissements, with the Woodcuts Belonging to Them*. Another, in his native French, was *A Practical Guide to Mobile Artificial Eyes*. Shortly afterwards, his advertisement appeared in the *Manchester Courier*:

> M. BOISSONNEAU of LONDON, appointed by the Committee of the Manchester Eye Hospital, ADAPTER of ARTIFICIAL EYES, will be there on the 21st, 22nd and 23rd instant, in order to supply such poor persons as have need of them. All such as have had the misfortune to lose an eye, and wish to remove the defect by wearing a movable enamel one will do well to present themselves at the hospital, at twelve o'clock on the above days, in order to have the advantage of M. Boissonneau's presence.

And having successfully entered the orbit of Manchester's cosmetically challenged, his further adverts attained a greater confidence:

> CHEERFUL PROSPECT FOR PERSONS DEPRIVED OF AN EYE – THE ARTIFICIAL EYES OF M. BOISSONNEAU (ocularist, knight and officer of several orders) completely regenerate physiognomy; they are full of expression,

more in accordance with the natural eye, may be applied by the patients them-selves, without any preliminary surgical operation, without causing the least pain, and even children do not complain. Mr Boissonneau will be in Manchester, Brunswick Hotel, to see patients on the 9th and 10th instant.

In fact his self-promotion was ever more hyperbolic. *Manchester Courier*, March 1853:

LE CHEVALIER BOISSONNEAU'S MOVEABLE ARTIFICIAL EYES – Mr BOISSONNEAU will be at the Manchester Eye Hospital on the 11th instant, in order to RESUME his labours, for TWO DAYS ONLY… application of artifi-cial eyes has been entrusted by Royal and Ministerial decrees to Mr Boissonneau at the hospitals of Paris, London, Liverpool, Manchester, Edinburgh and Germany.

Pierre-Auguste Boissonneau had some cause for his claims. He was the second genera-tion of the family to work in this occupation, his father Auguste, from Paris, being the first to manufacture an enamel prosthesis. The development of artificial eyes was very much a Parisian skill in the first half of the nineteenth century, and Boisonneau the younger won the first prize at the Paris Exposition in 1855, where it is said, the quality of work caused a sensation. The business thrived. In the ophthalmic journal *Klinische Monatsblatter* in 1863, Professor Boissonneau's European itinerary was advertised, and starting with Manchester on 26th March, he then travelled to Leeds, Sheffield, London, Brussels, Cologne, Berlin, Königsberg, Wilna, St. Petersburg, Moscow, St. Petersburg, Warsaw, Breslau, Leipzig, Frankfurt, Trier, Dieppe, Rouen, Le Havre, Lyon, Marseilles, Toulouse, Bordeaux, Nantes, Münster, Hanover, Berlin, Hamburg, Copenhagen, Gothenburg, Stockholm, Berlin, Mainz, Weisbaden, Coblenz, Düsseldorff, Lüttich, Rotterdam, Haag, Amsterdam, Utrecht, Arnheim, London… and back to Manchester in September. His truly international business was nevertheless doomed because in persisting with enamel as a material for manufacture, he had fallen behind the times. In 1835 the invention of cryolite glass, a lighter and superior material, led to rapid development in Germany, and it was craftsmen from that country that began to domi-nate, cryolite becoming the universal replacement for enamel.

In July 1856 a significant change was made to the medical staffing of the hospital, initiated by the Assistant Surgeons, who presented a letter to the Committee:

Gentlemen

We the Assistant Surgeons of the Manchester Eye Hospital beg to call your attention to the following statements and hope to receive a favourable answer to our request. For the last 12 years we have acted as Assistant Surgeons to the Hospital our duties being to assist the Surgeons in seeing the Outpatients, and also to assist in their operations, we have not the privilege of operating ourselves, and merely the privilege of observing the cases which remain in the house after operation. During the time we have thus been connected with the Institution the number of patients has increased. Upwards of 300 were counted by Mr Morris one Monday morning lately, and nearly the same number on the following morning. As Wednesday is a day on which

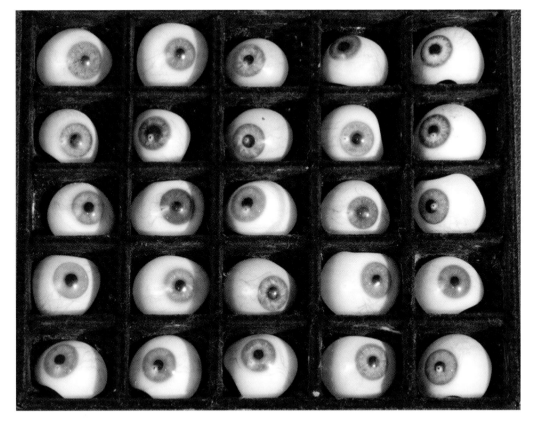

A sample box of wares from a German artificial eye supplier in the mid-nineteenth century; these prostheses were made of cryolite glass, which had replaced the enamel used by Parisian manufacturers. (Reproduced with permission of Mr Richard Keeler, Royal College of Ophthalmologists)

no Surgeon attends at the Hospital, and as Saturday is the day for operations, on which only a limited number of patients are seen, we think it would be of great advantage both to the patients and ourselves, if we were to be elected Surgeons for those days heretofore. By distributing the number of patients over six instead of four days it would give a smaller proportion for each day and thus enable them to be attended to more speedily than is the case at present, and also prevent their standing so long in the yard, which is sometimes unavoidably the case even during rain

Hoping you will kindly take these matters under your consideration

We remain, Yours Most Obediently

Chas Redfern, James Bent

Whereupon it was moved by Mr Hoyle seconded by Mr Leppoc and resolved that in consequence of the large increase of Patients in this Charity the following alteration be made in the 7th rule namely that the Medical Officers consist of one or more consulting Surgeons, two or more Surgeons, and two assistant Surgeons, but when a Surgeon has fulfilled the duties of Surgeon or successively those of Assistant Surgeon and Surgeon during a period of ten years he shall be entitled to become at his own options a consulting Surgeon

And in September the appointment of these two gentlemen as Honorary Surgeons was confirmed. Little is known of Charles Redfern, who resigned only a few years later.

James Bent was from a line of doctors; his grandfather, the surgeon James Justin Bent had famously amputated the leg of Josiah Wedgwood. James Bent was to die in 1864. In due course the promotion of these two gentlemen made it necessary to appoint two replacement assistant surgeons, and these appointments were made by election in September 1856, being awarded to Mr John Birch and Mr Thomas Windsor. The former was to be on the staff for only six years before his premature death; the latter was to continue a family tradition at the hospital for some years.

Thomas Windsor was born in Manchester in 1831, the eldest child of John Windsor, Honorary Surgeon to the Manchester Eye Hospital. He undertook his medical education at the Manchester Royal School of Medicine and qualified MRCS in 1853, then being apprenticed to his father, who was clearly ambitious for his son. The need for new assistant surgeons having been decided, it was arranged that Thomas Windsor be presented with a "Diploma of the Manchester Eye Hospital" (a document apparently invented specifically at Windsor's request), and this was signed by four of the surgeons, including of course his father, on September 18th 1856. It was precisely one week later, on September 25th, that "having previously examined the Diplomas &c of the (8) beforenamed gentlemen" the Committee appointed him as Assistant Surgeon. This is the only known official diploma presented to an apprentice surgeon from the hospital. The nature of the competition is unknown, but this was unashamed nepotism, and an appointment decision that the Hospital would come to regret.

Windsor was tall and thin, and was very much an outspoken and strongly opinionated man, apparently in contrast to his phlegmatic and self-assured father. It could be stated euphemistically that he was not a committee man, and his intolerance of bureaucratic method and establishment structures (including the church) was occasionally to explode into confrontation. Allusions to this from existing hospital records are of course never direct, but in due course the appointment of another surgeon of similar temperament (Adolph Samelson) would create enough friction to light fires, let alone create a dysfunctional Medical Committee (some readers may, as they browse, bring to mind parallel events from their own experience, and to misquote Wilde; to appoint a single such individual (if brilliant) is unfortunate [but tolerable within an organisation]; to appoint two is careless). His own nephew, Frank Windsor, later described his "intense conceit" and his "habit of riding roughshod over those who disagreed with him".

Windsor would be promoted Honorary Surgeon in 1862 and rapidly developed a reputation as one of the finest eye surgeons in the country. He was a prolific author of papers and was editor of the *Ophthalmic Review*. However, he resigned from the Eye Hospital in 1867 following a dispute with the Board over the duties of the house surgeon, then becoming Honorary Surgeon to the Manchester Royal Infirmary and Lecturer in Ophthalmology at Owens College. He retired from clinical practice at the early age of 47, financially well-endowed not only from his own highly successful private practice, but presumably from his father's legacy. He did so complaining that he was "much out-of-health and overworked" but in fact wished to pursue his real love, which was his collection of medical books. Already Honorary Librarian of the Manchester Medical Society (a post which he would occupy for 25 years from 1858, pausing briefly to be President in 1866) he had purchased widely and intelligently on their behalf, at one point adding 10,000 volumes in 5 years, often purchased at a pittance during his travels in Europe and America, the earliest being from 1480. The library in his hands became of international importance, and passed into the John Rylands Library of the University of Manchester in 1875, under his supervision. However, he resigned his position at MMS in anger after a petty argument over the topography of the new library.

Windsor's home was no less impressive a library; he never married, and the few visitors seeing inside his house commented not only on the impressive shelves full of books, but on the great piles of tomes from floor to ceiling; almost more hoarder than collector. The quality of his collection however was beyond dispute. He was a polymath and linguist, buying and reading in French, Italian and German as well as English. He became one of the great English bibliophiles of the nineteenth century, travelling internationally to secure his purchases and to deal on behalf of clients. In particular he developed close relationships with several American libraries which ultimately bene-fitted from his enthusiasm, especially the Library of the Surgeon General of the USA, for which he acted as buying agent.

He retired to Great Budworth in Cheshire. In 1907 he was presented with a hand-crafted illuminated testimonial from the Manchester Medical Society in recognition of his long and expert service as librarian; he received it with bad grace and refused a dinner offered in his honour. He died in 1910 aged 79. Difficult to the end, he instructed his executors that as little money as possible should be spent on his funeral (preferring to be cremated but only if no additional expense was incurred) and that nobody should be invited to it. After his death, over 20,000 volumes were distributed, on his instruc-tion predominantly to Washington DC and several other American university libraries (the John Rylands Library already has one of the finest historical medical libraries in the world following its acquisition of the MMS library collected by Windsor; had it also been able to retain his friendship and acquire his personal collection, its holdings would have been unsurpassed). He directed that his estate was to be used for the relief of suffering "provided that nothing should go to any hospital, medical society or insti-tution, or to any church or to any charity subject to any religious body or sect". One wonders how his executors ever managed to distribute the £20,000 estate (about £2M today). The only known image of him is shown here. He had repeatedly refused to have his portrait painted.

Heinrich (Henry) Julius Leppoc was born in Brunswick in Germany in 1807, son of a Jewish business family, and in 1834 was sent over to Manchester to manage the firm of Samson & Leppoc, a subsidiary company. He stayed here for the rest of his life, becoming Director of the Manchester Chamber of Commerce. A friend of Friedrich

Engels, he may have shared some of his political views, and developed a lifelong involvement with a variety of Manchester charities, notably the Manchester Board of Guardians, the Eye Hospital and the Deaf & Dumb Institution, He had been active as a committee member of the Eye Hospital for some time and was to be elected Chairman in 1863, a post which he would hold for 6 years before resigning in favour of his work at the Board of Guardians, in which role he laid the foundation stone of Crumpsall workhouse in 1876.

In 1862 a major row arose between some of the surgeons, and the Committee which was essentially a power struggle over the ability of the Committee to appoint, to dismiss and to require honorary staff to become consulting surgeons (essentially retired). In this year John Windsor was 65. He was confronted at the Committee meeting of January 9th 1862 and requested to retire. Robert Rumney JP, subscriber and future Board Secretary, was the provocateur, supported by Henry Leppoc. Rumney was a rich industrialist, the owner of Ardwick Chemical Works. He had proposed a series of amendments to the Rules, predominantly suggesting the abolition of the distinction between assistant and honorary surgeons; it was clearly felt that the more junior of these felt disadvantaged, and since there had been a rumour circulating that a second eye hospital was planned in Manchester, he wished to avoid losing medical staff to it. The more senior medical staff felt in contrast that a few years as assistant surgeon was entirely appropriate and that considerable experience was gained by it; to appoint directly to a full honorary post might permit the inadequately trained to be appointed. Windsor had been on the staff since 1818 and some substantial undercurrent of ill feeling would be necessary to culminate in such an insulting question. Windsor's response was that he had no intention of doing so, that he had been appointed Consulting Surgeon in 1857 against his will and that if the Committee so dealt with him "he would commence another Eye Hospital of his own for which he had ample means". The heated exchanges which followed led to the adjournment of the meeting, and its regrouping on January 13th when all had had a chance to cool down.

It is clear from the next minutes that the intervening 4 days had only given the various camps opportunity to retrench and reinforce. The opening gambit of Chairman Mr Leppoc was a proposal that the appointment of the honorary medical staff be vested entirely in the Trustees. There followed an intimate dissection of the wording of the Hospital Rules, each side proposing amendments unfavourable to the others, including the right of the Trustees to dismiss a surgeon. Despite some amendment to this resolution, it was passed by vote, and immediately both Richard Hunt and John Windsor, Surgeons, passed letters of resignation to the Chair. Mr Charles Redfern also resigned verbally. It was then resolved that any surgeon over 65 should be placed on the list of consulting surgeons (ie forcibly retired). This meeting ended with the suggestion of the creation for the first time of a Medical Board, divesting responsibility for medical matters onto the honorary staff, and simultaneously reducing their input into the Hospital Committee. All was not well, and the Annual Meeting loomed.

Thomas Windsor, Honorary Surgeon to the Eye Hospital 1862–67. The only known image, taken in old age

Henry Julius Leppoc,
Chairman of the
Eye Hospital Board
1863–9 (Reproduced
with permission of
Manchester Town Hall)

When held in the Town Hall on January 30th, the dispute continued to be aired in public, but the Board was determined to win this battle against its honorary medical staff. Proposed, seconded and resolved was the motion which expressed ultimate defeat for the doctors:

"That the following words be added to rule 6, "That on any question relating to the election or displacement of the Honorary Medical Officers and other Officers or Servants of the Institution, the Honorary Medical Officers shall not as Members of the Committee or Board of Management be entitled to vote"

This executive emasculation of the medical staff was reinforced by the official creation of the Medical Board, which thence sat separately from and reported to, the General Board. In other words, the message to the honorary medical staff was "you stick to your medical business, and we will run the hospital". At the Committee meeting immediately following in February, Messrs Rumney and Leppoc proposed and seconded that one or two additional surgeons be appointed. Further to this, the rule stipulating that applicants for these posts need no longer be Fellows of the Royal College of Surgeons, but merely "a legally qualified Medical Practitioner". The benefit of the change, it was argued by the proposer (Mr Rumney) was to permit those with degrees from Edinburgh, Glasgow or Dublin "candidates whose talents were quite equal, perhaps, to those from London" to apply for posts. John Windsor objected, but the change was voted in unanimously. A parochial, conservative protectionist versus the inexorable need for change? We shall see. The medical gentlemen held their tongues, or at least their pens, after these strategic losses, and neither John Windsor nor others, despite threats, opened another eye hospital. The recent written resignations of Windsor and Hunt were politely ignored, but Redfern departed. The wheels of change rolled inexorably on. Later that month, the very tiniest of advertisements appeared in the Manchester Courier:

MANCHESTER EYE HOSPITAL – WANTED, One or Two SURGEONS to this Charity – Testimonials to be sent in, addressed to the Honorary Secretary, Boardroom, South Parade, St. Mary's, not later than Saturday, the 22nd March 1862

And at the Special Meeting of the Committee on March 24th:

Moved by Mr Leppoc seconded by Mr Rumney and resolved that in accordance with the alteration of Rule 7th which abolished the distinction between Surgeon and Assistant Surgeons Mr Thomas Windsor and Mr Birch formerly Assistant Surgeons be now declared Surgeons to this Hospital

The Medical Board was permitted to scrutinise the applications for the new post(s) of Honorary Surgeon and to make recommendations to the Board. Unfortunately, the records of this meeting, if any were kept, preceded the first Medical Board record book. At a brief meeting on March 27th:

Moved by Mr Leppoc seconded by Mr Bowker and unanimously passed that Mr McKeand and Dr Samelson be elected Surgeons of this Hospital

In the blink of an eye the Honorary Surgeons of the Manchester Eye Hospital had expanded from two to six. Who were these newcomers?

Robert Heywood McKeand was a surgeon of low profile who was Manchester Police Surgeon, and was honorary surgeon to several insurance firms, presumably making most of his income from the examination of the injured rather than from direct treatment. His qualifications remain unknown, and there is no evidence of previous experience in ophthalmology. One can only imagine the views of the long-established eye surgeons of the Manchester Eye Hospital, on his appointment as their equal without any prior appraisal as assistant surgeon.

Adolph Samelson however, was an entirely different kettle of fish. He was born into a Jewish family in Berlin in 1817 and studied medicine at that university, graduating MD in 1840, his dissertation being *De Noma Historica Quaedam*, a study of cancrum oris, submitted in Latin of course, as was still required at the time. He moved to Brandenburg, where in addition to practising medicine he became politically active as a liberal, forming a cooperative society and a newspaper. In 1848, the May Uprising in Dresden was only one of a series of civil disturbances leading to riots which were ruthlessly put down by the Emperor's Prussian troops. Samelson made the mistake of publishing a polemic newspaper article in 1849, condemning the events, which led rapidly to his imprisonment for six months. One immediately sees parallels with the journalists attempting to report after Peterloo in Manchester 30 years before. He found on his release that he remained *persona non grata* locally and his medical licence was revoked. He moved back to Berlin and took up the study of ophthalmology under the great Albrecht von Graefe, who became his mentor and close friend. However, he was not permitted to remain undisturbed; he was harried by the Prussian authorities and eventually left Germany, initially attempting to work in Paris but then moving to Manchester in 1857. He rapidly became involved in several local institutions including those attempting to improve mining conditions, sewage works and others. He was a polymath and a born debater with a great interest in classical literature. He joined the Manchester Literary Club and spoke frequently there. In 1867 he provided an English translation of von Graefe's *The Study of Ophthalmology* and was a frequent contributor to the medical literature. He was not a Fellow of the Royal College of Surgeons and yet admirably qualified for this appointment. It seems highly likely that the recent change in qualification rules were made specifically with him in mind, and this draws the inescapable assumption that he and Leppoc, of very similar background, were well known to each other socially.

The already incumbent honorary staff ensured that the two new appointees did not disturb their already established professional relationships.

Adolph Samelson MD, Honorary Surgeon to the Eye Hospital 1862–76 (Reproduced with permission of the Portico Library, Manchester, ref Qr6 vol7)

Messrs McKeand and Samelson were allocated the Honorary Surgeons in attendance on Wednesdays and Saturdays at the Eye Hospital, the others not being in contact with them except at Medical Board meetings. The proximity of these two new surgeons was to prove incendiary, as the Committee would learn to their cost.

Soon afterwards, in April 1862 the Committee considered another substantial change in medical staffing; the appointment for the first time of a House Surgeon to the Hospital. The question arose partly from the resignation of JH Neild who had been Assistant Secretary and Collector for 14 years, and the Committee wondered whether the post of House Surgeon could be combined with that of Secretary. The sudden death of John Morris, House Steward for 11 years, highlighted the need for a redefinition of House roles. The Medical Committee were requested to give their views on this, and their initial decision, for reasons unknown (but possibly simply because they felt that there were now 6 Honorary Surgeons and one Consulting Surgeon, which were entirely adequate in terms of medical staffing), was to reply that by 4 votes to 3 their decision was that a House Surgeon was not necessary. However, the Committee were not satisfied. In their view the appointment would probably be financially neutral, assuming the combination of functions and some savings on dispensing drugs. A Sub-committee was appointed (to include two Honorary Surgeons) to reconsider the question, and responded as follows:

The Sub Committee to which was referred the subject of the vacancies now existing in the Hospital in consequence of the Death of the House Steward and resignation of the Secretary and Collector beg to report that they have again considered the appointment of a House Surgeon and are of opinion such appointment would be conducive to the interests of the Institution especially contemplating the future expansion and extended usefulness of the Hospital. As a matter of expense the Committee believe a competent Surgeon can be obtained who shall devote the whole of his time to the Hospital as Surgeon and Secretary without entailing any additional burden upon its resources. The following statement of present and estimated expenditure will place the matter clearly before the Council:

	Present Expenditure
House Steward and Matron	*85..0..0*
Dispensing Medicines	*15..0..0*
Secretary	*50..0..0*
	£150..0..0
Estimated	
Matron	*50..0..0*
House Surgeon	*120..0..0*
Payment for Collecting	*30..0..0*
	£200..0..0

Deduct profit on medicines saved   *50..0..0*

£150..0..0

> *The Committee are assured the Council will agree with them that there are advantages connected with the presence of a Surgeon on the spot which cannot be possessed in the absence of such Officer. They regret however to report that having submitted the question to the Medical Officers the opinion they have expressed is adverse to the views of the SubCommittee and the only course now open is to refer the subject back to the Council for its final decision as no other appointment can be made until this matter is settled. Should the Council agree to the appointment of a House Surgeon the SubCommittee would recommend that the mere Collecting the Subscriptions should be disconnected with the offices of the Institution and entrusted to some respectable Agent who would be paid the usual percentage for the Collection.*

The matter was returned to the Medical Board, who again rejected the appointment of a House Officer by 4 votes to 3. However, in June the matter was forced upon them:

> *Moved by Mr Bowker seconded by Mr Potter and resolved unanimously that in the opinion of this Committee it is desirable to appoint a House Surgeon to this Hospital who shall devote the whole of his time to the interests of the Institution, shall conduct the correspondence, act as Secretary to the Committee taking minutes of the proceedings, keep the books and generally discharge all such duties as may be devolved upon him by the Medical officers and Committee*

> *Moved by Mr Rumney seconded by Rev^d G M Johnson and resolved that the following advertisement be inserted in the Manchester Newspapers on Saturday next. Wanted a House Surgeon and Secretary to the Eye Hospital, he must be a legally qualified practitioner and devote the whole of his time to the Hospital. Salary £130 per annum without Board and Residence. Application with testimonials to be forwarded to the Hospital St Marys on or before July 10th 1862*

The honorary surgeons accepted this decision and proceeded to examine the testimonials of four applicants, from whom Dr Newbold Pickford was elected. This appointment had rearranged some tasks within the house; the post of Steward no longer existed (and therefore the steward's wife, who had acted as housekeeper, had also disappeared from the staff). It was necessary to find a replacement, and for the first time a Matron was appointed individually, who fulfilled the advertised requirements for "an active and well-educated female without encumbrance as the Matron to live on the premises, salary not exceeding £25 per annum". From a total of 37 applicants, Mrs A Hall was appointed. Presumably she was widowed and therefore without the "encumbrance" of husband or children in residence. The subscription-collecting duties (previously a part of the steward's work) were now undertaken by a Collector. In order to define precisely these new roles, in August 1862 a sub-committee was appointed to draw up a new code of instructions for the House Surgeon, the Matron, the Dispenser, the Collector and the Servants. It is reproduced fully here as an illustration of the many tasks performed by each, and of the discipline expected of the incumbents:

The House Surgeon and Secretary

The House Surgeon and Secretary shall attend at the Hospital on every week day from 9 to 11, again from half past 11am to 3, and from 5 to 8 o'clock pm, on Sundays from 9 to 10 o'clock and from 5 to 6pm except one of the Surgeons volunteer to officiate for him. He shall have his private residence at no greater distance than a mile from the Hospital. He shall during the daily time of his duty at the Hospital have the Board Room at his disposal, except when it is engaged for Hospital Business

He shall have the exclusive use of the following Cupboards; those in the lobby except the one beneath the staircase, but including the two safes, 2nd the one in No 5. 3rd the one in the Operation Room

He shall regularly visit all the InPatients every morning at and from 9 o'clock, every week day evening at and from 7 o'clock, on Sundays at 5 o'clock. He shall superintend generally the patients sitting, Beds, Bath, Waiting Rooms, and Closets as to temperature ventilation, cleanliness etc

He shall report to the Surgeons individually in reference to their respective Patients, and to the Medical Board with regard to general questions

He shall assist the Surgeons on their respective days of admission in their attendance on Outpatients. In the Surgeons' absence he shall attend to their Outpatients in accordance with their orders

He shall be the only person whom any of the Surgeons may in case of necessity substitute in his stead to prescribe for or attend to his patients

He shall assist the Surgeons in their operations, and shall attend to the cupping, administration of remedies, dressings etc according to the directions of the Surgeons

He shall have the entire care of the instruments of the Hospital, which subject to the orders of the Medical Board he shall continuously maintain in a state of thorough efficiency; he shall keep the Stock Book and the Entry Book of instruments

He shall superintend the Dispensary and the working of the same, promptly report on deficiencies and attend to the orders of Medicines etc as made by the Medical Board. He shall have the Dispensary swept every day and thoroughly cleaned every Saturday afternoon

He shall conduct the entire correspondence and keep all the accounts of the Hospital, convene the Meetings of the Board of Management, the Medical Board and occasional Sub Committees. He shall further receive all Subscriptions and Donations paid to him either directly, or indirectly through the Collector, shall produce the balance sheet duly audited every Month at the Meeting of the Board, and pay the accounts passed without delay out of the receipts in his hands; every receipted bill he shall insert in the Receipt Book

He shall keep the following books, 1st on behalf of the Board of Management, the Ledger, the Subscribers' Ledger, the Cash Book, the InPatients Entry and Discharge Book, the Diet or Weekly Victualling Book and the Report (or Monthly Statement) Book; 2nd on the part of the Medical Board, the Reception Journal, the Register of Applicants for admission as Indoor Patients, the Record of InPatients, the Record of Operations on OutPatients, the list of patients discharges and the Entry Book of Instruments

He shall enter the New Patients Numbers, Names, Ages, Occupations and Residences on the Prescription papers, he shall insert respectively remove the InPatients' Bed tickets and Diet slips. He shall sign and keep a duplicate of all orders given out for the Hospital, and shall for such purpose employ the printed form provided in the Order Book

He shall prepare the weekly, Monthly and Annual Reports

He shall check all recommendations as to whether they are in accordance with Rules 13.15.16 or otherwise, and submit those which are not to the Board of Management

He shall address all his remarks, suggestions, reports etc unless they merely concern the individual Surgeons or other Honorary officers, either as the case may require to the Medical Board, or to the Board of Management through their respective Chairmen

He shall have in his possession all the Letters, Reports and like Papers as well as the blank Forms in use at the Hospital, together with the filled up Books of the same

He shall also keep and contingently correct the Inventory of the Hospital, which he shall produce at every Monthly Meeting of the Board

The Matron

She shall have the large front room on the first floor for her sitting and Bedroom, and further at her own disposal, of the Cupboards in the house, that under the staircase in the lobby, and all those in the first storey

She shall not except in case of necessity absent herself from the Hospital before 9 o'clock am or after 8 o'clock in the evening, and shall invariably be on the premises on week days between 3 and 5 o'clock pm and, on Sundays all day except during Church time

She shall have the Bell rung and read prayers for those of the Indoor Patients who are able (respectively allowed by their Surgeons) to attend, in the Prescription Room every morning at 10 o'clock and every evening at 7.30 o'clock

She shall order the provisions for the Hospital ,respectively from the Contractors, cook the meals according to the diets prescribed and distribute them to the patients, attend to the cleanliness of the House and apartments as well as of the Servants' and patients' persons

She shall take care of the Household Furniture and goods according to the Inventory (a copy of which is to be placed in her hands) and shall, subject to the approval of the Board of Management, engage and dismiss the Servants of the Hospital, over whom she shall exercise the immediate control

She shall receive the payment for Board from the respective Indoor Patients at the rate of 5/6, and 6^d for washing per week, and shall deliver cash and account every other Saturday to the House Surgeon. She shall further keep the account of all the Inmates' Board and respective *wages, and shall send out the necessary provision tickers, also the Clergymens' and Ladies' circulars*

She shall furnish the House Surgeon and Secretary with all the materials in her possession and knowledge for insertion into the Diet book, respectively the Monthly Balance Sheet

She shall give prompt notice of any requirements or deficiencies she observes in her own department to the House Surgeon and Secretary who at the earliest opportunity shall report thereon as the case may require either to the Board of Management or to the Medical Board

She shall in any case of urgency during the absence of the House Surgeon send for him to his private residence or respectively to where on leaving the Hospital he may have stated that he can be found

She shall not at any other times than her Annual Vacation absent herself for an entire day from the Hospital without the previous consent of the Medical Board or in a case of particular emergency of the Chairman of the Medical Board. She shall under no circumstances permit during her own absence any of the Nurses to leave the House for a whole day

House Surgeon & Matron (Joint Observers)

The House Surgeon and Matron shall each have a separate leave of absence for three continuous weeks at any time according to their option or mutual agreement, within the period from 1st July to 31st August. The Medical Board shall exercise the immediate control over both, the House Surgeon and the Matron, as regards the discharge of their several duties. In any case of neglect the Medical Board shall report to the Board of Management.

Any differences which may arise between the House Surgeon and Matron shall be decided on by the medical Board. From their decision either party is at liberty to appeal to the Board of Management

A full month's period of notice to leave shall be given respectively to or by the House Surgeon or Matron

The Dispenser

The Dispenser shall attend at the Dispensary on every week day at 12 o'clock, to prepare for and effect the delivery of medicines as prescribed by the Medical Officers of the Hospital, to whose directions he shall strictly adhere

He shall observe the utmost cleanliness and precision in connection with every item belonging to the sphere of his duties

He shall promptly report by means of the Want Book on any deficiency which may occur to him in his department. He shall be under the immediate orders of the House Surgeon

He shall charge one penny for every bottle delivered by him from the Hospital stock to OutPatients, and shall render an account of the cash thus received to the House Surgeon every Saturday

The Collector

He shall render his monthly account and deliver the cash he holds for the Hospital, to the House Surgeon & Secretary and from him receive his discharge, as well as the Commission due to him on the first of each month

The Servants

Three strong and efficient female servants shall continuously be kept in the establishment, one to attend to the Kitchen and the general service of the house, two to act as nurses and housemaids and in particular to attend to the requirements of the Surgeons and patients

Of these Nurses one is to be more especially attached to the male, the other to the female wards; they shall obey the orders of the House Surgeon who in any case of remissness or neglect of duty on their part shall refer to the Matron

The Servants shall have their BedRoom adjoining to that of the Matron in the first story.

Not more than one of the servants shall have temporary leave of absence at a time.

Any vacancy occurring in the number of servants, shall be promptly supplied by the Matron and any changes amongst them shall without delay be reported on by the House Surgeon & Secretary to the Board of Management.

The Patients

Every Inpatient not admitted according to Rule XI free of charge, shall to the Matron pay in advance 5/6 per week for Board and after the first week 6ᵈ for washing. Every InPatient shall on admission bring a change of linen to the Hospital.

The Patients shall conduct themselves quiet and orderly and in all respects obey the directions of the House Surgeon and the Matron.

The breakfast, dinner and tea time for the InPatients shall be respectively 8¼ o'clock 12 o'clock and 6¼ o'clock. Prayers shall be read at 10am and 6pm

The InPatients who by their respective Surgeons are allowed to be up during the day shall as a rule repair to Bed at 8½ o'clock at night.

Those InPatients who by their respective Surgeons have been ordered to exercise in the open air, without any particular time being assigned for it, shall only be allowed to absent themselves from the House between 10 and 12 o'clock am and between 1 and 5 respectively from 1st October to 31st March 4 o'clock pm

No InPatient shall be put to work of any kind in the House, except with the express permission of the acting Surgeon.

A Pint jug of fresh filtered water shall every night at 9 o'clock be placed on the table near each Patients' bed.

The Boxes and Bottles containing remedies for InPatients shall be placed for or respectively by them in the tin cases suspended over their beds.

The InPatients shall be served with the remedies ordered for them as much as possible at stated hours, and on that floor to which their wards respectively belong. In furtherance of this end a moderate supply of the dressings and applications most frequently employed shall be kept in one of the Cupboards on the ground and second floor.

No more than two persons at a time shall be admitted to visit any Inpatient and such visits shall only take place on Wednesdays and Saturdays between 2 and 5 o'clock pm.

Any new applicant for the relief of the Hospital arriving after the admitting Surgeon of the day has left shall either in the name of the latter be admitted and provisionally prescribed for by the House Surgeon, or, if he judge the case to be one of importance, sent to the private residence of the Surgeon of the day.

Any Patient coming to the Hospital with the wish for private advice shall be shown the list of the Honorary Medical Officers' names and residences, as suspended in the Prescription Room, to resort to any one of them according to option.

Any case of gravity amongst OutPatients requiring in the opinion of the acting Surgeon an immediate operation and subsequent careful observation, shall, if there be any bed in the hospital at liberty, be admitted at once, irrespective of sex, and of capability to pay for Board. The bed fixed upon to receive such Patient shall, if required, be transferred from a female into a male ward or vice versa. Should there be more than one bed at liberty, that which was vacated the last, shall receive the Patient. In any such case however the respective Surgeon shall be bound at the earliest convenience either to discharge or else transfer the Patient into one of the beds at his own disposal, and respectively into the proper ward.

No Patient admitted to the gratis assistance of the Honorary Medical Officers, shall be made to pay for Medicine delivered to him by the Hospital.

The acceptance by any of the paid officials or servants of the establishment of any gratuity or remuneration from any Patient of the Hospital shall be visited with immediate dismissal

The intention to move the tasks of the former Dispenser onto the (somewhat onerous) job description of the House Surgeon highlights the need amongst Victorian doctors not only for contemporary knowledge of drug usage, but of the pharmacopoeia that contained instructions on manufacture. Ingredients were mixed by mortar and pestle if necessary, boiled in water (infusion), or dissolved in alcohol (a lincture), or mixed into various fats (ointment) or urea paste (cream). The great majority of ingredients were either alkaloids (derived from plant extracts, such as opium, belladonna or digitalis) or elements including mercury and arsenic. Apart from the use of local emollients and ointments, the medical management of ocular disease was little different at this time from the physic dispensed elsewhere, with what would today be viewed as an eyebrow-raising proportion of poisonous mercury, astringent chemicals and unpleasant purgatives.

The Reverend Richard Basnett had served the Eye Hospital faithfully for many years. He had been its Secretary, and now subsequently its Chairman since 1848. He had chaired most of the meetings recently during which major changes to the staffing of the hospital had occurred, instigated by some of the more forthright of the Committee, in circumstances of some stress and confrontation. He had had enough. From his Rectory in Gorton he sent a brief note to the Committee:

Gentlemen

From its inconvenience, I now must respectfully resign the Chairmanship of the Eye Hospital, & have the honor to subscribe myself,

Your obedient servant

R Basnett

Henry Julius Leppoc was happy to take over the Chairmanship. He was undoubtedly the main force behind what his colleagues on the Committee would call the modernising efforts which had led to the reconfiguration of the honorary medical officer grades; the abolition of ranking, and their demotion to honorary staff rather than fellow members of the Board; the introduction for the first time of the posts of House Surgeon and Matron; and the creation of a Ladies' Committee to oversee the House and its standards of cleanliness, Godliness and probity. On looking back at this period today, it is surprising that this was achieved in such a short time and without the disappearance of more surgeons than merely Charles Redfern; the risk of an alternative eye institution becoming created by disgruntled medical staff must have been significant and this high-risk strategy was perhaps fortunate in maintaining the Eye Hospital intact. Conflicts with and between the Honorary Surgeons were however far from over.

The Ladies' Committee was to become an essential supervisory body for the House, and was composed largely of the wives of members of the Board and the honorary medical staff. Other well-to-do ladies would also become involved, and for quite some years after this the Honorary Secretary to this Committee was Miss Julia Gaskell, daughter of the late Mrs Elizabeth Gaskell, prominent Manchester author of *Cranford*, *Mary Barton* and other novels. One can only imagine that the relationship between the members of the Ladies' Committee and the House staff and patients, who were regularly and summarily inspected, must have been somewhat "formal", rather in the way that the ladies would deal with their own domestic staff. Perfect cleanliness, efficiency and probity were expected. It was of course not only a supervisory arrangement, but also a very firmly reinforced class distinction; the upper middle class ladies supervising the lower middle class staff and working class patients, who were (perhaps not always mistakenly) referred to as "inmates" on occasion. Doubtless several of the ladies also served on the Board of Guardians of a workhouse or two, explaining in part the lack of distinction, but in truth the injured or unwell inpatient, not able to earn to keep his family, was only a few steps from the workhouse door where he would truly become

Miss Julia Gaskell (on the right) with her sister; Secretary of the Ladies' Committee of the Eye Hospital and daughter of Elizabeth Gaskell; from a drawing by Michael Rothenstein (Reproduced with permission of National Portrait Gallery)

an "inmate". The ladies at one stage attempted to insist that all male patients should, like the workhouse occupants, wear uniform serge jackets rather than their own clothes, but this change did not take place owing to a lack of funds. All House matters from sanitary arrangements, supervision of whitewashing, obtaining replacement hearthrugs and prayer books, requesting House communion from local vicars and the disciplinary supervision of the Matron and nursing staff, were within the remit of the Ladies' Committee. They were to remain the formidable controlling body of House order and presentation for many years.

CHAPTER FOUR

South Parade to St. John Street

No internal plan of the hospital at South Parade exists, but the diligence of the Board in arranging occasional inventories permits a description to be created, and gives a flavour of lifestyle, furnishing, hygiene, facilities and methods of treatment. A very comprehensive survey was undertaken in 1863. The inpatients were housed in separate female or male bedrooms; the former had two rooms of 5 and 6 beds respectively (the bedsteads were iron, the mattresses either hair or straw, and the pillows straw or flocking of wool or cotton). Other comforts included a bedside table each, chamber pots and a single Windsor chair. The men were housed in 3 bedrooms of 5, 5 and 3 beds respectively. The women and men had separate dayrooms including table and again, hard wooden Windsor chairs, but a fireplace and cupboard. The 24 inpatients were served by two water closets including washstand and footbath; and a single bathroom including a large bath with running water from a cistern.

There were three resident staff (the House Surgeon did not live on the premises, because there was not enough room – the medical staff would have preferred his constant availability). Two servants shared a bedroom with fireplace, one Windsor chair, washstand with water jug, slop-pail, cupboard and a chair each. They were at this time paid £8 10s 0d per year, with board and lodging. The matron in contrast was quite well-served: her salary was £30 per year. Her room was carpeted, lit by gas, and provided with table and chairs, inkstand, a tea service with cutlery and glasses. Her bed was curtained in green damask and was entered via mahogany bedsteps; she had two chests of drawers and a linen press; in addition to washstand, chamber pots and sundry items for personal hygienc she was the keeper of the key to the bathroom. If she required reading matter, the hospital offered a bible, a prayer book and a copy of the hospital rules. The matron, Mrs Hall, was later in the year censured by the Chairman, having been discovered by one of the surgeons to have a grandchild staying with her at the hospital. It was described as a grave dereliction of duty, to keep a child at the expense of the hospital, and he or she was removed forthwith.

The kitchen had a Dutch oven (or large casserole dish for hanging over the fire), a baking oven, steamer, coffee mill and the expected accoutrements. Next door, the scullery contained an iron water boiler, coal boxes and all expected scouring, blacking, washing and storage facilities of the Victorian era. Underneath were two cellars: a meat cellar for food storage, and a washing cellar, again with a boiler, a wash tub and accompanying maidens for hanging and drying linen. There was a "utensil and crockery store" which seems not to have been limited to sanitary ware, including urinals, bedpans and chamber pots, but also mugs, pill jars and facilities for washing the same. The servants did not appear to perform all of the domestic work; a charwoman was employed, and staff came in to do the washing.

For the outpatients, there appeared to be two entrances into the hospital. The front door proudly bore the plate "Manchester Eye Hospital" and the entrance opened into a lobby adorned with a stag's head, its tiled floor covered in straw matting, and on the wall was a box for donations. Opening off the lobby was the Board Room, its table made of birch and covered with American cloth, surrounded by 11 chairs. In here was the hospital safe, and a cupboard with various records. There was of course a fireplace. Also opening off the lobby was the ophthalmoscope room, windowless. The patients' waiting room contained three long wooden forms on which to sit (a level of comfort adhered to at the hospital well into the 1980s). The ophthalmoscope room was a relatively new development in ophthalmology – a dark space permitting the use of a new instrument to examine the retina. The frustration of every ophthalmologist until the mid-nineteenth century was the inability to examine the back of the eye in

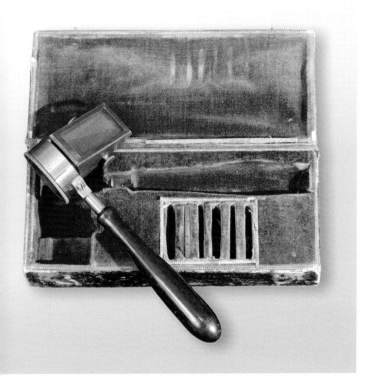

A Helmholtz ophthalmoscope of 1851 or later; the first instrument to permit examination of the living retina (Reproduced with permission of Mr Richard Keeler, Royal College of Ophthalmologists)

vivo. It was recognised that occasionally a "red reflex" could be seen in a person's pupil (and hypotheses for the cause of this ranged from phosphorescence to intrinsic electrical activity), but the normal blackness of that aperture prevented any examination of the retina. Ophthalmology, until that time, was entirely concerned with the treatment of diseases of the anterior segment, eyelids and orbit. It was Charles Babbage, he of the famed "Difference Engine", the world's first computing machine; a mathematician, scientist, polymath and generally inquisitive genius, who first hit upon the notion that coaxial illumination was necessary to enable the ophthalmologist to examine the fundus. He manufactured a tool, essentially a cylinder with a side-aperture opening onto a 45° mirror, through the centre of which the observer could see. He showed it to the London ophthalmologist Wharton Jones in 1847 but he could not obtain a view of the retina with it and Babbage took the matter no further.

It was left to a German ophthalmologist, Herman

von Helmholtz, to invent a usable instrument, which in 1851 he called an Augenspiegel (eye mirror). The principle was identical to that of Babbage but Helmholtz recognised the need to refract the image for the observer. Immediately the instrument's usefulness became known, and within a few years dozens of eponymous versions had been designed and produced by British and European ophthalmologists, many of greater usefulness than that of von Helmholtz. However, compared to modern instruments the degree of skill required to obtain an image was high; a good directed source of light onto the mirror was crucial, and low ambient light, preferably darkness, facilitated this, hence the introduction of ophthalmoscope rooms to such as the Manchester Eye Hospital. A new era in ophthalmology was born – diseases of the retina.

The Dispensary was well-equipped for the storage and preparation of medicines: its jar case contained various base materials. Its ointments were contained in kegs with taps. There were 80 glass bottles containing medicines. Ointments were prepared in 4 stewpots, 5 mortars and pestles were provided, with various glass measures, spatulas, Winchester bottles, a hand mill for powders and a "pill machine, complete". Next door was the Prescribing and Dressing Room, which seems to have been furnished with duplicate writing desks, chairs, stools, washstands and the like indicating that two patients at a time were dealt with. Basic eye examination took place here – there were two test types and a Donders' stenopaeic disc (a pinhole occluder) together with stethoscope, ear speculum and spoon. In addition to the application of various ointments, lotions and dressings, some instruments were stored here indicating that minor surgery was also performed: Desmarres and Jaegers elevators, conjunctival and dissecting forceps, and scissors.

The majority of surgery however undoubtedly took place in the Operating Room. Unlike modern rooms built for surgery, it was not entirely free of comforts for surgeon or spectator – A sofa with two cushions was a prominent piece of furniture, as was a spittoon (enamelled). The operating table had a mattress and this was covered for surgery in black mackintosh. The surgeon had a choice of stool or armchair. He was provided with a washstand with jug, bowl and soap basket. The surgical instruments, in 47 cases, were housed in a mahogany chest. They each had the letters M.E.H. and a set number indicating contents, each stamped in gilt on the box lid. Chloroform inhalers were provided for anaesthesia, and tin roses with India rubber tubing for eye douching. The contents of Case C (Cupboard XVI) were particularly varied:

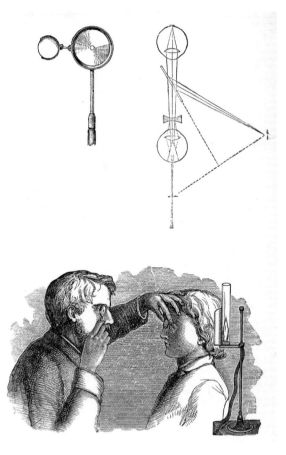

An early engraving of an indirect ophthalmoscope in use, c1870. The illumination is precisely one candle-power, hence the need for a darkened ophthalmoscopy room

At this time, a pedestrian on South Parade who was unaware of the usage of the building housing the Eye Hospital would be excused for dismissing it as an ordinary Georgian town house on an open church square. Only the door sign, and perhaps the unusual number of visitors, would signify the conversion of the large dwelling into the hospital that it had become.

Perhaps the church square in which the hospital was situated was not always quite as pleasant as may be assumed. The following letter was sent to the Mayor later in the year, concerning the local atmosphere during what presumably had been a hot summer:

To His Worship The Mayor of Manchester   *Manchester 14th Sept 1863*

Dear Sir

 Thanking you for the courtesy shewn to the deputation from the Manchester Eye Hospital which waited upon you to-day, I avail myself of your suggestion that the grievance then brought to your notice should be submitted in the present form

The Hospital, as you are aware, is immediately contiguous to St. Mary's churchyard, in which, by an order in council, internments have for a considerable period of years been discontinued. Recently however the graves are not infrequently reopened and internments take place, during which, effluvia of the most noxious and pestilential character are emitted, and during the recent weather it has been particularly offensive. The Committee of the Hospital submit, in the interest of their charity, that the health of their inmates and officers are thereby endangered as well as materially affecting that of the neighbourhood and town in general.

The Committee appeal to you as Chief Magistrate to use your authority that the serious nuisance referred to be discontinued

I am, Dear Sir, on behalf of Committee of Man^er Eye Hospital

Yours respectfully, H Leppoc, Chairman

The contents of case C, in the operating room, shows that surgeons were equipped for cupping, bleeding and enemas in addition to eye surgery

Case No. C (Cupboard XVI)
1. Enema Syringe
2. Anatomical Injection Syringe
3. Iridodesis
4. Mounted Suture Needles
5. Bone Instruments
6. Cupping Case
7. Bruecke's Loupe
8. Ophthalmoscope
9. Heurteloup's Artificial Leech
10. Anels Syringe, Tube, Extractor, glasses' Probes, Stilettes
11. Spectacle Case

Unfortunately the hospital was rebuffed, and presumably continued to suffer to some degree. The problem may have contributed to the decision in the not too distant future, to look for other premises.

The longstanding combination of the posts of House Surgeon and Secretary into a single job sounds very onerous today. The gentlemen of the Medical Board had previously suggested that the posts be separated so that the young doctors occupying the post of House Surgeon could concentrate on the medical tasks without the administrative interference of the Secretarial post. The Hospital Board however had not agreed, presumably on the grounds of cost; the combined post paid £125 per annum at this time, and presumably separation would increase expenditure. The incumbent in 1863 was certainly dissatisfied, for a variety of reasons:

To the Committee of the Manchester Eye Hospital   *April 13ᵗʰ 1863*

Gentlemen

Your determination not to acquiesce in the Recommendation of the Medical Board "that the offices of House Surgeon & Secretary be henceforth disunited" together with the never-ending superintendence of, and interference with, the duties of those Offices, as practiced by one of your officers, induce me, with feelings of regret, to lay before you my Resignation of the double office; for the honor you did me by electing me to fill which, I beg to return you my sincere thanks, I am

Gentlemen, Yours very Respectfully

Newbold Pickford, House Surgeon

The resignation of Dr Pickford was of course followed by the advertisement of the vacant post, as usual in the Lancet, Medical Times and Manchester newspapers. Four applicants were selected for interview, and Dr David Little was appointed. He would become one of the most prominent members of the honorary medical staff of the hospital, in its history.

One of Dr Little's early tasks was to send awful news about a young patient, and the contents of the letter make all too clear the dangers of general anaesthesia during this period, where both equipment and knowledge were basic. The 14 year-old boy had suffered a penetrating eye injury caused by a twig, while out hunting rabbits. The eye was irretrievably lost, but unfortunately the dreaded complication of sympathetic ophthalmia (inflammation also affecting the uninjured eye) set in and was threatening total blindness. It was felt necessary to remove the injured eye in the hope that the other eye would settle. The events were described by Dr Little in his letter to the Reverend Crossley:

Manchester Eye Hospital, 3 South Parade

10th January 1865

Reverend Sir

I am most grieved to have to inform you of a very sad occurrence, and solicit your cooperation thereabout

This afternoon between 2 and 3 o'clock it was resolved without delay to perform the operation necessary for the removal of the boy......'s right eye. For, it had just been ascertained that the left eye hardly retained more vision than to enable the patient to find his way about. He was in the operation room of the hospital in the presence and with the aid of the two nurses of the establishment placed upon the couch and prepared for the operation in the customary manner, chloroform being administered to him by myself. When after about 10 minutes, the boy appeared to be in a fit state for it, the operation was by Dr Samelson proceeded with, and the first stage of the same, a circular and superficial incision, was completed. Thereupon an interruption and the renewed administration of chloroform was necessitated by the boy (who vomited) beginning to appear sensible again, when he exhibited so much power in his movements that some force was required to keep him down. After chloroform had for a few minutes been given again, it appeared opportune to continue the operation. But scarcely had Mr Samelson set to work, when the boy began to gasp for breath and obliged us to resort to the customary means of admitting air from without, whereby and some slapping of the face (with a wet towel) he appeared in a minute or two to rally – the danger, with the imminence of which we are not unfamiliar, seemed to have passed. Yet, the breathing of the boy continued to be laboured, the pulse, at first plainly felt, passed away, and in spite of all the exertion, could not be recovered, although for better than a quarter of an hour respiration was kept up, partly by natural effort, partly by our assistance. During three quarters of an hour, Dr Samelson, myself, the Matron and the two nurses were in every sort of way employed to reawaken the spark of life, so recently extinct; but – it was to no avail – the boy is no more.

The direction of the present is to request you, kindly to communicate the fact to the parents. The examination of the body can hardly be deferred beyond Thursday morning. Let the extraordinary and mournful nature of the event be my apology for thus intruding on your peace and time, and believe me

Reverend Sir, respectfully yours

D Little MD, House Surgeon

It transpired that the poor parents did not receive this news quickly, as Reverend Crossley was away from home. The boy's father only arrived after an inquest had been held, refused a post-mortem and took the body away. A blow-by-blow account of the affair, including the names of the patient and doctors, was published in four Manchester newspapers, as was the contemporaneous habit. There is little doubt that the intrinsically dangerous and relatively unskilled methods of anaesthesia during this period, together with the lack of resuscitation equipment taken for granted today, led to the boy's death. However, the conclusion of the inquest was that "a functional infirmity of the heart, which during life had not revealed itself by any symptom whatever" had been the cause. We should not judge too harshly in retrospect. Perhaps the greatest sadness is that it is now generally accepted that the removal of the injured eye does not help the other to recover from sympathetic ophthalmia – the poor boy would not have been helped by this operation and would have in any case been blind.

Early in 1865 Dr Samelson informed the Board that "I shall leave this day for the Continent" for the purpose of resting and nursing an eye problem which he attributed to overwork. He had described it as "granular lid". His decision to seek treatment outside Manchester may have implied a less than amicable relationship with his colleagues, or it may simply have given him a reason to travel home; he took himself to Berlin, to seek assistance from the great Professor Albrecht von Graefe, with whom he had studied ophthalmology before coming to Manchester. He chose to stay in Germany for 4 months, and during that time he spent several weeks observing the clinical practice of von Graefe at his Eye-Clinique. On his return he published by instalments in the *British Medical Journal* a series of articles entitled *Reminiscences of a Four Months' Stay with Professor A. von Graefe in Berlin*. Every aspect of the great man's practice was detailed including clinic topography, staffing, throughput and treatment methods. Most importantly, von Graefe was at that very time experimenting with his new method of "modified linear extraction" of cataract, in due course using the cataract knife designed by himself for the purpose, and for which he is now most remembered. It is likely that Samelson was the first British surgeon to employ the technique, and the articles above were the written introduction of von Graefe's new method of cataract extraction to England. The method was to be largely adopted worldwide within a few years. It is either a tribute to its longevity, or perhaps a criticism of the slow pace of development, that the first cataract extraction witnessed by this author, 110 years later as a medical student in 1975, was performed using the same knife, making the same *ab interno* section, and performing the same broad iridectomy. On his return to Manchester Samelson brought with him a treasured souvenir, a signed photograph of Albrecht von Graefe, which was hung in the Manchester Eye Hospital board room. Unfortunately it has been lost.

The availability of free eye care at the Manchester Eye Hospital, together with the professional coexistence, sometimes conflict, of private and honorary tasks for the surgeons, was the cause of occasional problems, not to say friction, in defining who paid for what. The Hospital was dependent upon the judgement of various bodies including Poor Law Guardians, committee members of cooperative societies etc to decide whether a particular patient came with written recommendation for free treatment. In one case, discussed at a meeting of the General Board 10th March 1865:

> *Mr Barton attended the meeting to complain in the case of a poor woman whom he had sent to the Hospital as a fit object of charity & who was made to pay a surgeon's fee. He was of opinion that the person was not in circumstance to pay any such fee, and moreover that any fee taken by any of the surgeons on the premises ought to go to the funds of the Hospital. The House Surgeon was requested to inquire into the above case & report at the next meeting of the Board.*

And on 21st April, the opposite problem, declared via an anonymous letter read to the Board:

> *Sir*
>
> *You have a patient of the name of S…[1] M…… a Plumber & Painter (now retired from business). He has 12 or 18 Cottages in Tatton St, Hulme, also a quarterly house near Chorlton Road, and has a beautifully furnished house. He has had a stroke & is I think under Mr McKeand. He is not a proper object of charity and therefore hope you will enquire into the matter*

Later in the same year, another anomaly:

> *Mr Hunt stated that at present there is an In-patient in the Hospital who has been charged more than the amount usually paid for board, and that he had been informed that the Surgeon whose*

patient she was, intended to charge her for the operation and his attendance. The meeting was of opinion that no private patient of any Surgeon should be admitted as a Hospital patient, and the Chairman undertook to communicate with the Surgeon referred to by Mr Hunt by letter or otherwise

And a final example of the occasional denunciations, either of patients of means seeking free medical care, or of a genuinely poor patient simply being "undeserving"; the anonymous letter, and then a letter of apology from those who inadvertently recommended him:

J W………, Stonemason.

This man ought not to have had a recommendation. He is not an object of Charity, half the money he regularly spends in drink would have more than paid for doctors bills during the time his wife was under treatment

Dear Sir

We are obliged yours of this day in reference to the case of J W……… & regret excessively that a recommend was given to him, agreeing with you that he is not a proper object of Charity, it appears he applied to some of our people at our Mills, Warrington, who wrote to us here for a recommendation which was sent duly signed, trusting to their discrimination if not knowing who it was for, so soon as I found out what had been done, I wrote to them a note a copy of which I give you on the other side. I am extremely sorry that you have had this trouble & am Sir Yours etc

W Armitage

In relation to the specific concern about surgeons receiving any payment from patients within the premises of the charity, the conflict between honorary (unpaid) work within charitable institutions such as this, and private work (that is, the self-employed doctor's means of income) and the sometimes blurred margins between these two areas, would continue, with occasional stresses, not only until 1948 and the creation of the National Health Service (when surgeons were no longer "honorary" but salaried) but long beyond, and some critics continue to argue that the amicable and fair coexistence of both salaried (NHS) employment and self-employment is not possible.

The patients seeking treatment who were found to be poor, deserving and in need of inpatient treatment, were admitted for as long as necessary (and at this time the average inpatient stay was 20 days). Whilst inpatient they were expected to adhere closely to the regulations of the hospital; for those who could read (between one half and two thirds of men at this time, fewer women), copies were readily available for them and doubtless Matron would leave those who could not read, in no doubt following each misdemeanour. These long inpatient stays, in enforced low light while subject to strict supervision, must have led some, predominantly male patients to seek respite or entertainment elsewhere. However, they risked being found out and were duly admonished for their brief moments of freedom. The penalties could be severe; House Committee May 1863:

Resolved, that Richd Griffin be discharged, & that the Barton-on-Irwell Guardians be informed that R.G. has already been 8 months in the Hospital, & that on one occasion lately he came drunk to prayers.

Resolved, that Messrs J Munn & Co be informed that Geo. Moore has been discharged by the Committee on account of his coming home drunk to the Hospital on Saturday night last at 8 o'clock, being accompanied to the door also by a woman of loose character.

In 1864 the untimely death of Mr Bent, one of the two assistant surgeons, led to an attempt to reorganise the days of attendance of the Honorary Surgeons. An unseemly scrabble then developed for the preferred days of consultation. Mr John Windsor laid out his stall at a meeting in September, giving a prolix dissertation on a long career well served, eventually cutting to the chase:

"From long experience I am convinced, that there is particular advantage (pecuniarily) from the occasional calls of paying patients on market days viz. Tuesday and Friday, but I am of opinion that the priority of days should be allotted to seniority of appointment to Office, in accordance with the general practice – a practice hitherto pursued by the medical officers themselves without any discrepancy of opinion, and, I believe, any reference to the decision of the General Board"

Further bargaining took place, with the result that Mr Windsor was to be in attendance every Tuesday, and alternate Fridays, an arrangement that he doubtless viewed with satisfaction (pecuniarily). It was at the same meeting that discussion ensued on the increasing inadequacy of 3 South Parade for the Eye Hospital's purposes. Dr Samelson had been asked to draw up a report on the situation, which was duly delivered:

The Manchester Eye Hospital has completed the first half century of its existence. It is nearly 25 years since it transferred to the premises which it at present occupies. At that time the space which they afford may have appeared sufficient, but they were never planned for the purposes of a hospital. For several years their utter inadequacy has been manifest to the administrators of the Charity. Not only is the room so limited as to prevent the accommodation of more than at best half the number of patients beds really needed, but the 25 beds actually maintained are most inconveniently crowded together and distributed over the building in a manner glaringly inconsistent with the object of the Charity, viz. the leading to a successful issue of the greatest possible number of operations or other cases of eye-disease. Nor is the inconvenience experienced every day in the control of and attendance on the round of out-patients less to be lamented. Again, it is actually impossible to accommodate the number of nurses and servants indispensably required for the proper and salutary working of the establishment, even within its present limits. By the want of room the house surgeon is most unfortunately debarred from residing in the hospital, and the accommodation which it affords for the matron, is no less detrimentally deficient. The medicines required for the whole of the patients have, of necessity and at a great loss, to be procured from without. The Inpatients not confined to bed, as eye-patients but seldom are for any lengthened period, and more particularly, the convalescents have no opportunity afforded them for making exercise. Without entering into further, though perhaps not less convincing, detail, the Board feel themselves justified in affirming that on the grounds of humanity and public interest the transfer of the hospital into an edifice of considerably more than double the size of the present structure is a matter of immediate urgency. The M. E. H. is the only institution to which in cases of eye-disease the poor population of M. & Salford, of the greater part of Lancashire, and of the adjoining portions of the counties of Cheshire, Yorkshire, Derbyshire & Staffordshire can and do regularly resort. Thus, the hospital extends its operations over a district at once the most populous and the most wealthy… within its sphere of action the growth of pauperism by warding off blindness or else restoring sight to the curable blind. The rapidity of progress made within the last ten years in the knowledge and treatment of eye disease is perhaps unparalleled in the history of the healing art… Within recent times the kindred institutions of Liverpool, Birmingham, Leeds – to say nothing of the Metropolis – have been considerably extended and improved. In the town of Bradford simple means have been found for erecting a suitable structure to receive the eye-hospital which was started there only a few years since.

He was preaching to the converted. The Board strongly agreed with the need to expand, but the timing was not good; Dr Samelson's proposal was deferred "on account of the present state of trade". These few words economically described what was in fact a disastrous period for the mills of Manchester and the northwest of England; the so-called "cotton famine" of the 1860s. The causes were two-fold: firstly an overgrowth of Lancashire milling had led to an over-supply of woven cotton cloth and a subsequent fall in price; secondly the American civil war had interrupted the importation of raw cotton, mainly by a Union blockade of Southern state ports; both together caused a substantial fall in the industry's turnover between 1862–65. This had a real effect very quickly, with workers laid off in large numbers, leading to destitution and starvation; the effect outside Manchester was even worse, cumulating in riots in Stalybridge, Dukinfield and Hyde earlier in 1864. The Poor Law Guardians were stretched to their limit in raising funds to support the destitute, and this was not a good time to attempt to divert charitable donations towards the Eye Hospital.

The cotton trade between America and Great Britain was of huge importance to both. Despite the calamitous effects of the civil war upon the people of Manchester and the surrounding towns, and despite the loss of cotton supply from the Confederate states, there was a strongly held anti-slavery sentiment and therefore a Unionist sympathy in Manchester, expressed in a message of support sent to Abraham Lincoln himself, to which he replied:

"I know and deeply deplore the sufferings which the working people of Manchester and in all Europe are called to endure in this crisis… whatever misfortune may befall your country or my own, the peace and friendship which now exists between the two nations will be, as it shall be my desire to make them, perpetual.

These exchanges of friendship at a time of adversity were commemorated by a statue of Lincoln, standing now in Manchester town centre. The cotton shortage would have a far more long-lasting effect on the mill towns outside Manchester, because the eventual restitution of cotton imports would be concentrated mainly on Manchester itself. The trade situation later in 1864 was improving enough for the Eye Hospital Board to reconsider its decision on fundraising in the light of pressing need for more space.

An illustration of a Manchester Quaker soup-kitchen supplying gruel to the starving during the cotton famine. From the London Illustrated News, November 1862

THE SOCIETY OF FRIENDS' SOUP-KITCHEN, BALL-STREET, LOWER MOSELEY-STREET, MANCHESTER.—SEE PAGE 558.

A large appeal for charity was therefore initiated, including a circular letter from Mr Leppoc sent to 500 clergymen, requesting congregational donations. After enquiries a potential buyer of No. 3 was found: Mr Hampson, a neighbour in South Parade, who offered £2,800. The sale was agreed in April 1865 with the helpful caveat that the buyer permitted the hospital to remain in residence until new premises could be found. That search continued; initially a proposal to buy land in Quay Street opposite St. Mary's Hospital, was mooted (it had moved away from South Parade in 1856) but it was not considered sufficient. An advertisement was placed into the newspapers in May:

> SITE WANTED FOR BUILDING A NEW HOSPITAL – The Committee of the Manchester Eye Hospital are desirous of receiving OFFERS OF LAND of not less than 1,000 square yards, within a radius of not more than 1½ mile of the Manchester Exchange, for the purposes of erecting a new hospital. – Offers to be addressed to DR LITTLE, Eye Hospital, Manchester

In due course it was a property of Thomas Agnew, he of art dealing fame, which attracted the attention of the Committee. After due consideration, in October 1865:

> *The following Resolutions were passed*
>
> *1st That the house & land no 24 St John Street be purchased for the sum of £2200 for the purposes of an Eye Hospital*
>
> *2nd That it be left with Mr Leppoc & Mr Heron to negotiate with Mr Agnew for the property*
>
> *3rd That the architectural work be given to Messrs Mills and Murgatroyd, and that a building Committee consisting of Messrs Leppoc, Rumney, Potter & Goldschmidt, be appointed to confer*

with those gentlemen, as to the requirements & construction of the new building, and that a plan & report of the intended building be made out by the Architects and laid before the Board

At the Annual Meeting of the Hospital in January 1866, the choice of St. John Street was reported as being somewhat removed from the railway stations and dense working population to the east of the city, but had the advantage of great quietness and pure air. The site had a house on it, but considerable extension and redesign was required. The purchase cost was £2,200, but the total outlay proved to be £7,300. The vigorous and repeated searches for new donations, subscriptions and bequests to meet this sum need not be enumerated, but this period was to be one of the most active of the Committee for years. In the meantime, South Parade was becoming increasingly unpleasant:

It was reported that during the hot weather there was an intolerable nuisance arising in the cellar from stoppage of some of the pipes & accumulation of filth in a deep well & that since the last meeting of the Board, this filth had been removed by the formation of a new drain communicating with the main sewer

The Boiler in the kitchen was said to be in a bad condition & should there ever be a difficult supply of water, it would be extremely dangerous, but Mr Hampson undertook to have the cistern examined working, as the Committee did not wish to purchase a new boiler at present

Manchester Royal Eye Hospital, No. 24 St. John Street (the tallest building on the right) seen from the junction with Deansgate. St. John's Church, to be demolished in 1930, is seen at the end of the road

The contracts required for fitting-out of the new building in St. John Street are testament to the cutting-edge technology available at the time: Bells and speaking-tubes were the method of internal communication (£45); lighting was by gas (£45); heating was by a coal-fired boiler, and distributed by water pipes (£139). Changes to plans, strikes by joiners and sundry irritations were but minor inconveniences in a time of cheap labour and Victorian efficiency. The completed building was visited and inspected on January 7th 1867:

> *Present Messrs Leppoc, Bannerman, Dyson, McKeand, Samelson, Parlane, Aitken, Hampson & Murgatroyd*
>
> *The premises were examined & the wants in each room carefully noted. Mr Hampson was instructed to see after the kitchen furniture etc & chair & table for patients sitting rooms. Mr Dyson undertook to furnishing of the Surgeon's & matron's Rooms. Mr Murgatroyd was requested to have the panelling on the Wall of the Board Room done.*
>
> *The meeting agreed that a removal to the New Building should be made on Thursday next*

And so it was. There is no description of the move itself, but one can imagine a stream of porters with their backs laden or their trolleys loaded with furniture, rolling noisily along the cobbles between the hospitals; a group of patients possibly being led on foot to their new temporary abode. On January 11th the first meeting was held in the new hospital, closely followed by the AGM in February, also at the house, and to mark the occasion, presided over by the President, Lord Edward Howard MP. More was to be done, and alterations continued after occupancy. In the meantime, a rather important matter had been quietly pursued on behalf of the Hospital, and in May 1867 the response that the Committee wished for, arrived from the 4th Earl Belmore, secretary to Spencer Walpole, the Home Secretary. From the minutes:

> *The following letter was forwarded by Mr Heron, to be laid before this Board -*
>
> *Whitehall*
>
> *9th May 1867*
>
> *Sir*
>
> *I am directed by Mr Secretary Walpole to inform you, with reference to your letter of the 21st March last, that he has had the Honor to submit to the Queen the request of the Board of Management of the Manchester Eye Institution that the Institution may be permitted to assume the Title of "Royal"; and that Her Majesty has been graciously pleased to accede to the request of the Board, and to command that the Institution shall be styled the "Royal Manchester Eye Institution"*
>
> *I am, Sir*
>
> *Your obedient Servant*
>
> *Belmore*

This momentous occasion of the assumption of the royal title was therefore accompanied by an unfortunate misunderstanding as to the name of the "Institution" which had ceased to be so named several years previously. However, the Committee were not to be distracted; the Hospital immediately took the name of "Royal Manchester Eye Hospital", and did so until a simple typographical error in the publication of the annual report the following year. Perhaps the Board then considered that, as their great neighbour the "Manchester Royal Infirmary" had chosen, unusually, to commence their title with the name of their city, they should do the same. Whatever the reason for the decision, the title which the Hospital retains to this day is the "Manchester Royal Eye Hospital"

Not long after the hospital had moved to St. John Street, Dr David Little, who had performed diligently the onerous job of House Surgeon and Secretary (and who had seemed rather less stressed by the experience than either his predecessor or, as it would transpire, his successor) wrote to the Board:

> *Gentlemen*
>
> *I beg to lay before you my resignation as House Surgeon & Secretary to this Hospital and it is with some feeling of regret that I do so, but I am led to it from a desire to enter into private practice. It is now upwards of 4 years since you did me the honour of electing me to this Office, and as I have endeavoured to perform the duties of the appointment to the best of my ability, it will be a pleasure to know from you that I have given satisfaction. I thank you most cordially for the confidence you have placed in me, and for the uniform kindness & courtesy which I have all along experienced at your hands. I will always take a warm interest in the welfare of the Hospital, and do what lies in mu power to add to its success.*
>
> *I am, Gentlemen*
>
> *Yours respectfully*
>
> *David Little*

The Board expressed their gratitude to Dr Little in the most courteous terms (as well they might; Little had clearly performed the near-impossible combined job of House Surgeon and Secretary with considerable skill and fortitude for a long period), and immediately advertised for his successor. Now that the Hospital had more commodious accommodation, the House Surgeon and Secretary was resident, and in reflection of that the salary was reduced to £70 per annum, with board, lodging and laundry provided. Christopher William Calthrop, from Lincolnshire, was duly appointed. He was to last a mere four months in post before departing, exhausted.

A schism had been developing between various medical and committee personalities over a period of months, perhaps years. Thomas Windsor wrote to Mr Leppoc:

> *Mr Dear Sir*
>
> *When, towards the close of last year, I spoke to you about resigning my office at the Eye Hospital, you requested me not to do so for two or three months. Now, however, more than six*

have passed:- will you therefore be so kind as to give in my resignation at the next meeting of the committee.

Yours Truly

Thomas Windsor

Mr Leppoc was not amused by this attempted mode of resignation and his reply gives a flavour of the recent relationship between these two:

Mr Dear Sir

I have not laid your letter before the Board, hoping that you will reconsider your determination, but if you persist in resigning, pray address your letter to the Board & state at once the reasons which induce you to take this step

Yours Truly

H J Leppoc

However, Windsor was not a man to be summoned before the Board. In reply:

Mr Dear Sir

Having explained to you my reasons when I saw you some time ago & having nothing more to say and request you to give in my resignation

Yours Truly

Thos Windsor

The resignation was accepted by the Board with a mere nod to courteous acknowledgement. It is not known whether the resignation of Richard Hunt immediately following (nominally as he approached 65, at which time he was required to retire) was connected with the Windsor debacle, but his fulsome thanks, and the assurance of his continued interest, made a stark contrast with the abrupt resignation of Windsor. In response the Board were equally prolix, and Mr R T Hunt became an honorary Consulting Surgeon. Mr T Windsor did not. In the meantime the Board made a pragmatic decision: two Honorary Surgeons had departed in rapid succession, and in July, Dr Little, a man whom they clearly regarded with both affection and respect, had departed from the post of House Surgeon. He was approached again, and in September, without competitive application, he was reappointed as Honorary Surgeon.

The honorary medical staff at this time were not working in harmony. In particular Dr Samelson and Mr McKeand appeared unable to work amicably on the same day, with claims by one of inappropriate use of facilities by the other. The Medical Board decided that they should be separated and arranged that they consult on different days. The precise timings permitted for consultation were debated, and the House Surgeon was asked to ensure that any approaches by private patients were distributed to the surgeons in a pre-arranged manner. A further debate centred on the number of beds to be allocated to each surgeon, to the extent that each bed was allocated a number, and each set of numbers allocated to named surgeons. At the Medical Board meeting of October 12th, the flurry of trivial minutes descended into farce:

Dr Little proposed, Dr Samelson seconded a motion as follows -

That a microscope be obtained for the Hospital at a cost not exceeding £20

Mr Hunt moved as an amendment, seconded Mr Windsor –

That no microscope be purchased for the Hospital

The amendment was put & lost & the original proposition was then carried

Conflict also arose in October 1867 over the preferred contents of the hospital pharmacopoeia, each apparently requiring some drugs to be discontinued, and others objecting. The detail of this meeting need not be related, except to record its ending, and the beginning of the next:

The proposition was put & carried – Considerable confusion followed & the meeting was abruptly broken up.........after much discussion & confusion Mr Hunt & Dr Samelson leaving the meeting under protest.

The remaining doctors did however continue in their absence, and in due course a list of drugs to be discontinued was minuted. Their names give some flavour of the contemporary medicines available to doctors which were "not kept any more for Hospital use":

October 1867: Drugs to be discontinued from the Hospital pharmacopoeia

Matters rose to a head in November, at which time the frustration of the Board became evident, with an open threat to the doctors of a new, and for the nineteenth century, novel form of contract which would presage the National Health Service by 70 years:

> *The SubCommittee appointed to investigate the differences arising at the meetings of the Medical Board beg to report that the want of harmonious action on the part of the Medical Board has suggested to the enquiry whether the Honorary Medical Officers might not be advantageously superseded by paid Surgeons practising only in & on behalf of the Hospital. It is submitted that by the appointment of one or more first class men adequately remunerated the Hospital might be better served than at present, while the difficulties constantly occurring would be avoided. In such case all fees from patients able to pay for treatment would be received by the Hospital & would go far to reimburse the expenditure incurred in the House*

> *Other source of income might be from making the Hospital educational, the Surgeons giving sessional Lectures to medical students. In this respect the Manchester Royal Eye Hospital does not occupy the position it ought to do, considering the importance of its operations & the district in which it is situated*

The threat was however expressed more in irritation than in expectation; sabre-rattling is ineffective if the blade is blunt. The "first class men" at this time were invariably successfully self-employed practitioners and would deride the prospect of salaried employment at a charitable institution, firstly because the remuneration could never compare, and secondly because the fall in status and loss of professional freedom would be intolerable. Those doctors willing to fill any such posts would not be of the same level of qualification or skill. The matter was quietly dropped. The Board also suggested that the Chairman, Mr Leppoc, should chair the Medical Board meetings, presumably in an effort to instil some maturity into proceedings, but the response from the doctors (for once speaking with one voice) was so antagonistic that this too was dropped, the comment from Mr McKeand being:

> *Mr McKeand thought that the General Board ought not to interfere with the Medical men about their mode of conducting their own business*

The onerous nature of the combined post of House Surgeon and Secretary (and quite likely, the stress of dealing with the honorary medical staff) was in the meantime claiming another victim. In December 1867 the Board received the following:

> *Gentlemen*

> *When some four months ago you did me the honour of electing me your House Surgeon, I thought myself most fortunate in obtaining the post of responsible Officer to the largest Eye Hospital in the United Kingdom & fully intended to keep my appointment for eighteen months. From the very first day that I commenced my work I have endeavoured to do my duty to the Hospital to the best of my ability, not by sycophantic timeserving, but by respectful suggestions as to what might be for the real good of the Charity & to merit tour approbation and reward by faithful service.*

Several circumstances have however combined to force me to abandon this idea, & I now beg of you to accept my resignation

Briefly stated the principal are these. The differences that have lately occurred between the members of your Medical Staff, & the continued interference of one of them in matters with which professional men acquainted with common usage do not busy themselves has made my position uncomfortable in the extreme. A second is disappointment in the amount of experience & improvement to be derived from my situation. The immense field for practice afforded by the Midland & Northern Counties, naturally presented to the mind of a stranger a correspondingly great <u>personal</u> experience & improvement. That this is not afforded is at once evident from a comparison of the number of patients annually relieved & operations performed in this & other Ophthalmic Hospitals. Further the relative proportion between the duties required from the House Surgeon & from the Secretary is so extremely small as to render a long continuance in the combined offices by any <u>qualified</u> man except under most special circumstances exceedingly doubtful

Therefore, with great regret at having thus disabled from fulfilling my original intentions, & with the great respect that I feel to be due to the individual members of the Board, I beg to tender my resignation of the Offices of House Surgeon & Secretary

I am Gentlemen

Your most obedient servant

Christopher W Calthrop

The Board decided not to replace him pending further discussions. Whether his brief but traumatic experience at the Eye Hospital changed the career plan of Dr Calthrop is not known, but not long after leaving Manchester he was commissioned into the Bengal Medical Department, rising to the rank of Colonel as Principal Medical Officer for Assam, and adopting a hyphenated surname. In 1904 Christopher Carr-Calthorp CBE MD MRCS retired to write a genealogy of the Calthrop and Calthorpe families of Norfolk and Lincolnshire.

Dr Anstey was appointed as House Surgeon and Secretary in February 1868. He could not cope – he was reprimanded for absenting himself for three days, and by March had resigned, leaving immediately. The Board were finally getting the message that the combination of these two distinct posts was an unreasonable expectation, and the next post of House Surgeon was advertised separately, at a salary of £70 per annum with board & lodging. The occupant was Dr Charles Glascott, who would go on to become a long-serving member of the staff.

Problems amongst and with the medical staff continued. Dr Samelson was upbraided for using hospital servants in his own private practice, a few doors away in St. John Street. The medical staff responded vigorously to an overbearing Board resolution (instigated by Messrs Leppoc and Heron) requiring all of them to assemble at lunchtime every Saturday to discuss amongst themselves any patient thought to require an operation, before it was performed. The Board backed down. Dr Samelson and Mr McKeand had a nose-to-nose altercation over the use of hospital space at particular times, McKeand's threat to "make mincemeat of" Samelson leading to an official complaint to the Board by the latter. The Board described McKeand's language as "violent and unjustifiable" and demanded an apology, which was duly delivered to them but not, notably, to Samelson. The Board nevertheless hoped "that there may henceforth be harmonious cooperation on the part of the Honorary Medical Officers which is in fact essential for the effective promotion of the prosperity of this Institution".

In 1870 a documentary piece about the Manchester Royal Eye Hospital appeared in the *Manchester Guardian,* as part of a descriptive series on charitable institutions. The following extracts give a flavour of medicine at the time, in an entirely supportive and uncritical fashion:

> The in-patients have sleeping accommodation in roomy, well-ventilated wards, of which there are two large ones and one small one for each sex. They assemble in sitting-rooms, which are also dining-rooms, during the day; and in the evening those who are able amuse themselves in the large reception-room with music and singing. The windows of the dayroom are coloured so as to produce a toned light; and the light in the sleeping wards is also regulated by coloured blinds. The average stay of in-patients is three weeks, and during that time they are supplied with every need.
>
> For nearly six hours each day the patients occupy the time of the honorary medical officers. Three surgeons attend severally two days a week... They are assisted by the house surgeon, Dr Glascott, and by two nurses, the senior of whom, Margaret Somerville, has displayed such a faculty for ministering to this particular ailment, that the medical officers have confidence that she would wisely prescribe for and could effectually deal with any disease of the eye short of a surgical operation. It fell to our lot to see the course of procedure when Dr Samelson was in attendance, and we cannot forbear expressing our admiration of his genial kindness not unmixed with the rarest but most genuine humour, and directed with intuitive skill to each patient in such a manner as to remove all constraint and fear... This daily levee is attended by from 100 to 150 persons, including on an average about 15 new cases.
>
> Dr Samelson related to us a typical illustration of the usefulness of the Institution. When a patient comes, as is often the case, suffering from an ulceration of the cornea, there is often found a deposition of pus in the anterior chamber of the eye. If such a one followed his occupation, he would probably lose his sight. The Institution takes him in, puts him in a warm bed, gives him good food, beer and wine, administers quinine mixture, applies atropine to the eye and a lotion of camomile flowers; and in about a fortnight the patient is able to return to work, and the sight is saved. The Institution is found to do more good in this way than by operations.

The annual expenditure is about £1,800, and the subscriptions at present are £1,350. Thus there is an immediate need for £450 per annum more; and, considering the extensive area which this Institution benefits, there should be no difficulty in raising the subscription list to the required amount.

Or thus it was hoped. Such pieces were in theory invaluable advertisements for the needs of the Hospital, but in practice the funds were constantly under stress. The imbalance tended to be made up by (naturally unpredictable) bequests and ad hoc donations, but one particular problem arose recurrently, as was made clear in a following Annual Report:

The Chairman said that he understood the institution, however much it was valued in and out of Manchester, did not receive that support in the out districts, and in the neighbourhood of Manchester, that it ought to receive. He believed that only 40 percent of the cases treated in the hospital belonged to Manchester, and the remaining 60 percent came from the districts round about. He thought the wealthy people residing in those districts ought to be able to afford the institution a very adequate support.

Occasionally such appeals were successful. In 1871, a donation of £1,000 (about £110,000 today) was made by a Mr Nicholls, and a similar amount from a Mr Hatton. These unusual but immense donations were lifelines to solvency, swelled by sums ranging from £5 to £500 from individual legacies, collective votes of thanks, and wealthy benefactors. At the same time the regular subscriptions and donations were pursued vigorously by the Collector, who presented accounts to each Board meeting.

In 1872 the Hospital's Matron, Miss Bishop, retired, and the Head Nurse Margaret Somerville was promoted to fill her place at a salary of £40 per annum. She was to fulfil the post for ten years. In the same year, medical students were officially permitted to attend the Hospital for instruction, at a charge of £2.2s for six months. Originally intended to be limited to students of the Manchester Royal School of Medicine, it was in fact opened to any medical student. Although students had attended intermittently prior to this, 1872 can be considered the year that the Manchester Royal Eye Hospital became an undergraduate teaching institution.

In the same year, conflicts amongst the medical staff again reached a head. The severity of the mutual accusations enforced the creation of an investigatory subcommittee. Dr Samelson attempted, unsuccessfully, to have Sir Joseph Heron removed from that group. Heron, knighted in 1870, had been a prominent Board member for some years, and had been the Town Clerk of Manchester since 1838. A lawyer by trade, he was a persuasive member with a keen eye for organisation. Several previous matters had brought him into conflict with one or other members of the medical staff, and his presence on this body was objected to. The subcommittee uncovered a variety of irregularities, and were concerned that operations were being performed by the House Surgeon, and that indeed a significant portion of the duties assumed to be performed

Sir Joseph Heron, Town Clerk of Manchester and Royal Eye Hospital board member

by the honorary medical staff, were being delegated. The correspondence to the Board by each of the doctors was referred to but was not kept, perhaps because of some of the accusations within. It was therefore suggested that the number of honorary staff should be increased, and the Board came within a whisker of sacking all the doctors and starting again:

> *Although it appeared upon many grounds to be desirable your subcommittee have been unwilling to recommend that the present Honorary Medical Officers should be requested to resign, in as much as it was possible that such a course of proceeding might, if adopted have been misunderstood or misconstrued, and that injustice might unintentionally have been done to Medical Gentlemen to whom, whatever may be thought of the present grounds of dissatisfaction the Board are certainly indebted for valuable services rendered for many years to the Institution. In addition to the publicity which would necessarily have been given to the unfortunate disputes and quarrels which have arisen could not have been otherwise than prejudicial to the best interests of the Hospital.*

Messrs McKeand, Little and Samelson were censured by the Board, special ire being reserved for Dr Samelson to whom it was made clear that any further complaint might be the last. However, Mr McKeand's services (the quality of which one suspects, were not quite up to the mark, a matter which may have contributed to these conflicts) were considered dispensable and his retirement was enforced with immediate effect. He practised for a little while further in Manchester, and then retired to Southport where he opened a cottage eye hospital. It did not survive his death in 1880. In due course the House Surgeon, Charles Glascott, was promoted to fill his place (in the absence of other applicants). Glascott was born in Constantinople, the son of John Nassau Glascott, surgeon to the British Hospital there. Charles was brought home to Edinburgh for schooling and university, graduating there in 1868. He came straight to Manchester (one wonders whether he was the acolyte of Dr Little) and the two were well-known to work well together at the Hospital. He was regarded as having "a somewhat brusque military manner", said to conceal a tenderness and real interest in the welfare of his patients. He was to be in post for 35 years.

The departure of Mr McKeand had achieved in part what was necessary at the Eye Hospital – the "peace and harmonious cooperation" of the remainder. Now however, a further attempt was made to increase the number of honorary staff to six, and Drs Little and Samelson exploded – it was clear that from their perspective, the constant sniping and interference by the Board had gone too far. Their rebuttal, signed by both and this time printed and circulated to all Board members (with the clear threat of wider circulation), verged upon the limits of tolerable language in Victorian times. It has to be said that their arguments against the proposal, although partly motivated by self-interest, read logically and are supported by the absence of applicants for Glascott's post. The lengthy arguments however are less important than the way in which the letter was concluded:

We do not wish to be wanting of courtesy to the Board. We sincerely appreciate the private worth of many amongst you whose respect for our position, services, and well founded opinion we would no less sincerely appreciate. It is from the relentless partisanship of Sir Joseph Heron, for the last twelve years, as you are so well aware, the irrepressible helpmate of Mr McKeand, that we desire to appeal to the untrammelled judgement of those who for the time being are the guardians of the interests of the Eye Hospital, and of those of the population concerned in its working. If unsuccessful, we shall be constrained to lay the case, with what elucidations may further come to be called for, before the medical profession and the public at large.

We have the honour to be, gentlemen,

Very obediently, yours

A SAMELSON MD   D LITTLE MD

Both Charles Glascott and Richard Hunt gave their support to these arguments in separate, more conciliatory letters. Nevertheless the Board were incensed:

Resolved..That the Board regret that any Honorary Medical Officer connected with this Institution should have so far forgotten what is due not less to himself than to the other members of the Board as to address a communication in every respect so unjustifiable and so objectionable in its terms to the Board of Management.

Messrs Little and Samelson backed down and apologised. Fifteen-love to the Board. They went ahead with their plan to appoint new surgeons. However, the existing honorary surgeons' views were not to be so easily over-ridden; having been asked to consider the applicants, they reported to the Board that they "fail to show that they are competent to undertake the duties of surgeon to an Eye Hospital". Fifteen-all. Nevertheless the Board were not so easily defeated. They merely altered the job description:

It appears that there exists a difficulty in getting Gentlemen who are willing to undertake the duties (and so the Board) *now recommend that instead of Honorary Medical Gentlemen, Honorary Assistant Surgeons be appointed and that under the direction of the Chairman advertisements to be put into the papers inviting application accordingly.*

Thirty-fifteen. The Medical Board were not asked to review the applications; Forty-fifteen. On December 3rd 1873, three were appointed: Dr PH Mules, Mr R Crean and Mr H Estcourt (the first two having previously been rejected by the surgeons as "not competent"). The Honorary Surgeons were then asked to offer guidance to the Board concerning rules governing the new Assistant Surgeons, but replied:

That as there is at present no rule recognising the appointment of Assistant Surgeons, the Medical Board beg respectfully to decline assigning any duties to such, until the rules may have been so altered as to constitute Assistant Surgeons as regular Honorary Medical Officers of the Hospital.

In other words, Assistant Surgeons did not actually exist. Forty-thirty. Here however, the Board drew their trump card. Mr TC Morgan, an applicant from Moorfields Eye Hospital for one of the Assistant Surgeon posts, was duly elected by the Board, without consultation with the existing surgeons, as a full Honorary Surgeon. Game, set and match. In fact he was a mere pawn in this battle, a mere transient, resigning less than one year after appointment. The three Assistant Surgeons were "allocated" to the Honorary Surgeons by the Board, again without consultation. The medical men silently admitted defeat. It is difficult to understand why they chose to do so; each was now well-established in private practice and work at the Royal Eye Hospital was onerous and time-consuming. The institution could have been destroyed by a walk-out of medical men. That they did not do so in the face of over-aggressive management by the Board is either a tribute to their dedication and ethics, or a pragmatic realisation that honorary status at MREH continued to be of social and financial value.

Notwithstanding this public medical acquiescence, all seemed rather too quiet – Medical Board meetings now went inquorate or merely did not happen, six months at one stage passing without the doctors meeting together. Messrs Crean and Estcourt resigned in short order and one gains the impression of an unhappy House, presumably with ongoing conflicts and factions, and perhaps with unbearable pressure being brought onto the unwanted newcomers in the corridors of the Hospital. However, in contrast Dr Mules was made of sterner stuff; he was promoted Honorary Surgeon after only one year in post as Assistant Surgeon. A Devon man, he had been trained at St George's Hospital and Edinburgh University, and was a true polymath, contributing many papers and case reports to the medical literature, being a liberal contributor to the Transactions of the Ophthalmological Society. In 1884 he was awarded in Paris the Prize Medal of the International Society for the Amelioration of the Condition of the Blind. He lived in Bowdon, where like John Windsor before him he pursued his private love of botany. Most of his spare time was spent tending an extensive garden and over-seeing a nursery locally, from which were raised two species of Aubrieta, thus named after him. He resigned his post at the Eye Hospital after fourteen years, moving further west where he continued practising ophthalmology in both Chester and Wrexham. He also wrote on local history, but his main ophthalmological landmark was an attempt to replace vitreous after evisceration with a solid implant.

The Board were regularly frustrated by the increasingly uncooperative behaviour of Dr Samelson and he was reprimanded on several occasions for various misdemeanours. Matters came to a head in June 1876 following a complaint against him by the House Surgeon, then a Mr Hex. The details are unknown but the matter was severe enough for the Board immediately to suspend him from duties, and for him to resign his post shortly afterwards. He remained in practice in Manchester for over ten more years. He left a confusing legacy – clearly a highly intelligent man and a dedicated ophthal-mologist who contributed much to the people of Manchester not only at the Royal Eye Hospital but at the Sanitary Association, the Liberal Association, the Manchester &

Salford District Provident Society, Henshaw's Society and other institutions. He was an active member of the Manchester Literary Club and read many papers to it. It is from his obituary in their Quarterly Review that his portrait here is taken. He retired to Cannes, where he died only a few months later in January 1888. He left sums of money to many charitable institutions, including £300 to the Manchester Hospital for Incurables, £100 to the Manchester Warehousemen and Clerks' Orphan Schools and £100 to the Strangeways Boys' Refuge. Clearly a complex man, a hard worker with a strong sense of public responsibility and a skill for organisation, yet impatient and intolerant, he remains an important part of the history of the Royal Eye Hospital, and as an importer of the techniques of von Graefe, important to British ophthalmology.

In 1877 the Hospital was visited again by the press. The Manchester City News wrote a series of articles about Manchester institutions, of which this was the first, appearing in February of that year. Extracts give a flavour of the times:

> A professional aspect and a professional quietude cling to St. John's Street, Deansgate, in spite of the great wave of turbulent and unthoughtful existence which washes its very doorsteps… Large, roomy, red-brick houses, browned with age, the family mansions of a past generation, bright doorplates, dainty uniform window-curtains, a sombre church at one end, the solitude of a silent street situated in the very heart of Babylon, and one building brighter than the rest, at once more cheerful and more dignified, and you are ringing the bell of the Royal Eye Hospital.
>
> It is eleven o'clock in the morning, and the day is Monday. Between 250 and 300 people are seated in the reception-room. Strong men, patient women, babies who solve the riddle of human suffering by crying, boys and girls who seem to be more struck with the novelty of the situation than with its inconvenience, this unhappy crowd is assembled in a large square room, and a grand sense of community in pain and trouble and patience almost stills the air.
>
> Following the footsteps of a small batch of these outdoor patients, you find yourself in the consultation-room, where an honorary surgeon is devoting all his skill and care to the relief of suffering, and, in some case, receiving murmurs where he is wont to receive guineas. Not that it would be just to imply that appreciation is not the rule with the patients, only that here and there a mother seems to be disappointed when the physician plainly intimates that uncleanliness or ordinary neglect is the cause of the ailment, and appears to wish that the diagnosis were more complex.
>
> With prescription papers in hand, the patients succeed each other, one by one, in front of the surgeon. In the majority of cases his practised eye detects at once the cause of ailment, and the short dialogue which ensues is less in the form of interrogation than in the form of half a dozen brief diagnostic sentences from the surgeon, to all of which the patient assents. If it is a simple case of external disease the surgeon writes a prescription, the patient is passed on to the dispensary, and then leaves the building with instructions as to his return visit. But when the patient

complains of impaired sight, before presenting himself to the surgeon an assistant tests his eyes by placing him at a distance of twenty feet opposite a card upon which are printed letters and figures of various sizes. A standard or normal measurement of good eyesight having been agreed upon, it is plain that the precise extent of the patient's departure from this standard can be expressed in a mathematical formula. If this examination shows that glasses remedy the defect, a suitable pair of spectacles is prescribed for him, and given to him without charge. If glasses are of no avail, he is shown into a room lighted by gas where, by means of a simple and wonderful instrument called the ophthalmoscope, the surgeon is able to explore the whole interior of the eye, to see the back of it as clearly as the front, and to trace the very nerves which communicate with the brain. This examination results in either medical treatment or surgical operation, and it is consoling to know that, as sensitive as the eye is to pain, few eye diseases and few operations are accompanied with acute or prolonged suffering.

The visitor is introduced to the Matron, Miss Somerville, and enters the indoor department of the hospital. The first room that we enter is called the female sitting room. Seated in a semicircle round the fire are about twenty persons, of all ages, from children in arms to women of eighty. Eyes bandaged and resting their heads upon their hands, a few of them are chatting in undertones, but on most of them a listless, weary vacancy seems to have settled, the effect of this enforced idleness. The men's sitting-room is a repetition of the women's, but it is much more fully occupied. The various trades of Lancashire are peculiarly trying and threatening to the sight, and a large majority of the male in-patients are the victims of accident.

The operating room is splendidly adapted for its purpose as regards light and appointments, and so exquisitely formed and so ingenious are the dainty surgical instruments that the imagination is not here terrified as it is apt to be in similar chambers of horrors. Nor must we omit to notice the large and admirably-fitted kitchen and scullery on the ground floor, the pans in which you can see your face, the clean floor off which you might eat, the magnificent sirloin which was roasting before the fire, and which subsequently formed the dinner of the patients. The remark probably applies to all well-managed hospitals, but it is certain that the good food, the cleanly habits, and the kindly treatment which rule in this institution, contribute largely to hasten and to complete the cures inaugurated by scientific skill and happy medicines.

These happy medicines; what were they and how were they prepared, stored and administered. The Medical Board and other minutes are liberally scattered with references to the high costs of these medicines, and various dispensers were employed over the years in an attempt to reduce the outlay. For example, the same year:

The Medical Officers agreed to use Cinchona instead of Quinine as much as possible owing to the high price of the latter.

INFUSUM GENTIANÆ COMPOSITUM.

℞ Gentianæ concisæ,
   Aurantii corticis exsiccati,
   Limonum corticis exsiccati āā ℥ ij,
   Aquæ ferventis Oj.
Dosis f ℥ j.

     INFUSUM NUCIS VOMICÆ.

℞ Nucis Vomicæ contusæ ℥ j,
   Aquæ ferventis Oj.
Dosis f ℥ ss.

     INFUSUM QUASSIÆ.

℞ Quassiæ concisæ Ɵ ij,
   Aquæ ferventis Oj.
Dosis f ℥ j.

     INFUSUM VALERIANÆ.

℞ Valerianæ ℥ ss,
   Aquæ ferventis Oj.
Dosis f ℥ j.

     LINCTUS PAPAVERIS.

℞ Opii contriti gr. j,
   Aquæ,
   Theriacæ āā f ℥ j,
   Misturæ Acaciæ f ℥ ij.
   f ℥ j continet Opii gr. ¼.
Dosis f ℥ j ad f ℥ ss.

A page reproduced from the pharmacopoeia of the Manchester Royal Infirmary 1840, to illustrate contemporary instructions for drug manufacture

The efficacy of Cinchona bark as an antipyretic had been known for 200 years. Containing a mixture of alkaloids, the bark was crushed and dissolved in alcohol to form a tincture. The chemical extraction of quinine, the most effective of the alkaloids and already identified as antimalarial, was expensive. Native only to Central and South America, the bark was in limited supply and could not be harvested without killing the tree. The expansion of the British Empire into India, with its accompanying fevers, had pressurised supplies, and indeed earlier in the nineteenth century, a Dutch/English expedition to South America had been organised specifically to obtain saplings and seeds to be introduced into the Eastern colonies of both nations, so that more local supplies could be guaranteed. Still at this date the difference in cost between raw Cinchona tincture, and purified quinine, was substantial, hence the decision.

For a flavour of other substances then used in medicine and ophthalmology, one only has to read the list of those discontinued in 1867 from the Eye Hospital formulary. No copy of the formulary is still in existence, but a page from the Manchester Royal Infirmary Pharmacopoeia (1840) is illustrated, to show the almost alchemical instructions for the creation of potions, which are unintelligible to the modern doctor or pharmacist. Some examples of the Eye Hospital drugs were:

Pulv Helleb Alb (Powder of White Hellebore) – a severe gastrointestinal irritant and poison, sometimes administered with laudanum to treat either gout or manic disorders

Tinct Aloes (Tincture of Aloe root) – crushed Aloe dissolved in alcohol, with liquorice, used as a cathartic

Ext Aconiti (Extract of Aconite [Monkshood]) – a deadly poison, a substantial diuretic, but then applied locally to skin, sadi to diminish the pain of arthritis or neuralgia

Tinct Lavand Co (Tincture of Feverfew) – to treat severe headaches and migraine

Antim Sulph (Antimony Sulphide, Kohl) – used already for two millennia as a black eye cosmetic, in this context it was used as an emetic

Pulv Digitalis (Foxglove powder) – now used in its purified form to treat cardiac arrhythmias, at this time is was used variously to treat boils, abscesses and poorly-healing wounds, headaches, as a diuretic, and for several other complaints

Infus Gentian Co Conc (Concentrated Gentian Compound Infusion) – a boiled solution from the Gentian flower, mixed with cardamom, orange peel and other flavourings, which contains caffeine, nicotinamide and other active ingredients; to settle the stomach and as a general tonic

Pulv Myrrh (Myrrh Powder) – powdered resin from the bark of Commiphora trees, believed for millennia to treat multitudinous diseases, but known at this time to be antiseptic, to treat gingivitis and mouth ulcers, and used to treat syphilis

Oc Amygdalae (Oculentum Oleum Amygdalae; Almond Eye Ointment) – an ophthalmic salve made from the oil of sweet (cultivated) almonds, used as a dressing for eyelid inflammations. To be distinguished carefully from the oil of bitter (wild) almonds, also used with great care orally as an analgesic, expectorant and anti-tussive, prepared diligently to ensure that no cyanide is included!

There are common trends here; the preponderance of unrefined alkaloids; the hair-raising toxicity of some; and the wide range of inventive possibilities available to the doctor prior to the isolation of active ingredients and their purification. The prescriptions were taken away by patients, not in standard containers, but in those brought by themselves. The outpatient record sheets of this time instructed: "You are to bring with you clean bottles, with corks, for your medicines. One penny is to be charged for each bottle delivered from Hospital Stores".

In 1879 we return to a common theme – the need for more inpatient beds. Turning to the rear of the building, the Committee looked at adjacent cottages on Artillery Street and undertook to lease them for additional accommodation. It is a characteristic of Georgian and Victorian Manchester architecture, and by no means unique to this city, that many main residential and business streets had narrow roads running parallel, behind the large houses there. Commonly referred to as "Back South Parade", "Back Princess Street" or the like, these streets acted firstly as rear access to these large houses, for tradesmen, servants, suppliers; in general those who were permitted nowhere near the main entrances; and collections of small, dark cottages there often acted as servants' quarters. Artillery Street served this function for the houses on St John Street and still runs parallel to it. A recess off Artillery Street named Span Court contained four cottages which backed onto the Eye Hospital. All four were leased from a Mrs Roberts, for a period of 11 years at £45 per annum. Alterations included knocking-through and floor strengthening, after which the cottages were converted into additional dining and sitting room space, allowing space for the creation of several new beds within the main building, giving 66 in total.

The inpatients at this time languished in the Hospital for an average of nearly three weeks. We have some insight into their care, but are fortunate to have retained one volume of inpatient records, those of Dr Little in 1883. As

The Royal Eye Hospital in St. John Street, showing the cottages in Span Court behind

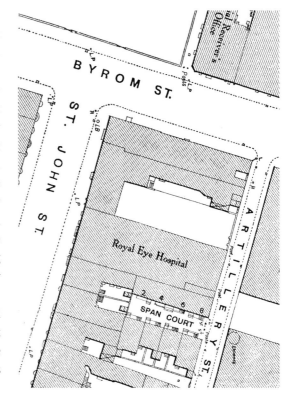

with all records during this era, the pages are carefully designed, well-presented and beautifully bound in half-leather with gold-tooled lettering. The records are brief but diligently kept, and of the several hundred in existence there are obvious trends: The first is that although the ophthalmoscope was available, the vast majority of patients did not undergo fundus examination, and ophthalmology at this time was overwhelmingly concerned with the anterior segment of the eye and its surroundings. Within this group, there are two main problems, of infection and injury; both problems typically presenting for the first time after weeks or more, with advanced complications such as perforated corneal ulcers or sympathetic ophthalmia. A further obvious feature is the large number of children, sometimes with irretrievable blindness, many with congenital syphilis, many with ophthalmic neonatorum. Two examples are illustrated:

An inpatient of Dr Little in 1883. Diagnosis: painful right eye after previous iridectomy & cataract surgery. Treatment – removal of eye

The drawings made for each patient are diligent and descriptive, and the diagnoses of anterior segment disease seem almost entirely in keeping with those that would be made today with vastly superior equipment. Occasional laconic notes are made after admission, either by Little or by the House Surgeon.

Another inpatient during the same year. Diagnosis: Large cottonball ? cysticercosis. Treatment – removal of eye

Although the abbreviations R and L are inserted onto these printed sheets, the ophthalmologists had a tendency to retain the Latin OD (oculum dexter) and OS (oculum sinister), a system which today, quaintly and anachronistically, is used only by our transatlantic colleagues (who also still adhere to the British Imperial notation of visual acuity)

In these notes the vision (metric Snellen notation by this stage) is recorded for each affected eye. Near vision might also be tested, and in the 1850s Professor Eduard Jaeger of Vienna had introduced a standardised method of testing the acuity for reading. A copy of a reading type from this period at the Eye Hospital still exists, and shows that the entire reading type, ingeniously constructed from a virtually continuous extract from *The Vicar of Wakefield* by Oliver Goldsmith (1766) is as much a test of literacy as it is of visual acuity! A paduasoy (this author has learned for the first time) is apparently a form of corded silk textile. One assumes that the clientele of the time would not have been familiar with either the more exotic of textiles at the time, nor of the terms used to describe them (even in Manchester).

The elegant reading test types devised for patients at the Manchester Royal Eye Hospital in about 1880. The passage is taken from *The Vicar of Wakefield* by Oliver Goldsmith

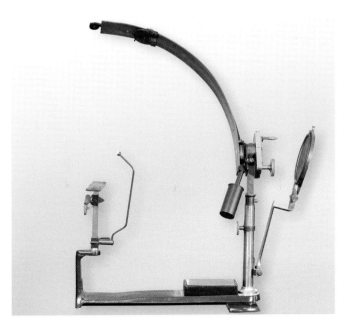

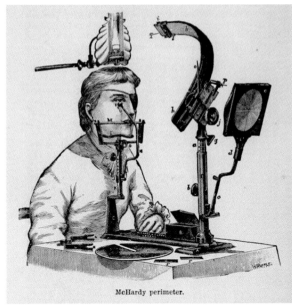

McHardy perimeter.

The Professor McHardy perimeter of 1882 (Reproduced with permission of Mr R Keeler, Royal College of Ophthalmologists) and a contemporary engraving of it in use

Patients with glaucoma were assessed by digital measurement of intraocular pressure. Although von Graefe had introduced a crude method of tonometry as early as 1862, it was not widely adopted, and the first accurate tonometer, produced by Schiøtz in 1905, was still 20 years away. The intraocular pressure or "tension" was recorded as normal (" T N") or raised from slightly (" T+1") to stone-hard (" T+3"). Treatment was by iridectomy. At this time the assessment of visual fields by perimetry had recently become available in various forms, and records of typical end-stage glaucoma with tunnel vision are recorded in the 1883 volume. At this time the Hospital was equipped with cutting-edge technology, the McHardy perimeter, designed only the previous year. It and several similar types were the fore-runners of the Lister perimeter whose use would persist until almost the end of the twentieth century. Bjerrum had yet to define the importance of central field analysis (his paper would be published in 1889). This author remembers with mixed feelings his experiences as an SHO new to ophthalmology in 1982, when despatched into the twilight of the one extant matt black-painted Bjerrum room, where he stood like the Sandeman man, caped in black, attempting to map the central field of a patient in front of a 6' vertical black felt carpet stitched with concentric circles. One sometimes wondered whether this was the ophthalmological equivalent of being sent for a "long stand".

The slow but inexorable increase in patient numbers was reflected and congratulated in successive annual reports as published in the Manchester newspapers, at which time the inestimable value of the institution was inevitably commented upon by the Mayor of Manchester and others (Hear hear!). Very occasionally however, were contrary views expressed; both patients and alternative practitioners were free to advertise in the newspapers, and in respectively the *Burnley Advertiser* and *Bury Times*:

–To the Inhabitants of Burnley and its Vicinity–

PERMIT me to call your attention to a few important facts. Within the last twenty years I have had under my treatment upwards of 1000 cases of Fevers and Stomach Complaint, which I have treated with unparalleled success…

Mary Smith, No 8 Holt St Burnley, was totally blind; two doctors attended her and she then went to the Manchester Eye Institution but could meet with no relief. I cured her in two months, and she is now going to school…

HL SMITH, Water Doctor

TO ALL SUFFERING FROM BAD EYESIGHT John Ashworth, of Britannia, Bacup, begs to inform the public that his wife has been nearly blind for three years, and having been to the Manchester Eye Hospital, and been treated by doctors round about for two years, without any good effect, at last she visited Mr DENNIS HIGSON, of Accrington, whose treatment in a fortnight has almost restored her to perfect sight. He with confidence recommends all sufferers to visit Mr Higson.

It was somewhat later, in 1881, that the attention of the Committee was drawn to the proximity of a suspicious-looking personage who was probably the same gentleman…

> *Dr Glascott informed the Board that for some time past patients attending the Hospital had been supplied with pamphlets by a man who stationed himself in Artillery Street for the purpose. These pamphlets, a copy of which was shown, were written by a person styling himself Professor Higson of Ashton and contained numerous testimonials purporting to be from patients who had been speedily cured by Professor Higson after prolonged and unsuccessful treatment at this Hospital. The Board thanked Dr Glascott for having brought this subject before their notice, and Mr Bannerman kindly offered to speak to the Detective Department*

… who then presumably had his collar felt and was not heard of again locally. He did however ply his trade elsewhere – Dennis Higson and his son "described variously as quack or botanical doctors" were fined £1.10s with costs in Burnley in 1882 for "exposing objectionable and obscene placards". They then clearly felt that the Northwest was becoming a little too "hot" to practise, and they moved to Sunderland, where they advertised in 1884 in the *Sunderland Daily Echo*:

BE WISE IN TIME –

If this should meet the eye of anyone requiring advice, or those who have been disappointed, neglected, or pronounced incurable, they should go to or write AT ONCE to

D HIGSON & SONS
MEDICAL HALL, 9 HUDSON-ROAD
(opposite the skating rink) SUNDERLAND

Who can you blame but yourself if you refuse the opportunity now offered you, when you can consult one (at the above address) – who will give you, free of charge, every instruction that will enable you to grasp the GRAND REMEDY which has saved thousands from future repentance and an untimely grave, and gives them that VIGOUR and STRENGTH which is so essential to happiness in all grades of society.

Etcetera. They probably also handed their pamphlets to patients "not cured" at the Sunderland Eye Infirmary (est 1836). But we must return to Manchester, where the new post of Secretary and Collector had been created, at a salary of £100 per annum. The previous Collector, John Lawton, who had served the Hospital for 16 years, was summarily given 3 months' notice, and Mr William Burgess was appointed to the dual post. The Hospital had now been in St. John Street for some 15 years; initially hailed as a massive improvement over the accommodation at South Parade, the total number of patients had progressively risen from 3,872 in 1867 to 12,961 in 1882, an enormous, three-fold increase in such a short time. The building could not cope, and on January 27th 1883, a special meeting was held, at which the Medical Staff presented to the Chairman a missive via Dr Little:

Dear Sir

I am desired by the Medical Staff to appeal to you respecting the insufficient accommodation afforded for patients at the Eye Hospital & to urge upon you and your Board the pressing need for the erection of a larger and more suitable building.

I In consequence of the large increase of patients of recent years both outpatients & in-patient departments are in a constant state of overcrowding, and the result is, the air throughout the whole building becomes most offensive.

II The present hospital contains 65 beds, & these are kept constantly filled, a state of things which materially interferes with the general health of the patients, as well as their recovery from Eye Disease & operations.

III On account of the small number of Beds, we are obliged every week to send patients back to their homes, who ought to be admitted into the House for operations – this becomes a serious matter to these patients, regarding expense & loss of time.

IV The Sitting-Room accommodation is most inadequate & the ventilation bad, & altogether the sanitary condition of the Hospital generally is far from what it ought to be.

V To provide for the <u>present </u>wants of the numerous patients attending the Eye Hospital, we should require a building provided with not less than 100 beds.

We trust these foregoing considerations will receive your earliest attention

Signed on behalf of the Medical Staff

Faithfully Yours

David Little

The Board were immediately in agreement with these sentiments, and it was apparent that a new building was required. The search for land began.

CHAPTER FIVE

Out of Town

THE ANNUAL REPORT OF 1882 drew attention, as had been perennially attempted, to the geographical disparity of the funding of the hospital. Of the 12,961 patients dealt with (of which 1,264 had been admitted as inpatients) about three quarters resided outside Manchester. The Board had frequently exhorted the cooperative societies and other institutions of the outlying towns to arrange more subscriptions to the Hospital, but perennially these had not been forthcoming. During the previous year, 138 patients from outside Manchester were completely unfunded, and a further 73 were from towns which submitted minimal subscription. Overall there were about 300 cooperative societies in the areas which the Hospital served, of which only 24 subscribed at all. This problem, which had existed since the first years of the hospital, would never be entirely resolved.

At the same meeting, the urgent need for a new Hospital was reiterated, though the likely cost of £15,000 was a great concern. The Board had rapidly considered a number of available pieces of land for building, mostly out of town. These included Ardwick Lodge on Upper Brook Street, and York Place fronting onto Oxford Street. However, after careful discussion it was unanimously agreed that a site on Oxford Street, bounded on the North side by Nelson Street, offered the best prospects. The medical officers pointed out that they tended to reside in town, and their private practises were currently a few moments walk at most, from the Hospital in St. John Street. However, the advantage of "superior air" and better accommodation to the patients outweighed such matters, and they agreed to the site, albeit suggesting that the retention of the St. John Street building be considered, for outpatient use. While such suggestions may not have been entirely altruistic, they transpired to be prophetic, as the continued usefulness of the arrangement would prove for many more years. Negotiations were undertaken and the site, totalling 3,700 sq yds, was purchased for £6,300. Since the Manchester Corporation were in the process of widening Oxford Street for the installation of tramlines, it was possible to offset some cost by selling 280 sq yds of frontage at £980.15s 6d., and to defer payment for the site for one year.

The purchased site was in Chorlton-on-Medlock, an area bounded in the north by

the River Medlock, and in the South by Victoria Park, a rich residential estate of large Victorian villa-style houses in large gardens. To the West was Moss Side, to the East, Ardwick. To the South along Oxford Street (shortly to become Oxford Road, continuing into Wilmslow Road) were almost exclusively large houses, the Northern border of such affluence being some houses on Nelson Street, including the previous residence of John Owens, benefactor of Owens College, now the University of Manchester. To the West, North and East were terraced residential streets for the middle classes. The area was well away from the crowded city with its mills still spewing smoke, its rivers still running with unclean water and its overcrowded streets. There was a house with several stables on site.

Considerable further discussion took place about the possibility of running two hospitals simultaneously; the necessary to-and-fro of the medical staff, the probable need for two House Surgeons, the duplication of furniture and equipment were all of concern. The Board decided that it could not be afforded, and planned to move entirely to Oxford Street. A New Hospital Fund was created and advertised widely, with an encouraging response from various Boards of Guardians and other potential donors. An instructions document was created for architects tendering for the project, and this included a requirement of 1200 cu ft per inpatient bed, and that the cost should not exceed £100 per patient bed. Five firms of architects competed anonymously for the tender, the successful firm being Pennington & Bridgen. Nathan Glossop Pennington

FRIBA and Thomas Edward Bridgen ran a large and highly successful Manchester firm on John Dalton Street, and were responsible for the design of several prestigious buildings in the town centre, several churches and at least one other hospital. The submitted plans were slightly amended and it was decided that the building should be cellared almost throughout. The final elevation drawing supplied by Messrs Pennington & Bridgen has become an icon for the Manchester Royal Eye Hospital over the succeeding 125 years.

The building was, as described by Pevsner, of Queen Anne style, of red Ruabon brick with steeped roofs and gabled windows on the third floor. The windows of the building were to be of clear glass in their lower part, and olive-green above. Enhancing the frontage at either end were two terracotta plaques by George Holding, the first showing Christ healing the eyes of the blind man (John Ch. 9); the second, at the southern end, showed the blinding of Elymas (Acts Ch. 13); this plaque would be removed during a future extension; it is not known whether it is still in existence.

The Chairman, Mr Goldschmidt, was doing his best to keep costs down, and objected to some of the more outrageous comforts proposed for staff and patients. In particular:

> *Hot & cold water proposed for each basin, I think quite unnecessary, and I would cancel the hot & then if required, let it be drawn from a pipe in the passage*

> *It was agreed that the separate Water Closet provided for the House Surgeon be dispensed with, and that the space be made of as a Hat & Cloak-room for the Board.*

The terracotta plaque designed by George Holding, of Christ curing the blind man (John 9:6), installed on the north gable of the new Eye Hospital

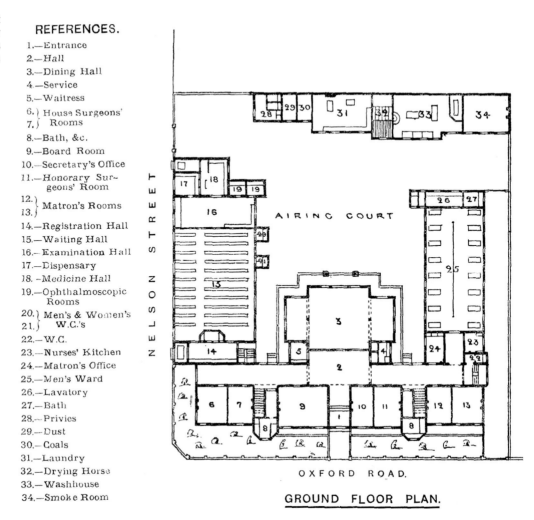

The original footprint of the new Manchester Royal Eye Hospital as designed in 1883

REFERENCES.

1.—Entrance
2.—Hall
3.—Dining Hall
4.—Service
5.—Waitress
6.⎫ House Surgeons'
7.⎬ Rooms
8.—Bath, &c.
9.—Board Room
10.—Secretary's Office
11.—Honorary Surgeons' Room
12.⎫ Matron's Rooms
13.⎭
14.—Registration Hall
15.—Waiting Hall
16.—Examination Hall
17.—Dispensary
18.—Medicine Hall
19.—Ophthalmoscopic Rooms
20.⎫ Men's & Women's
21.⎭ W.C.'s
22.—W.C.
23.—Nurses' Kitchen
24.—Matron's Office
25.—Men's Ward
26.—Lavatory
27.—Bath
28.—Privies
29.—Dust
30.—Coals
31.—Laundry
32.—Drying Horse
33.—Washhouse
34.—Smoke Room

GROUND FLOOR PLAN.

Notwithstanding the pressure on expenditure, the Board felt it necessary that the Boardroom of such an important institution reflect its status. Thus "for a sum not exceeding £50" that room was to be fitted with oak dadoes, glazed oak bookcases, a chimneypiece and ceiling cornices and rose. Fifteen builders tendered for the project, from whom Messrs R Neill & Sons were chosen at a quotation of £10,702. The original plans for the ground and first floors are shown here; alumni will immediately recognise the topography, but will remember the adaptation of space over a century later, when for instance the original laundry became for many years the "much-loved" Acute Referral Centre, the dining hall became the David Little Clinic, and the ground floor men's ward was to be the Day-Case Centre.

The first-floor plan was largely retained for over a century, but the operating theatre and women's ward were much later to become the Ophthalmic Imaging Department and Retinal Clinic, and the men's ward would become part of the Nightingale Suite.

The scale of the financial challenge presenting itself to the Board was now clear: the purchase of land and building costs would exceed £15,000, and after fitting and furnishing the total was predicted to be closer to £20,000, the hospital only having accumulated £9,000 to date. A wide appeal was made, but the difficulties of raising cash became apparent when only 50 of 14,000 leaflets printed and circulated, were successful. Much networking by the Board members was necessary, and matters were not made easier by the coincidence of three deaths; firstly of Henry Leppoc, stalwart in the Hospital's service for 31 years; secondly of Lord Howard, the Hospital President; and lastly of Mrs Goldschmidt, the Chairman's wife and Chair of the Ladies' Committee. Nevertheless the stalwarts of the Board girded their loins, made new appeals, secured new subscriptions and donations, so that by the time of the annual meeting in January 1885, the sum still to be found was reduced to £5,000. During this period considerable discussion took place on the wisdom of retaining part of the St. John Street Hospital as an outpatient facility (the patient numbers having increased yet again to 15,427, a 2% increase on the 1882 figure). There was a significant financial burden in doing so, ameliorated by selling or letting unwanted parts of the building. Nevertheless the

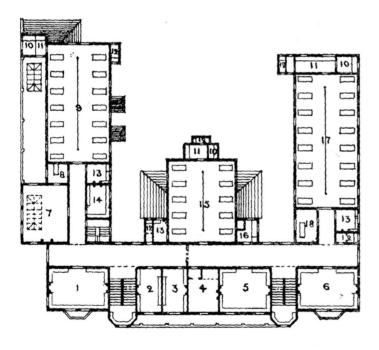

REFERENCES.

1.—Women's Day Room
2.—Nursery
3.⎫
4.⎬ Bedrooms
5.⎫
6.⎬ Men's Day Room
7.—Operating Room
8.—Recovery Room
9.—Women's Ward
10.—Bath
11.—Lavatory
12.—W.C.
13.—Nurses' Kitchen
14.—Waiting Room
15.—Boys' Ward
16.—Service
17.—Men's Ward

FIRST FLOOR PLAN.

PENNINGTON & BRIDGEN, Architects,
Manchester, London. and Liverpool.

The original first-floor plan shows the usage of the light and airy Nightingale ward pattern

The new Chairman's chair from the boardroom, engraved with the year 1885 and the intertwined initials "REH", and still in use

decision was made to retain that as an outpatient hospital. Unusually for a bespoke new building of the importance of the new Eye Hospital, a chapel was never provided, religious services being held in day-rooms and other common areas. The matter was never referred to in minutes and perhaps may have been simply an issue of cost.

The building of the new hospital took somewhat longer than expected, but prior to its occupancy, the Board held its first meeting there, in its new oak-panelled boardroom, with matching bespoke table and monogrammed chairs, on April 18th 1885. This author, some 113 years later, would be honoured to chair meetings in the same room as Clinical Director of the Eye Hospital. After recommendations from medical staff of several hospitals, who advised against "tainted" furniture being brought in from the old hospital, the building was furnished anew throughout. All walls in corridors and stairs were painted in Sea Green. The design of railings to be placed on the frontage was approved. The new hospital, it was decided, should be connected with the outside world by more than Her Majesty's Post, and therefore a quotation was agreed, from the Lancashire & Cheshire Telephone Exchange Company, to install the required apparatus at both Oxford Street and St. John Street, for a rental of £27.10s per annum (in due course the Board decided that the new-fangled apparatus should retain a direct link between the two branches of the Hospital, but that a connection to the exchange was an unnecessary expense). All treatment and waiting areas were floored in linoleum, but the Boardroom acquired a fine Turkey carpet by donation. Its bookcases were also filled by a donation of books from Mr Parlane, member of the Board. Shrubs were ordered for the front of the hospital and the railings painted green. The dispensary was stocked, the laundry equipped with a gas engine, the building contractors were berated for their delays and workmanship, indeed all traditional processes involved in "snagging" a new building were undertaken. The Mayor of Manchester and Hospital Chairman, Philip Goldschmidt, arranged to pay for the furnishing of one of the wards; this was named in memory of his wife, recently deceased, who had chaired the Ladies' Committee for nine years. The wards, of which there were 7, were designed on the new "pavilion" principle, later known as "Nightingale wards", and were to house 60 men and 40 women. Each was provided with an electric bell, and the men's day rooms (but not the women's) were provided with spittoons. Messrs Armstrong & Bro., opticians to the Royal Eye Hospital, donated clocks for Boardroom and waiting-room, and a barometer for the hallway.

The new headed stationery was delivered and the

The new Royal Eye Hospital headed notepaper of 1885

Hospital was opened for business on December 4th 1885, the outpatient department opening on December 21st. The Manchester Royal Eye Hospital had arrived at what would be its address for the next 124 years. The total cost of the land, the building and its contents was £22,000.

The official opening of the hospital was deferred until the date of the forthcoming annual meeting. It was fitting that the momentous occasion should be led by Alderman Philip Goldschmidt, Mayor of Manchester for his second term, Chairman of the Manchester Royal Eye Hospital and on its Board for 21 years. It took place on February 15th 1886, attended by many benefactors, friends and members. A golden key, made by Elkington & Co. of St. Anne's Square, the handle with a cat's eye design together with a rod of Aesclepius, was used to unlock the building. The throng moved into the dining hall for speeches, the hospital was inspected, and after luncheon the Annual Meeting was held. The Mayor provided the in-patients with a celebratory meal, and they gathered later in the dining room to give their thanks. The Secretary, Mr Burgess, "called upon them to express their thanks in right hearty fashion; a call to which they responded in a way which showed that, however it might be with the eyes, their lungs were in good condition".

The House Surgeon, now accommodated in pleasant rooms at the Northwest corner of the ground floor (which during the author's residency were the junior mess and consultants' dining room) had a much more daunting task than before, in caring for

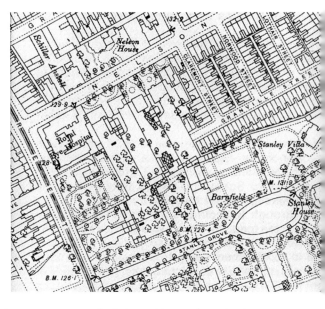

The Manchester Royal Eye Hospital, Oxford-Street, in its new location in a residential area of Chorlton-on-Medlock

The new Manchester Royal Eye Hospital, shortly after opening. The neighbouring householder on the right, somewhat overlooked, successfully sued for compensation owing to the blockage of light

up to 100 inpatients, and his salary was raised to £90 per annum, with board, lodging and laundry. It was decided that a fourth nurse was now needed, at a salary of £24. The hospital's finances, which had come through the building of the new hospital relatively unscathed, were now enhanced by an enormous bequest from the late Henry Hargreaves of Blackburn, whose £15,000 contribution (approaching £2M today) transformed the outlook of the Board. There followed a somewhat prolonged challenge to Hargreaves' bequest from his outraged family, settled only after several years in the Eye Hospital's favour, just before its final challenge in the House of Lords.

After a year or so of settling into Oxford Street, the Board turned its attention to altering the St. John Street "branch" of the Hospital. There were no in-patients there any longer, but it remained a busy out-patient facility and that aspect was adapted and expanded, retaining an operating facility. The alterations were complete by the end of 1887 and were described in the Manchester Courier:

> The old waiting rooms have been re-floored, re-furnished, re-painted and rearranged to accommodate the maximum of patients with the least sacrifice of space. There is lavatory accommodation for both sexes, and a box for voluntary subscriptions. Opening out of this large room to the southward are a suite of apartments divided into rooms for infants, for minor operations, testing &c. Cases requiring continued indoor treatment are sent to the Institution in Oxford Road. About 500 ocular operations per annum are however, performed on outpatients at the John-St hospital. One of the rooms is called the Ophthalmoscopic Room, where apparatus is provided for viewing the interior of the eye.

The porters of the hospital (there were two at Oxford Street, one at St. John Street) were expected to be resident, and normally worked from 6.30am until the patients were bedded down. Their jobs were physically onerous, and staff turnover was quite high. This was a time before employment rights came into existence, and yet an episode at this time illustrates that the Board was capable of generosity of spirit while needing to keep the hospital staffed at reasonable expense. Porter Oliver, who had worked well at Oxford Road for some time, became ill and was unable to discharge his duties for a full working day. His wife was a laundress at the Hospital. His difficulties were tolerated, but his illness worsened and when he was diagnosed with the consumption he was absent for treatment at the Royal Infirmary for several weeks. After discharge he was unable to work but was housed again at the Eye Hospital, and he attempted to return to work but found great difficulty, his health deteriorating again. Throughout these several months his wages were paid as normal and the Board were regularly informed as to his state of health. At the end he became moribund and died at the Hospital. The Board wrote a letter of condolence to his wife and included a gratuity of £5 for his funeral costs. She was retained as laundress.

In April 1888 the following advertisement was placed into the *Manchester Times*:

MANCHESTER EYE & EAR HOSPITAL
25, St. John Street – Patients enter via Byrom Street
CHAIRMAN OF COMMITTEE –
MR ALDERMAN BAILEY
HON. SURGEON – DAVID McKEOWN
M.A., M.D., M.Ch.

This Institution will be OPENED on Tuesday next, the 1st of May. Patients admitted on Tuesday, Thursday & Friday mornings, from 9 to 11 o'clock; and on Monday and Wednesday evenings, from 6.30 to 8 o'clock. NO RECOMMEND is needed. JOHN McDOWELL Hon. Sec

The Manchester Ear Hospital was in its 43rd year, and the Royal Eye Hospital in its 74th, yet a new institution providing care for both sense organs was set up next door to the St. John Street branch of the Royal Eye Hospital. The Board noted its coming, and instructed its solicitors to investigate the right of a new institution to use a name so similar; they were concerned about the addressing of post, particularly remittances relating to donations and legacies. Secondly they made it known by circulating to all Boards of Guardians, that a written recommendation was not required for the Royal Eye Hospital either. A deputation met Alderman Bailey, the Chairman of the new institution, making clear before their arrival that the encounter was "official and not merely a friendly visit". They attempted to pressurise him to withdraw his support. Who knows with what ammunition they were equipped; whatever coercion was applied, they were successful; in his written response he abjectly apologised, stating:

> *I have written and withdrawn my name because, if for no other reason, I think it would be improper for me to favour any movement which would be unpleasant to your good self and the excellent public spirited men who for years have been doing good work in Manchester*

However, if the Board of the Manchester Royal Eye Hospital thought that the withdrawal of Alderman Bailey's support would cripple the new institution, they were mistaken; others lent their time and resources. Objection was also made to the name of the new institution, but the request to change its name was refused despite legal approaches. The conflict petered out and the new hospital continued to work for 29 years, treating at one point over 3,500 patients in a year. The founding surgeon, Dr McKeown, died in 1906, after which there was some talk of amalgamation of hospitals. This was rebuffed disparagingly by the Royal Eye Hospital, but the institution continued to exist, now known as the "St. John's Hospital of Manchester & Salford for the Ear & Eye". At some stage during the Great War the hospital found itself unable to obtain services from an eye surgeon, and became a hospital only for the ear, but it ceased to exist in 1917. It was one of two specialist institutions in the Manchester area to have attempted to "compete" with the Royal Eye Hospital until the recent dismantling of the National Health Service structure (the other being the Altrincham & Bowden Eye Hospital).

The hospital of the late Victorian era ran like a well-oiled machine. Every situation

Manchester Royal Eye Hospital.

••••••••••••••••••••

NURSES' TIME TABLE.

A.M.

6 30.—The Day Nurses shall be called by the Night Nurse.
The Night Nurse shall prepare the Nurses' breakfast, and shall draw up the blinds in the Wards.

7 0.—The Nurses shall come to breakfast, the Day Nurses being fully dressed for the day.

7 30.
to
9 0.
—The Nurses shall during this time dress the eyes of the Patients, open windows in Wards, at 8 0 shall give breakfast to the Patients both in the Dining-room and the Wards, shall do their own Bedrooms, and shall turn the Patients' mattresses, with help, if possible, from the Patients, shall give out medicines and get ready for Surgeons.
The youngest Nurse or Probationer shall sweep and dust the Operation-rooms, and have them ready by 9 0.

9 0.
to
12 0.
—One Nurse attends the Out-patients' Consulting-room, the other Nurses attend to the In-patients upstairs. All Nurses attend the Surgeons, and are under their control whilst in the Operating-rooms, and at other times as long as required. Empty medicine and lotion bottles to be left at the Dispensary before 9 30.
Nurses' luncheon.

12 0.—Serve dinners to Patients in Wards.

1 0 to 1 30.—Nurses' dinners.

1 30.
to
4 0.
—Dress Patients' eyes and give medicines as may be required, and see to the comfort of their Patients.
The Nurses shall not do their own personal sewing or other work until after the Patients' tea.
The Nurses shall in the afternoon keep passing through their Wards and Day-rooms, and shall, when not thus occupied, attend to the bandages and pillow-slips of their Wards, sitting with their Patients, or in their own Kitchens or in their Day-rooms.

4 0.—Nurses' tea.

4 30.—Dress Patients' eyes.

5 0 to 6 0.—Serve Patients' tea. Give medicines.

6 0.—Attend House Surgeon in visiting Wards.

7 0.—Attend to bathing of Patients and sending children to bed.

7 30.—Serve Patients' suppers.

8 0.—Patients go to bed.

8 10.—The Nurses are off duty, but attend to any special case. Supper.

10 0.—The Nurses shall, when out for the evening, always return to the Hospital before 10 0 P.M.

10 0 P.M.
to
8 0 A.M.
—The Night Nurse is on duty, and shall visit the Wards every two hours, and oftener if required; shall call the Nurses and Servants at the appointed hour, and dust the Consulting-room before going off duty.

———————

N.B.—The Nurses' Holidays shall be granted by the House Surgeon in consultation with the Matron.

PATIENTS' MEAL TIMES.

8 0.—Breakfast.   12 0.—Dinner.   5 0.—Tea.   7 30.—Supper.

had a rule, carefully considered by the Board and amended if necessary by resolution; every member of staff knew their place, their time of work, their time of rest, their proper apparel. They knew when they were permitted to leave the building, and when they must return, subject to disciplinary action if necessary. As an example, a copy of the Nurses' Timetable of 1889, overseen by the Ladies' Committee and ratified by the Board, is seen:

Later in 1889 Dr Philip Mules, Honorary Surgeon for fourteen years, resigned, stating that he found the strain of his work too much. Having left, he did nevertheless set up a hospital of his own, the Altrincham & Bowden Eye Hospital, which survived for a few years before he moved in 1896 to North Wales. At that time the Committee of the hospital at Altrincham attempted to amalgamate with the Royal Eye Hospital, but were rebuffed, and the hospital closed. The Assistant Surgeon at MREH, Alexander Hill Griffiths MD, who had been serving at the Hospital for ten years, had been champing at the bit for promotion and was offered the post without advertisement. Born in Aberdeen (and one of several Scottish surgeons to serve the Hospital thus far), he obtained his medical degree there and had been immediately appointed House Surgeon at the Manchester Royal Eye Hospital. He was clearly a very inquisitive man, a keen histologist and microscopist. Although Donders had first introduced cylindrical

Alderman Philip Goldschmidt, Mayor of Manchester and Chairman of the Board of the Manchester Royal Eye Hospital 1870–89

lenses into the refraction trial case in 1864, the prescription of cylindrical lenses for astigmatism was not common, and Hill Griffiths was responsible for highlighting the need for this to his UK colleagues; he was to be awarded the Middlemore prize by the British Medical Association in 1897. He later became the first president of the North of England Ophthalmological Society.

Alderman Philip Goldschmidt JP, twice Mayor of Manchester, the Chairman of the Board of Management of the Manchester Royal Eye Hospital, died in March 1889. The name of Philip Goldschmidt has been mentioned in several places in this history, and his remains perhaps the most important name ever to be associated with the Hospital. His splendid portrait was painted in 1887 by Walter William Ouless RA, one of the best-known society portraitists of the late Victorian era. Born in Oldenburg in Lower Saxony, to a Jewish family, like so many others from Germany he came to England to pursue the textile business, initially in Bradford but subsequently in Manchester, where his business traded worldwide, very successfully. He was immensely

David Bannerman, Chairman of the Board of the Manchester Royal Eye Hospital 1890–7

The warehouse of Bannerman's in York Street. The company also had mills and warehouses throughout the northwest

generous with his time and energy to various charitable institutions, being Chairman of the Board for 19 years until his death. He was also the Treasurer at the Manchester Royal Infirmary and served with several other institutions. There is little doubt that his energy and persuasive powers, enhanced by his position as Mayor, ensured the affordability of the new Hospital and were it not for him, the move to its new premises might never have been possible. Renowned for kindliness, straightforwardness and generosity, his funeral was one of the most well-attended in Manchester's history. His portrait retained pride of place in the Boardroom of the Manchester Royal Eye Hospital for 122 years, and the room also bears a plaque paying tribute to his contribution. His son, Herman Julius, had already joined the Board before his father's death and would continue an unbroken family association of 74 years with the Hospital, serving as its Chairman from 1921 for twenty years.

The Board elected a new Chairman, David Bannerman. He was the son of Henry Bannerman, Scottish farmer who in 1808 had sold up and moved his family lock stock & barrel to Manchester to get rich in the cotton industry. He succeeded. Henry Bannerman & Sons were one of the most prosperous mill owners in town, their business also extending throughout the northwest with mills and warehouses at Wigan, Rochdale, Oldham, Preston and Bury. Their enormous Manchester warehouse on York Street continued well into the twentieth century until bought by Courtaulds. Bannerman had taken over the company on the death of his father and was to remain Chairman of MREH until his death in 1897. The Bannerman's warehouse and buildings like it defined then, and continue to shape now, the architecture of the centre of Manchester. Quite soon during his tenure the hospital benefitted from another generous legacy, from John Rylands: 200 shares in Messrs Rylands & Son Ltd, sold for £5,440. 7s 3d (over £500,000 today). Rylands was both during his life and via his wife after his death, one of the greatest Manchester philanthropists, and he could afford to be. Remembered as Manchester's first multi-millionaire, his wealth arose after the incorporation of his enormous cotton business, including at one stage 17 mills and employing over 5,000 people. His name persists today on the fine library on Deansgate, constructed as a memorial to her husband by Enriqueta Rylands, which houses a sumptuous collection (including the important Manchester Medical Society library collected by Thomas Windsor) within one of the finest neo-Gothic buildings in the world. The bequest to the Eye Hospital led to an entry in the Board minutes, the like of which had never before been seen, and for some period, drew a line under the constant struggle for funding which had characterised the first 70 years of the Hospital's existence:

> There being a large cash balance in the Bank to the credit of the Hospital it was resolved that the sum of £6,000 be invested in 2 ¾ % Consols 1903.

This history has not concerned the reader with the many discussions in Board meetings as to the placing of investments that the Hospital may from time to time have accrued, but the members of the Board were continually striving to obtain the best returns possible on its behalf, and of course as most of the gentlemen concerned were astute businessmen, they doubtless succeeded. All investments were carefully recorded in the Stocks Book and regularly reviewed. A position of relative financial comfort at the Hospital was now attained for the first time in its history. However, more prosaic matters continued to intervene:

> The Matron reported that she had found it necessary to give notice to the Cook and the Laundress on account of drunkenness. As it appeared that it had been the custom for the servants to send out for beer, the Board resolved that henceforth no nurse or servant should be allowed to send out for intoxicating drinks but that the Matron should be authorised to give beer or milk to the nurses and servants as they might choose.

> Gentlemen

> I have to report to you that about a fortnight ago I had to dismiss a patient, John Quarnby, for going out of the Hospital without leave. Our Porter William opened the back gates on purpose to let the man out. I have reason to believe that this had been going on for a long time.

> I remain, Yours obediently

> Edw Roberts

> The report of William Ashbourne (the Porter) general conduct being unsatisfactory it was resolved that he should be dismissed.

> The bathroom on the ground floor is so cold that it cannot be used during the winter months; if a coil of hot water pipes could be placed there it would be a great convenience

The workload of the Hospital inexorably rose (despite the novel co-existence with their new competitor in St. John Street) and both branches saw outpatients. Because the St. John Street branch retained most of the business of Salford and the northern towns, it dealt with 11,134 outpatients in 1889, compared to 7,523 in Oxford Street. The joint total however, at 18,657, was an 8% rise on the previous year's workload. There were 1341 inpatients at Oxford Street, a rise of 3%, the average stay remaining at about 20 days with a patient's cost of board at 4s 6d per week, a servant's at 5s 8d. The cost of running of the Hospitals was £3,389, 15s 9d but the income received was £4,271 11s 3d and this splendid balance reflected the current overall financial position. At the annual meeting in January 1890 the *Manchester Guardian* reported the words of one Mr J Mawdsley, whose words, though reflecting contemporary attitudes, were prescient and fore-ran the thoughts of those introducing the National Insurance Act over twenty years later:

> It had often occurred to him how little it would cost each person per annum if each contributed to support institutions of the character of the Eye Hospital. If that idea was carried out the charitable character of such institutions would be done away with, for each person receiving treatment there would have subscribed his or her share to the cost of maintaining the institution. For himself he would much prefer that the poorer classes should not be so dependent for these things on the people above them

These were days more than 50 years before the emergence of the first antibiotic, and well before most effective vaccines, but the infectious nature of some diseases was now well-appreciated following the work of Semmelweis, Pasteur and others. The minutes of the House Committee and Board make clear their diligence in ensuring cleanliness within the Hospital, and on occasion, direct action was taken to limit spread of infection. Reports of diarrhoeal illness resulted in the closure of a ward for disinfection; suspected diphtheria was met by the removal of adjacent patients; and a few cases of typhoid or scarlet fever were removed immediately to the Fever Hospital at Monsall. "Verminous patients" were refused admission in all except the most extreme circumstances. In this era all aspects of building maintenance and cleanliness were rigorously applied, and every attempt made to reduce disease. The suppliers of meat were re-tendered at regular intervals, the ventilation in storage larders (no refrigeration was possible) continually addressed. Whitewashing and redecorating at frequent intervals was a ritual. The provision of clean laundry for both patients and staff became an increasing challenge; laundresses earned little and worked in a very unpleasant environment, performing backbreaking work for long hours, using a selection of caustics and soaps in hot and humid rooms; long-serving staff were rare. The boilers for laundry regularly needed attention or replacement, and the volume of washing progressively increased. No photograph exists of the Eye Hospital laundry, but there is a contemporary image of the Royal Infirmary laundry in Piccadilly, which gives a flavour of the

level of technology available in the Victorian institution: massive tubs to be stirred,
mangles to be turned, hundredweights of sheets and clothes to be handled. Unlike the
laundry shown, no steam-powered axles powered the Eye Hospital facilities.

The new building at Oxford Street actually proved to have substantial problems in
building quality (collapsing fireplaces, re-laid corridors, sewage leaks into basements
and rainwater run-off around foundations); in temperature maintenance (frozen water,
uninhabitable rooms in winter, stifling heat and lack of ventilation in summer); so that
a veritable forest of additional water piping, pumped ventilation and drainage sprang
up over the succeeding few years. Nevertheless regular requests from medical and
nursing staff were made to improve the atmosphere in clinical work spaces. Clean
fresh air was not readily available, despite the expense and energy required to move
the Hospital "out of town". Deaths within the hospital were reported at a rate of 6–8
per year. The improved apparatus for the administration of chloroform anaesthetic
invented by John Snow had reduced those particular tragedies to a smaller number,
and most deaths were a result of concurrent illness in admitted patients with illnesses
which were then untreatable, especially diabetic coma, stroke, cardiac failure and
uraemia. There were occasional deaths from sepsis, and infrequent but tragic deaths
of infants, sometimes from febrile convulsions after admission with eye and systemic
infection. At one stage in the 1890s, owing to the practicalities of sometimes dealing

with corpses on the premises for longer than was desirable (with predictable unsa-voury consequences which troubled the medical staff), part of the cellar was converted to a mortuary. The very process of moving bodies was difficult and undignified. The House Surgeon requested of the Board:

> *I have to report that there is no stretcher in the Hospital, and that in removal of dead patients it is necessary to use a door, thus rendering an unpleasant duty more unpleasant and more laborious.*

The Secretary was instructed to procure a stretcher. Notwithstanding the comparatively huge rate of morbidity and mortality at this time compared to the twenty-first century, there is no hint of apathy in any of the written records of the hospital. The House Surgeon individually reported each death in writing to the Board of Management, and occasional changes to practice resulted from such discussions. All written complaints to the Hospital about individual patient care were treated with similar diligence, and individual staff members sometimes admonished, usually merely for rudeness. There appears to have been at all times a genuine wish to provide care for as many as possible, as well as possible.

CHAPTER SIX

Portrait of a Surgeon at Work – Dr David Little

I<small>T WAS ON A</small> Sunday morning in 1893, as recalled by his daughter Dora, that Dr Little, having been unable to complete all of his planned hospital work that week, went to the Eye Hospital to perform a cataract operation, and permitted her as a treat, to accompany him and to watch the surgery take place. As he arrived, a medical student, Mr JD Amenaber, requested permission to photograph the operation taking place. The resulting image may be unique in being the only photograph in existence of a cataract operation in that era. It shows a scene redolent of nineteenth century medicine; were it not for the presence of a surgeon and patient, the operating room would be unrecognisable as such. The walls are painted, with a dado rail, a mahogany door is glimpsed, and behind the surgeon is a desk with some books and papers. The light source is not seen but there was probably merely light from the window. The patient is bearded, dressed probably in his only suit for the occasion, a dapper check; his waistcoat is fastened, his fob chain across. He lies prone and one suspects, frightened and very still as instructed, on a quilted leather operating couch, his hands stiffly at his side. The couch was made to the specification of the Eye Hospital by Marris & Norton, furniture makers of Birmingham, was covered in American leather, and cost £23.13s 6d. The patient's head lies on a soft pillow covered in embroidered linen. On his forehead rests a white cloth. Dr Little, the surgeon, is standing behind his head, dressed in his frock coat with a white handkerchief in his top pocket. He too wears a waistcoat, a wing collar and tie but the cut of his clothes, his elegantly combed silver hair and his clean features place him on a different social scale to that of his patient.

Dr Little operating for cataract, 1893; a photograph by medical student Mr Amenaber

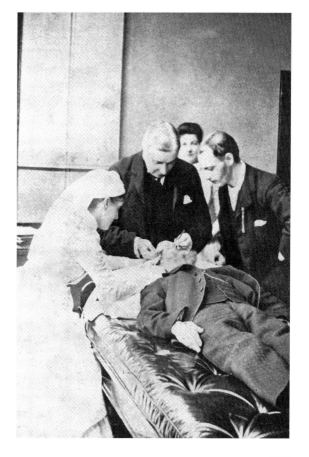

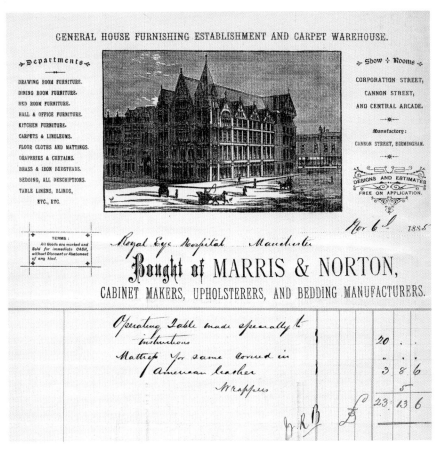

GENERAL HOUSE FURNISHING ESTABLISHMENT AND CARPET WAREHOUSE.

Departments

DRAWING ROOM FURNITURE.
DINING ROOM FURNITURE.
BED ROOM FURNITURE.
HALL & OFFICE FURNITURE.
KITCHEN FURNITURE.
CARPETS & LINOLEUMS.
FLOOR CLOTHS AND MATTINGS.
DRAPERIES & CURTAINS.
BRASS & IRON BEDSTEADS.
BEDDING, ALL DESCRIPTIONS.
TABLE LINENS, BLINDS,
ETC., ETC.

Show Rooms

CORPORATION STREET,
CANNON STREET,
AND CENTRAL ARCADE.

Manufactory:
CANNON STREET, BIRMINGHAM.

DESIGNS AND ESTIMATES
FREE ON APPLICATION.

TERMS:
All Goods are marked and
Sold for immediate CASH,
without Discount or Abatement
of any kind.

Nov 6th 1885

Royal Eye Hospital Manchester

Bought of MARRIS & NORTON,

CABINET MAKERS, UPHOLSTERERS, AND BEDDING MANUFACTURERS.

Operating Table made specially to instructions — 20 . .
Mattress for same covered in American leather — 3 . 8 . 6
Wrapper —

£ 23 . 13 . 6

The receipt dated 1885 for the leather-covered operating table seen in the photograph

In the background is the face of one of the nurses, or perhaps Dora Little herself, watching the surgery from a respectful distance. The picture is taken at the very point of cutting into the eye by a Graefe section.

Dr Little and the patient are attended by two others; Doctor Robert Edie, the House Surgeon, and Nurse Lizzie Isherwood. Dr Edie is smartly attired, again in morning dress, with handkerchief and lapel fob, and is watching with particular attention – perhaps there is an element of posing for this image, and one imagines the magnesium flare bursting into life as the frame is captured, and hopes that the patient did not jump!. Nurse Isherwood is smartly presented in her light blue and white-striped nursing dress, a starched white apron and a long white headdress. She leans over to steady the patient's head at this crucial point of the operation.

It is startling today to see a surgeon pictured operating in his day-clothes. Contemporaneously however, the dress of the surgeon was entirely chosen to protect himself from the various fluids of the patient, not vice versa. Joseph Lister himself, famed for his later theories of antisepsis during surgery, was noted by an observer in 1871 to don his old blue operating coat for surgery; that garment, previously morning dress but now delegated to the operating theatre rather as one does old clothes to the gardening shed; used many times before and splattered many times with sundry emanations, sanguine, alimentary or purulent, so that the coat was stiff with dried stains and malodorous, a feature which apparently was considered a badge of experience in some operating theatres. Lister was later to go on to describe the use of phenol solution (carbolic acid) both as a wound disinfectant and a hand-washing aid, and demonstrated the reduction in post-operative infections as a result. The medical profession was initially sceptical of these methods, absorbing their importance with resistance and suspicion (as is their wont with so many innovative developments), and the ophthalmological community in particular, mainly because their surgery was performed without touching the eye with the hands, would change their practices only very slowly. Even in the 1980s, some cataract surgeons were still operating without gloves. Dr Little is shown here not wearing an old coat reserved for the operating theatre, because this form of surgery would not risk the cleanliness of his ordinary garb. What old operating coat would display a pocket handkerchief, his clean shirt-cuffs exposed? Doubtless Dr Little had arrived in this coat, and would depart wearing it, accompanying his daughter to morning service. We can however surmise that he probably washed his hands before and after the surgery and that the instruments he used had been cleaned in disinfectant, or possibly boiled. Joseph Lister, by this time honoured with a baronetcy, and a famed London surgeon, would later be remembered at the Manchester Royal Eye hospital when Lister House was named after him.

The operation for cataract at this time had recently undergone a change which had made the patient's experience slightly less painful than had previously been the case – the introduction of cocaine anaesthetic drops. General anaesthesia was theoretically possible (both ether and chloroform had been available to induce general anaesthesia since the 1840s) but these drugs were used only when necessary owing to the risks involved, and then usually in low dosage; the post-operative vomiting that they commonly induced was too great a risk for an unsutured cataract operation wound, which may expel the ocular contents. The discovery in 1884 that cocaine was anaesthetic had been made by Dr Carl Koller, a Bohemian ophthalmologist (how appropriate) who, after experimenting unsuccessfully with topical morphine and other known analgesics, found that the cocaine alkaloid caused numbness after simple instillation of drops. The usefulness of this new treatment for eye surgery was immediately and internationally apparent. Koller moved in the late 1880s to practice in New York where he became a famed ophthalmologist. The *Manchester Courier* enthused about the drug in 1886:

The Coca plant, the leaves of which produce cocaine, the first local anaesthetic

> Soon after this he (Koller) commenced to employ cocaine in operations performed upon the eye of patients. The results were highly satisfactory; and since then cataracts have been operated on, squinting eyes put straight, foreign bodies upon the cornea removed painlessly and with ease, under the influence of the drug. In cataract especially cocaine is of great value, this operation can be performed by its means without the slightest sensation of pain, and yet the patient is fully conscious…

Whilst this description of pain-free surgery may have been somewhat overenthusiastic, it is true that the introduction of cocaine was a major step forward, and it is certain that the patient in this picture would have had them instilled. Decades later, the introduction of nerve block injections would give complete local

A contemporary section from the catalogue of John Weiss, ophthalmic instrument manufacturer of London, showing a selection of available cataract and other ophthalmic knives

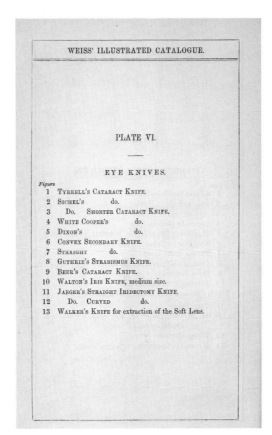

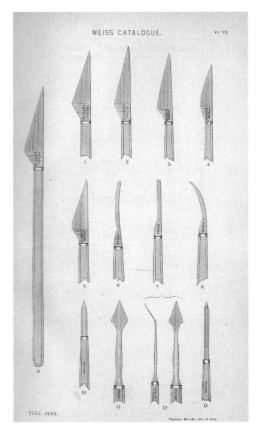

anaesthesia for cataract operations, but it is interesting that with the development of much more subtle, atraumatic surgical techniques, in the twenty-first century it is now common again to undergo cataract surgery using only topical anaesthesia.

Dr Little was 53 years old in 1993. He was therefore presbyopic. He is seen operating not only without any form of magnifying aid, but without glasses; he therefore needs to stay far enough away from the patient to prevent his vision blurring; he therefore cannot sit. In the twentieth century, magnifying glasses of increasing sophistication would gradually become available to facilitate the task of the cataract surgeon, but it was not until the invention of microscopy with coaxial illumination in the late 1970s that the operating microscope became commonly used in cataract surgery; operating loupes were still in use in the 1980s, and some surgeons preferred to stand for cataract surgery even then. Now, in the twenty-first century, both feet are required to operate machinery and so all intraocular surgery is performed with the surgeon seated.

Also prior to the surgery, atropine drops may have been instilled into the patient's eye in order to dilate the pupil. This was the only such drop available at the time and suffered from the disadvantage of being irreversible for some days postoperatively. If the surgeon intended to perform iridectomy with his Graefe knife, atropine was not used. The eye is being held open by a speculum of a design still used today (albeit not for cataract surgery). To begin the operation for cataract, the eye is immobilised by using a pair of toothed forceps to hold the conjunctiva below the cornea. A cataract knife was then used; a wide variety had become available during the middle nineteenth century but the design mostly adopted was that of Albrecht von Graefe, a famed Berlin ophthalmologist. This tempered-steel stiletto was inserted through the limbus, and then emerged from the other side, impaling the eye. Using a sawing motion, the knife then created a semicircular incision from the inside (*ab interno*), usually taking with it a flap of conjunctiva. It was not uncommon, during this process, for the anterior chamber of the eye to lose fluid and become shallow. If this happened, a large piece of the iris would also be removed, sometimes inadvertently but often deliberately to facilitate removal of the lens. In this picture the right eye is being operated upon. One disadvantage of the above technique was the requirement for left-handed cutting of the left eye, a considerable challenge to most surgeons. The re-usable cataract knives of this time required careful re-sharpening with a leather strop, as a blunt knife could be disastrous. The task was traditionally performed by a senior sister, and was still required in the 1970s. Disposable or gemstone knives came later.

The anterior capsule of the lens would then be disrupted with a discission knife or cystotome, and then using controlled pressure, both from below the cornea and above the wound, the cataract would be expressed, leaving the lens capsule in place.

In the late nineteenth century, a cataract was usually extracted only when "mature", or "ripe". A cataract usually develops slowly over a period of years. In doing so, more and more of the lens becomes opaque, and a very longstanding cataract takes on a deep

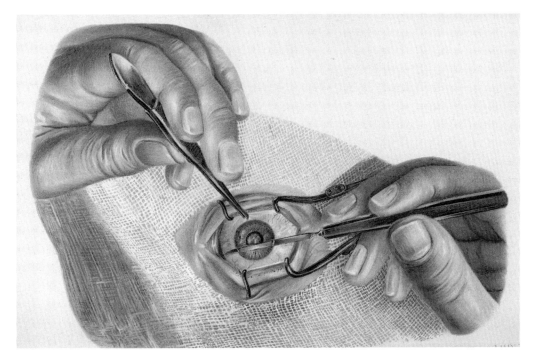

A contemporaneous drawing of a Graefe ab interno cataract section – the surgeon's view from behind the head

brown opacity, with consequent virtual blindness. At this stage, the lens has changed from being a soft, viscous material (impossible to extract properly with Victorian instruments) to a hard dense mass which can be removed in whole from the eye, simply by applying controlled pressure to an opened eye. The removal of this opacity would massively improve vision, if major complications could be avoided. Unfortunately, complications were not infrequent and arose for several reasons: firstly there was inadequate magnification and poor lighting, so that instruments could not be used safely inside the eye after the nucleus of the cataract was removed; secondly, sutures suitable for eye surgery did not exist, therefore the wound could not be repaired after the cataract had been removed and had to heal unaided; thirdly, antibiotics had not been discovered. In a report from the Hospital twenty years after this operation took place, of 306 cataract operations performed during one year, 41 eyes were unable to see any letters on the vision chart after surgery and 13 were irreversibly blinded by complications, including 4 from severe infection.

After the cataract had been expressed from the eye, any parts of the iris which had prolapsed would be excised by de Wecker's scissors, and any tissue remnants would be wiped from the wound. The wound would then be placed with its two edges in apposition, and any conjunctival flap would be brushed back into position. Crude suturing would only be introduced in the early twentieth century, using silk of about 4/0 calibre (0.2mm diameter), although some would use horse-hair, but later three developments would permit the extraordinarily fine sutures available today; firstly the ready swaged suture needle, which could be attached to one end of a suture by compression rather than threading; secondly the operating loupes and microscopes which would permit the surgeon to see with adequate magnification; and thirdly the development of synthetic monofilament sutures of exquisitely fine calibre (corneal suturing in the twenty-first century normally uses 10/0 calibre sutures [0.02mm diameter], which can only be seen properly under the operating microscope, and even finer sutures have been made).

This patient, having no sutures to hold the wound together, would require particular care and attention to permit healing without the wound spontaneously rupturing. Strict bed rest was enforced for days, sometimes including the immobilisation of the head with sand-bags. Usually both eyes were covered, because the unoperated eye, in moving to watch objects, would also cause the operated eye to move.

We are fortunate to know in some detail the method of extraction used by David Little, because only 4 years earlier he had given a detailed presentation on the subject to the Section of Ophthalmology of the British Medical Association, and later published in the *British Medical Journal*, based upon the audited experience of 1,248 cases. He was a supporter of iridectomy:

> The patient undergoes no special preparation; the operation is performed on a
> table in good daylight. A 4 per cent solution of cocaine in boracic acid is dropped

three or four times in the upper part of the cornea. Before the introduction of cocaine into practice, it was quite the exception for me to give chloroform or ether. The conjunctival sac and external parts of the eyelids are well washed with corrosive sublimate solution 1 in 5,000. Formerly I used 1 in 2,000, and I cannot say that I ever saw irritation caused by it. All instruments are carefully wiped or washed in the same solution. A stop speculum is introduced, and the eye fixed below with conjunctival forceps by an assistant. With a second pair of forceps I fix the eye at the horizontal meridian inwards, so as to ensure perfect steadiness and the making of a perfectly even incision. With a Graefe's knife the incision is made throughout its whole extent in the apparent corneo-scleral junction, and the iris extracted close to the periphery. If the incision is made too corneal in any part of the section, the iris probably cannot be excised close enough to the periphery, and adhesions or dragging may result. If the iris after excision does not retract well within the anterior chamber from the corners of the wound, I do not hesitate to excise more. The capsule is ruptured from below upwards with a Graefe's bent cystitome, and the lens expelled with a rubber spoon in the usual way. As soon as the nucleus has escaped the speculum is removed, and the pupil is cleared of cortex by pressure within the fingers over the eyelids only. I never introduce an instrument to remove cortex. Conjunctival flaps are avoided, if possible, as they hinder the exit of cortex. The wound is well-cleared of cortex and blood-clots by a piece of cotton-wool soaked in sublimate. The dressings consist, first, of a piece of lint soaked in corrosive, then a thin layer of dry cotton-wool and a single strip of plaster from cheek to forehead. The other eye is covered with a round piece of muslin, and both supported by a double flannel bandage. The patient is kept in bed for two days, and the dressing left undisturbed for three or four, unless unfavourable symptoms appear.

Corrosive sublimate was the contemporary name for mercuric chloride, used as an antiseptic since the middle ages, and at this time also as an anti-syphilitic. Post-operative inflammation was treated with camomile fomentations "as hot as the patient can bear it". At this time the theory of fomentations remained that of the middle ages; hot applications acted as a stimulant, cool was anodyne. Atropine was used routinely for analgesia, threatened infection was treated with applications of iodoform (but usually without beneficial effect). The bandages were normally removed after about ten days, and perhaps a fortnight after surgery, the cataract wound would be considered adequately healed to permit the patient to walk or ride home. He would then be fitted with thick-lensed

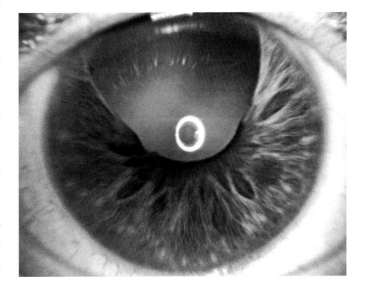

The post-operative appearance of an eye which has undergone cataract surgery combined with iridectomy, as described by David Little. This eye however underwent surgery in the 1970s

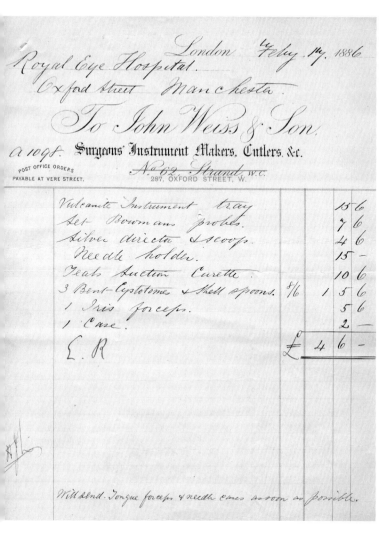

London Feby. 14. 1886

Royal Eye Hospital.
Oxford Street Manchester.

To John Weiss & Son.

a 1098. Surgeons' Instrument Makers, Cutlers. &c.

POST OFFICE ORDERS
PAYABLE AT VERE STREET.

No 62 Strand. W.C.
287, OXFORD STREET, W.

Vulcanite Instrument tray	15	6
Set Bowmans probes.	7	6
Silver director & scoop.	4	6
Needle holder.	15	–
Teals Auction Curette.	10	6
3 Bent Cystotomes & Shell spoons. 5/6	1 5	6
1 Iris forceps.	5	6
1 Case.	2	–
£. R	£ 4 6	–

Will send. Tongue forceps & needle cases as soon as possible.

A bill for surgical instruments from Weiss, supplied to the Manchester Royal Eye Hospital shortly after the opening of the new building. Dr Little may even have used one or two of the above during this operation

glasses, known colloquially as "pebbles" because of the high power required to replace the human lens which had been removed. Those who had undergone surgery without vitreous loss, who had avoided intraocular infection, and whose wound had healed without disruption and prolapse of eye contents, could often see very well with pebbles, and many could read a newspaper. Considering the starting point of almost total blindness before surgery, a successful cataract operation was almost "a miracle".

Dr Little, as for most of his contemporaries, had only recently begun to use antiseptics during surgery, and he commented in 1889 that:

> About the beginning of 1887 I began to carry out antiseptic treatment systematically in every case of extraction, and from that period I have performed 133 cases… There has been no case of suppuration of the cornea, and no absolute loss of the eye from any cause… The employment of antiseptics has at least largely diminished the risks to suppuration.

Little claimed good results in 90% of cases, but in a significant minority a second operation to cut the lens capsule was necessary, and only 13% achieved the "normal" visual acuity of 6/9 or better.

The instruments for use in ophthalmic surgery had by the late nineteenth century reached a high level of quality, and they were correspondingly expensive. The above selection of instruments from John Weiss illustrates only a small section of the varieties then available. This and other manufacturers supplied the Royal Eye Hospital, and a typical invoice from 1886 is shown here.

The gentleman undergoing cataract surgery in this picture is not known to us, but fortuitously an article was anonymously published in the *Manchester City News*, almost contemporaneous with this operation, by "A Cataract Patient" who clearly underwent an identical procedure, in the new hospital. He related that:

> "I went in on a Tuesday, and spent the afternoon and evening in becoming acquainted with my quarters in the new building in Oxford Road. The next morning at half past ten I was summoned with others to the operating room. Just before my turn came, the nurse injected some liquid into my eye – only one

was to be operated on – whispering at the same time words of good cheer. A minute or two afterwards I was lying on a high couch facing what appeared to be the strong sunlight. The physician placed cocaine in the eye – to deaden the pain – and then asked me to remain as quiet as possible. He put a little apparatus over the eye to keep it steady, and in a few seconds I distinctly saw him take a "black sixpence" gradually from my eye. I could see the light enter as the black disappeared. Remember, my other eye was perfectly useless for purpose of sight, so that I must have seen the operation with the eye operated on. The pain was rather severe, as I suppose the lens behind must have been cut away by a special and very sharp instrument. The sensation of something tearing away at the eye was not agreeable, and although the operation did not last more than a minute in all, I felt I could not have stood it much longer. The next minute the nurse had the eyes bandaged, and grasping my arms firmly, she led me to my room, giving me strict instructions to hold my head steady. At the door another patient, who could partially see, took me in charge, and I went to bed, where I remained two days."

Having undergone the surgery, the gentleman remained in the hospital for some weeks, experiencing the contemporary relationship between patients and staff with quiet acceptance:

"My five weeks' stay has left me with pleasant recollections only. I cannot speak too highly of the skill and assiduity of both doctors and nurses. Again, we patients were never treated as if we were mere objects of charity. Probably, at first, I thought the nurse under whose charge I was placed a little dictatorial. She requested me not to talk, and in particular not to ask questions. In fact, for some time it appeared to me that I was considered a mere baby, and all my movements regulated. But my views underwent a change after the first week. When my cataract had been removed, severe inflammation set in, and shooting pains through the head followed. I awoke in the morning to see constellations and lightnings innumerable though my eyes were closely bandaged. For the careful attention I received at that troublesome time I will always be grateful. It was just the same in the night. Nurses and doctors appeared to be wandering about at all hours. Soon a day came when the physician said I could go home. After a month's absence I returned to the Hospital a short time since for an order on Messrs Armstrong, and now I can read the newspaper, after an interval of several years. I am looking forward to the second operation with rather different feelings than I did to the first."

David Little was born near Lockerbie, Dumfriesshire, in 1840, the son of a cattle farmer. He attended Corrie School, and was able at 16 to attend Edinburgh University as his tuition fees were paid by his elder sister. He passed his final examinations in 1859, at nineteen years of age, but was not permitted to graduate MD until reaching the age of majority at 21. While waiting for this event he worked as a doctor's assistant in Sowerby Bridge. His graduation was witnessed by his sister Henrietta, who described him as tall

and thin, a thoughtful man of few words (the family motto was *"Multum in Parvo"* ["there is much in little", or perhaps the interpretation should be "there is much in Little"]). After graduating he worked in practice firstly in Stourbridge, Worcestershire, and then in Durham, but in 1863 was elected as House Surgeon and Secretary to the Manchester Eye Hospital, and four years later he was appointed Surgeon, and also practised at No. 21 St John Street, adjacent to the new hospital premises. He became Ophthalmic Surgeon to the Manchester Royal Infirmary in 1882, and was Lecturer in Ophthalmology at Owens College. He took a home in Victoria Park, comprising a large villa with tennis court. As a teacher he was well-liked, one student later writing "He taught us much by his words, but far more by the charming courtesy he always displayed in dealing with patients, rich and poor. His example lives with us still and I, with many another of his pupils, gratefully cherish his memory."

That he was an expert cataract surgeon is not disputed, and his skills were sought from patients throughout the British Isles. His other quite numerous papers encompassed such diverse ophthalmic conditions as corneal staphyloma, cataract, retinal detachment, iris sarcoma and cysticercosis.

Dr Little was one of the great Manchester surgeons of the late nineteenth century, and became President of the Manchester Medical Society in 1880, the fifth President from the Royal Eye Hospital. He was also very well-recognised nationally, and in 1901 was elected President of the Ophthalmological Society of Great Britain, the first in the twenty years of its existence to be appointed from outside London. His Presidential address was on "Primary Chronic Glaucoma". Unfortunately this appointment coincided with his virtual retirement from medical practice owing to the worsening symptoms of his pernicious anaemia, from which he died in 1902, aged 62. He had been associated with the Royal Eye Hospital for 39 years, of which 35 years as Honorary Surgeon. He was greatly missed, and the Children's Ward was immediately named after him. His wife presented to the Board a replica of the portrait of him painted by George Harcourt RA, fellow Scot and celebrated Victorian artist, which was to hang in the Boardroom at

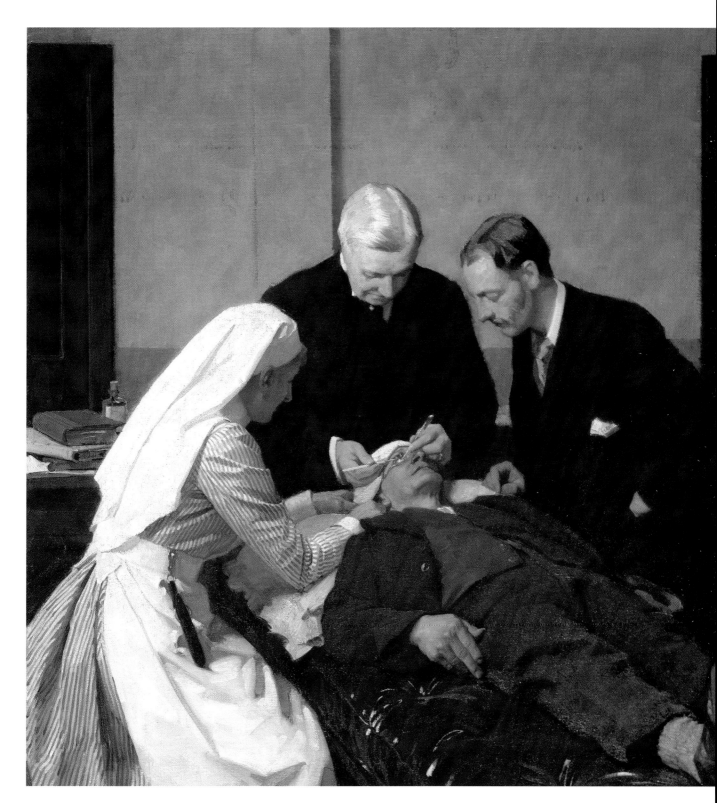

PORTRAIT OF A SURGEON AT WORK – DR DAVID LITTLE

From ROBERT WALTER DOYNE, Esq., M.R.C.S., L.S.A., Ophthalmic Surgeon, Oxford Eye Hospital.

KILCRONE,
OXFORD, 10th June 1892.

I HAVE known Dr. ROBERT EDIE for more than a year, during the time he held the post of House Surgeon to the Oxford Eye Hospital. I always found him a most reliable officer, one in whom I felt I could place implicit confidence. He is well qualified to fill any post that requires the special knowledge of an Ophthalmic Surgeon. He has performed with success several of the most delicate operations on the eye, and in my absence I had no hesitation in leaving serious and difficult cases to his judgment. Those with whom Dr. Edie may be thrown in contact will find him at all times a courteous gentleman.

ROBERT W. DOYNE.

A testimonial in support of Dr Robert Edie, provided by Robert Doyne, founder of the Oxford Eye Hospital

Oxford Street until the building was vacated in 2009. Much later in the 1990s, the Hospital's first bespoke preadmission clinic was also named after him.

The Royal Eye Hospital is fortunate to retain in its archives, full details of the process of appointment of Dr Edie as House Surgeon to the Manchester Royal Eye Hospital in 1892. This appointment followed the resignation of his predecessor, Dr Charles Ramage. It was the custom in nineteenth-century medicine to obtain, if possible, a testimonial from every teacher and employer for whom the doctor had worked. In contrast to today, where applicants will specify two or three named referees from whom a fresh reference will be requested, a doctor then would progressively build a portfolio of permanent testimonials which would be printed for presentation to potential employers, and sometimes following such an application, published in local newspapers. Dr Edie, on seeking appointment at the Royal Eye Hospital, presented testimonials from 14 doctors, including surgeons and professors from the University of Edinburgh, where he had trained. These included the eminent Professors Cathcart and Rutherford, and most prominently from an ophthalmic perspective, that of Robert Doyne, founder of the Oxford Eye Hospital.

Dr Edie was appointed in 1892 in competition with two others. His start was delayed somewhat as he recovered from typhoid fever, but in due course his contribution to the hospital was complimented in two annual reports, his standing doubtless owing in part to his previous experience in Oxford.

Unfortunately the future of Dr Edie was not a happy one. It transpired that he had developed a serious medical problem and had been advised by his physician that he would no longer be able to carry out his duties, and should resign. These facts only became known following the tragedy of April 1894, when he took his own life. He entered the Hospital dispensary early one morning and took a large draught of opium, then disappearing. The indoor porter, Edmund Firley, was suspicious and searched for him, finding him eventually locked into the pathology room on the fourth floor. He was extracted and attempts were made to revive him, but they were unsuccessful and he died later that day.

Nurse Lizzie Isherwood appears, in this image, the model of nursing decorum; her tidiness, cleanliness and efficiency are clear. Doubtless she was expert at her role, but she appears to have had a streak of independence in her; her name appears somewhat more times than are comfortable in the hospital records, following claims of insubordination, or a failure to follow orders, by the matron. She was guilty of inadvertently administering carbolic acid, instead of Black Draught (a purgative made from Epsom salts, cardamom, ginger and senna), to a child in 1885; his subsequent death two days later was however attributed to "exhaustion from suppuration", and she was merely reprimanded. On one occasion in the late 1880s she was made to resign after back-talking to matron, but then reinstated following an appeal by the medical staff, who clearly valued her services highly enough to interfere in the disciplinary process. She was to continue to be a stalwart of the hospital for several more years, perhaps with a somewhat strained relationship with her matron. However, in 1894 matters again came to a head because of her conflicts with other staff in the Hospital. The details are unknown. The Board wished to dismiss her, but again the medical staff made it clear that she was an excellent nurse, and requested that if it were considered necessary to dismiss her, she should be compensated. She was indeed required for the second time to resign. Rebel to the last, she did not comply and was therefore dismissed, in the same month in which Dr Edie died. The Board did however comply with the wishes of the medical staff, in substantial fashion; she was paid salary for the remaining eight months of the year. She moved to Dorset.

Harold Speed, born in 1872, became a well-known artist of the Edwardian and Georgian eras, firstly as a painter of romantic scenes, but more prominently as a society portraitist. He published on drawing and painting technique, and several of his works reside in the National Portrait Gallery. In 1919 he was asked by David Little's widow to paint a copy of the photograph of the cataract operation performed 26 years before, and the resultant fine large canvas was given to the City of Manchester. It now resides in the Manchester Art Gallery. There is some artistic licence in its composition – Dora has disappeared from the scene, the patient's clothes are slightly less worn, his fob-chain has disappeared and he has been shaven. Nevertheless it is a faithful rendition of a scene repeated many thousands of times in Victorian England – a doctor in his day-clothes, performing surgery before the days of effective anaesthesia, in an almost domestic setting. It is a treasured part of the history of the Manchester Royal Eye Hospital, and as a painted depiction of Victorian eye surgery in progress, possibly unique.

CHAPTER SEVEN

Jostling for Position

IN MAY 1894 THE medical staff of the Manchester Royal Eye Hospital made a proposal to the Board, because of their perceived inability to cope with the current numbers attending the Hospital branches at both Oxford Street and St. John Street. They suggested a change to the rotas of the Honorary Surgeons such that the three most senior surgeons (Messrs Little, Glascott and Emrys Jones) would deal only with Oxford Street outpatients, whereas the other (Dr Hill Griffith) and Mr Roberts the Assistant Surgeon, should deal with St. John Street. This was an interesting suggestion as the number of outpatients at St. John Street was regularly higher than at Oxford Street (3867 versus 2938 for the first 4 months of 1894). The proposed changes involved extending the opening hours at St. John Street, and it was therefore moved that a second House Surgeon was necessary. The Board was in agreement, and promoted Mr Roberts to Honorary Surgeon. Shortly afterwards he was moved to donate a piano for the nurses' sitting room.

These discussions were simultaneous with the advertisement for a House Surgeon following the death of Dr Edie, and this gave the Board the opportunity of appointing two; Dr Wallace Wilson, lately of Guy's Hospital (for Oxford Road, £70 per annum with board & washing) and Dr John Gray Clegg, lately medical officer of the Crumpsall Workhouse (for St. John Street, £150 per annum non-resident). The latter would become one of the most prominent and well-known surgeons of the Hospital, and certainly one of its great characters, who would be on the staff for nearly fifty years.

The annual report of 1895 showed the largest ever increase in patients seen, to a total of 21,575 at both branches. The changes made to the attendance by the medical staff, whereby both branches were open for six mornings per week, had assisted throughput, but the Board were concerned enough to demand that monthly attendance figures were now presented to each meeting. In the meantime, at the annual meeting in the Town Hall, the potential evils of the new-fangled electric lighting were addressed:

> Nor can it be said that the improvements anticipated from lighting by electricity
> have been altogether realised. Except in cases where the light is considerably

softened, its effect upon the retina of the eye is decidedly unpleasant, and complaints are rife amongst clerks in banks and mercantile houses that its constant use is injurious. It is true that under the climatic conditions of Manchester we are left with a choice of evils, the glare of electricity, or the fumes of gas, but the real solution would appear to lie in some better method of diffusing the electric light. In the meantime, advocates of both methods of lighting can rejoice in the successful report of the Manchester Royal Eye Hospital.

It was during 1895 that the first known photograph of the House staff was taken. The two recently appointed housemen, John Gray Clegg and Wallace Wilson, are seen flanking the back row, with the venerable secretary Mr Burgess sitting imperiously at centre. Some but not all of the nursing staff are also present, and the mount of the original photograph bears the signatures of all, including (left to right, back first): Rachel Eyre, Janet Tracey, Louise Edmondson, Rachel Birch, Eilonwy Hughes and Alice Kay. The Matron, notably, was not in the group.

Mr Burgess was very much the superintendent of the Hospital, the overseer of its efficient running. He and the Ladies' Committee were the conduit to the Board for all matters not passing through the Medical Board. He was a fount of strength to the Hospital, and no matter was too small for his attention. In August 1895 he wrote an epic letter to the Board, bringing their attention to various matters including the idleness of the outside porter Jones, who spent a good deal of his time "smoking and playing games with the patients. He is supposed to keep the yards and the outside places clean." The state of the hospital frontage on Oxford Street, overgrown with weeds, was an ongoing concern, and Jones, he said, ought to be weeding, but Jones had retorted that he "will do it if he is paid for it, but he is not going to begin gardening without." Alumni will remember fondly that this particular problem was not adequately addressed during the next 114 years. Perhaps Jones was allowed to set too much of a precedent, but the Board was so tired of dismissing porters for laziness, drunkenness, associating with loose women and sundry misdemeanours, and appointing new ones on low wages who had a distressingly short average tenure, that perhaps they overlooked his insubordination in the hope that he would at least stay longer than most.

Mr Burgess also alluded to the discomfiture of Nurse Birch, seen in the staff photograph here, who wished to leave the hospital because she was so unhappy with the Matron, Miss Black, who, it was said, was subjecting her to "petty persecution. The other nurses also complain of the Matron's treatment of them, and the indignities put upon them. They are constantly addressed in the most insulting terms, taunted with their low birth, their want of breeding, vulgarity and so forth, and told that the Board had informed her of this". Worse, the Matron was accused of traducing members of both the Board and the Ladies' Committee. A delegation of nurses and the House Surgeon appeared before the Board and confirmed these accusations. Miss Black was tried and judged in her absence, and was given three months' notice. Her successor, Miss Glover, was a great contrast in personality. She was very experienced, having trained at St. Thomas' Hospital and the Hospital for Sick Children, Great Ormond Street, before becoming Matron firstly to the Kent & Canterbury Hospital and then of Shrewsbury School.

The annual report of 1897 raised concerns about hospital funds. Expenditure had been necessary on the building, firstly to increase staff quarters (patient numbers continuing inexorably to rise); to install electric lighting; and to equip properly for the first time a pathological room. The cost of the dispensing of medicines had risen from £260 for 1893, to £466 in 1896. The period also coincided with sickness amongst the staff, with an outbreak of scarlet fever (cases being immediately removed to Monsall Hospital) and two cases of typhoid. For the first time since 1879, the annual budget was in debit, yet alterations to provide further staff accommodation and better patient isolation facilities, were considered.

By 1897 most of the nurses portrayed in the recent staff photograph had departed, and usually for the same reason: a perceived need to obtain more training in general nursing, so that they could obtain better future appointments. In July of that year, the Matron, Miss Glover, wrote at length to the Board making substantial suggestions to alter both the nursing structure and the quality of training. She pointed out that nurses having worked at the Manchester Royal Eye Hospital should be able to go on to obtain posts as senior nurse or Matron at similar establishments, but were not currently able to attain such appointments. She recommended that for the first time, two nursing

Sisters should be appointed at £30 per annum, the incumbents to be both generally trained and with ophthalmic experience. This compared to a contemporary maximum salary of £24 for the most senior nurses, excepting the Matron who received £80. In addition she requested 4 Staff Nurses with duties for inpatients only, of which one should be on night duty (previously a task often delegated to a probationer). Two or three probationers should be in training at one time, and an examination in ophthalmic nursing should be sat at the end of the first year, a year in general nursing then being required for those who wished to return to a substantive post.

These suggestions seem today to be very "modern" and entirely sensible, introducing both a nursing hierarchy that we would still recognise, and a genuine system of training and accreditation. The Board took her letter seriously enough to have it printed and circulated widely for comment, and in due course they accepted it almost to the letter, transforming the nursing structure of the Hospital, albeit at an additional £100 per annum.

Matron Glover's recommendations may now seem prescient, but the ideas were not entirely her own. She was a product of the Florence Nightingale School, at St. Thomas' Hospital, and it was Nightingale who established so many of the principles which are now regarded as fundamental to the profession of nursing. Glover was obviously well-taught, and she, like so many others trained in Nightingale's image, disseminated those ideas worldwide. She had been appointed Sister of the Ophthalmic Ward at St. Thomas' Hospital in 1891, but it appears that she left in 1893 following the enforced abandonment of a romance with one of the medical staff. The sainted Florence Nightingale wrote of her to the Home Sister in that year:

3rd January 1893

Private. Dearest "home sister", I am grieved beyond measure at the incident of Miss Glover, also perplexed… I think probably people do not recognise the principle upon which we had to act… I think Miss Glover's letter puts it somewhat differently from what was supposed. But I cannot see how the engagement being unhappily broken off makes a difference. We mentioned chaperons, but in fact the Ward Sister is herself the chaperon. But if the ward sister herself takes to marrying? I ask your best advice, dear home sister, as to what advice to give Miss Glover for her future career, as she asks.

Florence Nightingale

The advice, it transpired, was to leave, and she departed for Canterbury. Subsequent posts took her progressively further from London, but Manchester may not have been far enough for her to forget her abandoned paramour. She eventually left the country in 1898, leaving Manchester to take up a post as matron of a hospital in Cairo. She should be remembered as one of the key reforming staff in the history of the Hospital.

Since the death of Philip Goldschmidt in 1889, David Bannerman had served as Chairman of the Hospital Board. At this time however, largely owing to advancing

Philip Kessler, Chairman
of the MREH Board
1898–1920

deafness, he resigned his position and Philip William Kessler took his place. He was Lancashire born and bred, Managing Director of Sepert Shipping, and would remain Chairman for 22 years. He was a busy man: simultaneously for several years he also served on the Board of the Manchester Royal Infirmary. Unfortunately only shortly after this change the long-serving Secretary, William Burgess, died suddenly after 16 years in post. His loyalty and efficiency had been greatly appreciated, and for this author, his death brought an end to a period of unparalleled legibility of hospital records! His successor was sought by advertisement at a highly competitive salary of £120 with additional 5% commission on all subscriptions collected. Unsurprisingly there were 37 applications, from which W. Shelley Prophet was appointed.

The replacement for Miss Glover as Matron was Miss Bland. She had not been long in post before the Ladies' Committee informed the Board of complaints by patients against the Matron "of want of interest & sympathy", and a wave of resignations from nurses raised suspicions. The Board noted:

> *The Board is much concerned at the continual change of Sisters, which cannot be to the benefit of the Hospital, and would be glad to receive the Matron's explanations of the causes.*

An insight into part of the problem is given by an edict issued by the Board soon afterwards:

> *It was resolved that it be an instruction to the Matron that all orders to the Nurses should be issued through the Sisters, and that with a view to the facilitating of this arrangement it would be well if the Matron had an interview with each Sister every day.*

A problem which would nowadays be described as "undermining" was clearly present. The new Matron may have been unimpressed at the new nursing structure imposed by her predecessor in Nightingale style. The imposition of such a stricture on the Matron illustrates how severe the problem was perceived to be. In due course Rachel Birch, pictured amongst the staff above, rose to become Sister, and then Senior Sister. A conflict arose between her and the Matron, which on investigation by the Board left the Matron viewed in a poor light. The terse references to her further input into Hospital business left no doubt as to her standing, and a few months later her resignation was laconically tendered, and equally briefly accepted, without tribute. Her successor was rapidly appointed, and proved to have worked before at the Hospital; Marjory Sutherland, who had most recently been Assistant Matron at the Birmingham & Midland Counties Training Institution for Nurses. She immediately got along famously on her return to the Hospital and was to remain for 14 years.

It was now 1901. The old Queen had recently died, the Hospital had treated two patients injured at the Battle of Spion Kop and several others from the South African War, and Edward VII was now enthroned. Work inexorably increased, over 24,000 patients having been dealt with in 1900. The Oxford Street Hospital was considering expansion. In the spring, Miss Terry, the owner of the house south of the Hospital n

Oxford Street, died, and the Board investigated purchase. However, it transpired that the property rested in the Trust of Owens College, who refused to sell, informing that they intended to "reserve the house and grounds for possible future eventualities". An annually renewable rent as offered, was of no use to the Eye Hospital. It was no coincidence that the Royal Infirmary, still in Piccadilly (the oldest part of which was built in 1755) had been building up to a complete move for some years. In fact the first suggestion that the Royal Infirmary should move was made as early as 1876, but during the late 1890s a substantial conflict between their Board and Trustees would come to be known as the Great Infirmary Controversy, and would substantially delay what was an increasingly necessary step. The alternative, to extend and rebuild within Piccadilly, was controversial. Notably the representatives of Owens College were amongst the most vociferous opponents of such a scheme, and amongst the complex undercurrents within this argument rests the assumption that the College wished the Infirmary to move closer to its own site. Ultimately at a special meeting of Trustees, the Board were outvoted and a motion passed to build a new Royal Infirmary at Stanley Grove, just south of the Eye Hospital (the freehold of which, it transpired, rested entirely with Owens College). The MRI Board resigned en masse in protest, but the die was cast, both for the Royal Infirmary and for its neighbour-to-be, the Royal Eye Hospital, which was now to be hemmed in on all sides.

The state of crowding at the Oxford Street site of the Eye Hospital was becoming acute; the medical staff was requested for the first time to prioritise admissions on any given day so that patients requiring urgent help were not turned away, and the matron expressed to the Board her concern about an occupancy rate somewhat over 100%:

> *I desire to call your attention to the overcrowded state of the wards. I think the patients ought not to be admitted when there are no beds for them. Children lately have been sleeping two in one bed regularly and sometimes even three; also on occasion a child is put in bed with a woman and as the beds are single it is very uncomfortable and the woman objects.*

> *On the second floor there are several beds from the Women's side in the Men's Ward, and on the first floor several from the Men's Centre Ward in the Women's Ward. Then, patients are always being moved about from one bed to another to make room for a more urgent case, which does them no good, their clothing &c gets lost, and it gives a great deal of unnecessary trouble for the Sisters and Nurses; in fact it is impossible to them to do their work properly unless things are altered.*

> *Yours faithfully*

> *M Sutherland, Matron*

In the meantime, modernisation was afoot: more of the Hospital premises were electrified, the operating theatre was redesigned and equipped, and it acquired its first giant magnet at the request of the medical staff. David Little died and his post as Honorary Surgeon was taken by John Gray Clegg.

The Manchester Royal Infirmary had now acquired from Owens College the whole of the Stanley Grove site excepting that corner occupied by the Royal Eye Hospital, which had recently, unsuccessfully attempted to buy the next-door property. It therefore opened negotiations with the Royal Infirmary and requested that it should acquire 25–30 yards of Oxford Street frontage, in order to extend. The reply, from John Thomson, Chairman of the MRI Board, was that:

> *This Committee regrets it cannot accede to any request which will result in diminishing the Oxford St frontage of the Stanley Grove Estate but that it would be prepared to consider a proposal to sell the house No. 81 Nelson St on the East side of, and adjoining the Royal Eye Hospital.*

The house referred to, "The Limes", was next door to the Eye Hospital on the south side of Nelson Street. The MREH Board asked their architect to comment upon possibilities. The suggestion was that this house could be purchased in order to furnish accommodation for the nursing staff, releasing space for an additional 24 beds for patients within the main building, if extended somewhat down Nelson Street. The MREH Board thought this compromise most unsatisfactory, and appealed to the MRI Board again for Oxford Street frontage, offering both beds for MRI ophthalmic patients, and to offer clinical instruction in ophthalmology to MRI staff. They were again rebuffed, and essentially made an open appeal asking what they could offer in order to secure the required land, settling if necessary for somewhat more on Nelson Street, rather than any on Oxford Street. Presumably behind-the-scenes negotiations were also undertaken with contacts at Owens. The reply, received in May 1904, finally agreed to the sale of land on Oxford Street, with a variety of conditions, the most important being:

> *The Royal Eye Hospital shall provide such "reasonable facilities" for clinical instruction in diseases of the eye as shall from time to time be required by the Infirmary or by the Victoria University, these facilities being a condition of the transfer of the Stanley Grove Estate from the Owen's College to the Manchester Royal Infirmary.*

A meeting took place in June 1904 between Messrs Kessler and Goldschmidt from the Royal Eye Hospital, and Messrs Hopkinson and Thorburn of the Royal Infirmary, to set the conditions of sale of the required land. It transpired that the plans for the new Infirmary had left a space of 110 feet between the two buildings, of which the Royal Eye Hospital was to purchase 85. The memorandum of the meeting concluded:

> *The land… should be occupied by a Hospital giving "reasonable facilities" for clinical instruction, a condition due to the fact that this land was a part of the "Owens College Hospital Estate". They also indicated that the Infirmary would probably be prepared to abandon its in-patient eye department in view of the proximity of the Eye Hospital. They suggested therefore that it would be well if the Eye Hospital were to undertake to set aside a certain number of beds, not less than 6 for male and 4 for female patients, such beds to be used for purposes of clinical instruction to the students of the Manchester Medical School and to be under the control of the*

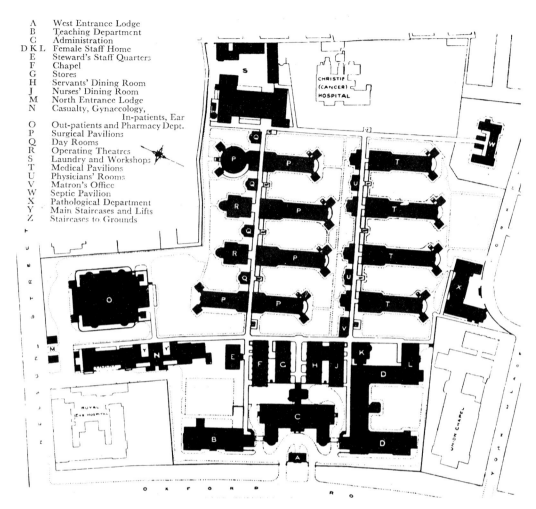

A   West Entrance Lodge
B   Teaching Department
C   Administration
D K L   Female Staff Home
E   Steward's Staff Quarters
F   Chapel
G   Stores
H   Servants' Dining Room
J   Nurses' Dining Room
M   North Entrance Lodge
N   Casualty, Gynaecology,
         In-patients, Ear
O   Out-patients and Pharmacy Dept.
P   Surgical Pavilions
Q   Day Rooms
R   Operating Theatres
S   Laundry and Workshops
T   Medical Pavilions
U   Physicians' Rooms
V   Matron's Office
W   Septic Pavilion
X   Pathological Department
Y   Main Staircases and Lifts
Z   Staircases to Grounds

The 1904 plan for the enormous new Manchester Royal Infirmary, dwarfing the Royal Eye Hospital at lower left. However, the new hard-fought boundary of its property is marked, with space for extension

Ophthalmic Surgeon to the Infirmary. This arrangement would meet the essential requirements
of the case, but a further use of the Eye Hospital for clinical instruction would be welcomed.

And so it was that nearly 90 years after the formation of the Eye Hospital, the Royal Infirmary would cease to house ophthalmic inpatients. It would not however cease to treat them – that would continue to take place within the premises of the Royal Eye Hospital, and their ophthalmic surgeon (usually also an Honorary Surgeon at MREH) would continue to see eye outpatients at the MRI. The longstanding but informal and irregular instruction of students at the Eye Hospital would now be changed so that a fixed responsibility for teaching undergraduates was now undertaken, and MREH would become the centre for undergraduate teaching of ophthalmology in Manchester. These steps permitted the Eye Hospital to make use of the land not needed by the MRI. Much discussion then took place on the need for specific accommodation of "teaching" patients, the necessity of providing a specific operating room allowing

PLAN OF ENLARGED HOSPITAL, OXFORD ROAD.
GROUND FLOOR.

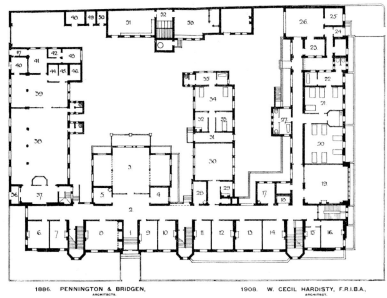

1886. PENNINGTON & BRIDGEN,
ARCHITECTS.

1908. W. CECIL HARDISTY, F.R.I.B.A.,
ARCHITECT.

KEY.

1.—Entrance.	15.—Matron's Office.	28.—House Surgeon's Room.	41.—Medicine Waiting Hall.
2.—Hall.	16.—Sisters' Room.	29.—Pantry and Service.	42.—Recovery Room.
3.—Dining Hall.	17.—Honorary Surgeon's Room.	30.—Nurses' Dining Room.	43.—Operating Room.
4.—Service.	18.—Lift.	31.—Disconnecting Passage.	44.⎫
5.—Waitress.	19.—Nurses' Sitting Room.	32.—Nurse.	45.⎬ Ophthalmoscopic Rooms
6.⎫ House Surgeons' Rooms.	20.—Men's Ward.	33.—Isolation Ward.	46.⎭
7.⎭	21.—Women's Ward.	34.—Isolation Ward.	47.—Out-patients' Exit.
8.—Board Room.	22.—Lavatory, &c.	35.—Lavatory.	48.—Mortuary.
9.—Secretary's Office.	23.—Ante-room.	36.—Out-patients' Entrance.	49.⎫ Dust.
10.⎫	24.—Students' Entrance.	37.—Hall.	50.⎭
11.⎬ House Surgeons' Rooms.	25.—Sterilizing Room.	38.—Waiting Hall.	51.—Ironing Room.
12.⎭	26.—Lecture Theatre.	39.—Examination Hall	52.—Drying Horses.
13.—Matron.	27.—Lavatory, &c.	40.—Dispensary.	53.—Washhouse.
14.—			

observation for students near to that, with separate access for students from the MRI site; and the necessity of identifying the Clinical Lecturer in Ophthalmology at the University as the MRI Surgeon who would participate in their care, that person also being required to be appointed to the honorary staff of MREH. The required land was to change hands for £2,500. The costs of extension were estimated at £20,000 and an appeal for contributions to the Extension Fund was circulated to 14,000 residents in Lancashire. Donations began to accumulate – £1,000 from a rich man's estate; £10 from a poor man in memory of his late wife's treatment at MREH; 5 guineas from a passer-by reading the appeal notice on the Nelson Street frontage; the Minnehaha Amateur Minstrels gave a performance at the Free Trade Hall, the proceeds of which went to the Extension Fund; and so, slowly the required costs were identified, and each donation recorded with equal standing, in the minutes of the Board.

The plans for the MRI were based upon the "pavilion system" whereby separate blocks were connected by glass-covered corridors with open lower sides. Although most corridors were progressively closed to the elements, this author remembers vividly the autumnal leaf-piles and wintry snowdrifts still being blown along the main corridor as late as 1979–80, when our freezing undergraduate group made its hasty way towards yet another round of teaching by ritual humiliation, on S4.

The requirements for the MREH extension were becoming clearer; in addition to the particular need for teaching beds and operating room, further beds were in any case required, as was additional accommodation for nursing staff. This was to be achieved by the construction of a new south wing, and the construction of a 3rd floor over the original south wing. The architect appointed was Cecil Hardisty, and his plans were approved by 1908 and sent out to tender. The style was to reflect the original construction, but in the process the second of the two terracotta plaques on the frontage was taken down, and its eventual destination remains unknown. The ground floor plan as submitted by Hardisty would remain largely unchanged in layout (but not in function) until the hospital's closure in 2009.

In the central wing, behind the nurses' dining room (to remain as the canteen until the 1990s) was the isolation block, comprising 3 beds, sanitary facilities and a nurse's room, the area only being reached via a separate outside staircase. The ground floor of the new south wing would comprise the teaching areas, with male and female beds for the University Lecturer, and the "lecture theatre" (literally the operating theatre for

The Manchester Royal Infirmary during construction, looking North along Oxford Street. The Royal Eye Hospital is seen in the background

teaching) would in due course become known as the University Theatre. The whole ground floor of this wing would in the 1970s be converted into the 4 operating theatres which remained until the hospital's closure.

The construction work on the new MRI began in 1906. The quiet residential area of Stanley Grove was converted into a cacophony of demolition and building, hundreds of labourers gradually constructing the neo-classical building from redbrick and Portland stone. A series of photographs were taken during this process, one showing the southern aspect of the MREH with its new neighbour rising imperiously beside it.

The extension work to MREH was commenced as the MRI was rising beside it. Financially the hospital was under strain again – not only was capital required for the building, but the increased expenditure required for staffing the higher number of beds was proving difficult to fund. Building was completed in 1908, and the enlarged hospital was trumpeted in the Annual Report of 1909 as now having 160 beds, more than Moorfields Eye Hospital at 140 and therefore the largest in the country and probably in the world. In practice however, the extension was filled only gradually as income permitted the staff to treat increased numbers of inpatients. In 1910 the annual income/expenditure was in deficit by nearly £1,000; the Hospital had over-reached itself. Increasingly urgent needs were expressed to subscribers and donors, and at the Annual Meeting in 1911 the Chairman found himself having to justify the construction of the extension to the beneficiaries, on the basis of ever-increasing need to treat patients. That justification was at least well-documented by the inexorable rise in numbers treated. There now appeared regularly at Board business an appraisal of the

The newly extended Manchester Royal Eye Hospital

inpatient waiting list, which required division into "urgent" and "non-urgent" to enable the medical staff to prioritise.

The building work of both MREH and MRI was completed in late 1908, and thus the whole appearance of this stretch of what was now called Oxford Road, was transformed from a quiet residential area into a busy hospital complex. St. Mary's Hospital joined them in 1910, creating a combined frontage stretching some 600 yards. The foundations for what would become one of the largest healthcare and education campuses in Europe, were laid.

The extended MREH catered for the "deserving poor" of the working population. In every annual report in this period, an appeal was made to the Trustees to ensure that only those who could not afford to pay for their care, were permitted:

> The Institution having been frequently IMPOSED UPON BY PERSONS WHO ARE NOT FIT OBJECTS OF CHARITY, Trustees are particularly requested, before they give a recommendation, to satisfy themselves (in compliance with Rule XXV) respecting the circumstances of the applicant. Subscribers are respectfully requested to bring this Report under the notice of their friends.

W. SHELLEY PROPHET, SECRETARY

ROYAL EYE HOSPITAL,

OXFORD ROAD, MANCHESTER.

In the annual report of 1909, the list of those considered "fit objects of charity" gives a flavour of the occupations of those treated (or their families):

V.—TRADES AND CALLINGS OF THE PATIENTS ADMITTED IN 1909.

[To the names of the married females, and of all juvenile patients who, when admitted, themselves follow no occupation, that of the husband or parent respectively is entered.]

Agents, Collectors, and Travellers	338
Artists, Designers, and Draughts-men	40
Bag and Box Makers	82
Bakers and Confectioners	168
Boatmen and Sailors	46
Boilermen and Engine Attendants	135
Bricklayers and Slaters	215
Brush and Basket Makers	29
Butchers	121
Calico Printers, Bleachers, Dyers, and Finishers	139
Capmakers	187
Carters, Cabmen, Coachmen, Grooms, Ostlers, and Nippers	1009
Clerks, Cashiers, Storekeepers, and Timekeepers	1038
Coach and Wagon Builders and Wheelwrights	117
Coopers	22
Dress and Mantle Makers	226
Electricians	106
Emigrants	25
Engravers and Stampmakers	71
Farmers and Farm Labourers	110
Frenchpolishers and Upholsterers	62
Fustiancutters	18
Gardeners	137
Glassworkers	43
Hairdressers	88
Hatters and Hat Trimmers	156
Hawkers	264
Joiners and Cabinet Makers	623
Labourers	6018
Lodging-house keepers	95
Masons	80
Metal Workers, Machinists, &c.	6593
Mill Employés	1578
Milliners	54
Miners and Quarrymen	602
Ministers, Missionaries, and Students	48
Nurses and Midwives	58
Office and Errand Boys (and Girls)	90
Painters, Paperhangers, and Sign-writers	369
Packing-case Makers	66

Paupers	47
Paviors, Asphalters, and Navvies	42
Plasterers	48
Plumbers, Bellhangers, and Glaziers	169
Policemen, Postmen, Soldiers, and Commissionaires	221
Porters	286
Printers, Bookbinders, Paper-rulers, and Pattern card Makers	376
Publicans, Waiters, Waitresses, and Hotel Employés	237
Railway Servants	568
Saltboilers and Miners	12
Sawyers	67
Scholars	162
Seamstresses, Shirtmakers, and Embroiderers	718
Servants (Domestics), Charwomen and Laundresses	1228
Shopkeepers and Dealers and their Assistants	703
Shoemakers and Cloggers	175
Slippermakers	38
Tailors and Tailoresses	875
Teachers and Governesses	149
Telegraphists, Telephonists, and Typists	51
Theatrical Employés, Musicians, and Vocalists	69
Tram Drivers and Guards	187
Umbrella and Stick Makers	39
Warehousemen, Hoistmen, Makers-up, and Packers	1070
Waterproofers and India-rubber Workers	210
Woodcarvers and Turners	24
No Occupation	966
Widows	1320
Orphans	227
Housewives	253
Sundry Occupations and Professions	1191
Total	33,094

An extract from the annual report of 1909 showing the occupations of those treated; a cross-section of pre-war industrial Manchester trades

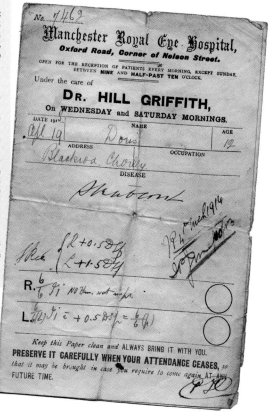

A pre-war patient record card from MREH

An appeal for funds for MREH in 1911, in the Manchester Guardian

All patients, when attending the Hospital for an outpatient visit, had a record card – an 8"×5" leaflet, numbered individually, on which essential medical information (and in this era, "essential" meant very laconic indeed) was recorded. The record became the responsibility of the patient, not the Hospital; the latter had negligible records storage facility, and the patient took the card home for safe keeping and to bring back with them if necessary. A few have survived, and an example here shows the style. Record cards of this type were to remain in service at MREH until the 1960s, and for some general practitioners, for far longer.

For several years in succession, the expenditure of the hospital was greater than its income, as witnessed by the summary of throughput and finances issued in 1911. The capital was being slowly eroded, and in this year a somewhat desperate advertisement appeared in the Manchester Guardian attesting to the financial difficulties of maintaining this extra workload.

The hospital now required a nursing staff of 19, and the monthly Matron's report contained regular indications of the difficulty in maintaining staffing. A salary hierarchy had been established in order to retain good nurses, but the need for general nursing training in addition to ophthalmic experience meant that every nurse was required to go elsewhere for the former before being accepted back as a Staff Nurse, and many stayed elsewhere. In the days before antibiotics, nursing carried risks of infection and injury, and a regular parade of such matters included the necessary time off work, or transfer to the Monsall Hospital, for such maladies as "septic throat", tonsillitis, purulent conjunctivitis, erysipelas, scarlatina, chickenpox, acute rheumatism, burns from Nitric acid, dislocated wrist, "septic finger" (a particularly common item, this), and the fairly frequent dismissal of nursing probationers as having been found "unsuitable". Nevertheless the staff somehow managed, and the introduction of a system of nurse education and examination by the medical staff led to accreditation as qualified ophthalmic nurses. At this time nursing probationers were paid £9–15 per annum, Staff nurses £18–24, Sisters £25–36, and Matron £70–80. The Matron and Ladies' Committee also oversaw the porters, charwomen and laundry staff. There were

4 porters at this time; Edward Firby, Head Porter received 32s 0d weekly including uniform; Second Porter and Engineer Thomas Alderson received 30s 0d; Third Porter and Boiler Attendant Alfred Hammel was paid 17s 0d; and Fourth Porter Frank Horn, 15s 0d (in other words, as much as a nursing Sister, albeit without bed and board). All were required to live in close proximity to the hospital.

The Hospital, as for all at this time, was almost entirely dependant upon coal for its heating. There were many eager suppliers, and highly competitive tenders were made on at least a half-yearly basis. In June 1910 Messrs Blight & Co. secured the contract to deliver No. 5 Slack (poor-quality small coal and dust for steam boilers) at 9s 7d per ton, No. 3 Burgy (slightly better, for furnaces and heating apparatus) at 11s 3d, House coal at 14s 2d and Good House coal (the least dirty to use) at 15s 5d. The back of the hospital contained the coal houses and the boiler house, and there were hoists up to each floor to supply the firegrates, the portering staff being responsible for its supply internally. The charwomen were doubtless kept very well-occupied in cleaning the ashes and smoky paintwork, and the regular bills for repainting reflected the atmosphere.

New technology did gradually intrude into this coal-fired and steam-powered system. Electricity was already supplied to the building, for lighting some but not all rooms. The Hospital was now on the expanding telephone exchange, its number being *No. 15 Rusholme*. The medical staff realised the need to obtain radiographs for some injured patients; X-ray radiography had been in clinical use for over 10 years, but MREH could not justify the purchase of the necessary equipment for its own use. It therefore negotiated with the MRI next door, who supplied X-rays at 5 shillings per photograph. The Board did decide to acquire a Remington typewriter, but on the subject of the new-fangled vacuum cleaner, they were elegantly unenthusiastic:

> *The Board have had the matter of the Vacuum Cleaner under consideration, but hesitate to order one as they are not convinced that in actual practice the utility of the appliance would be commensurate with its cost and the expense of the electric current required.*

It would be a further year or two before they did give way and permit the charwomen to use a vacuum cleaner, at the eye-watering cost of 18 guineas. Meanwhile, constant attempts to improve ventilation within the building reflected partly upon poor design, and additional expense was incurred in building repairs; the various contracts agreed with builders rather suggest that the Hospital was not well-built. Almost the entire second floor corridor floor had to be replaced after cracking and subsiding.

Contracts for the supply of meat, bread and milk were also regularly set, and in September 2010 the butcher J Bushill agreed to supply legs of mutton at 8d per pound, coarse meat at 4d, Canterbury lamb at 5d; the baker AJ Hamer brought best bread at 4s 4d per 4lbs and best flour at 1s 5d per 12lbs; E Burgess supplied the milk at 2s 7d for 12 quarts

During 1909–10, a conflict arose between a group of opticians, and MREH about the perceived monopoly of Armstrong & Brother, suppliers of spectacles to the Hospital.

Armstrongs had for many years been the preferred supplier; their staff attended the outpatient department to dispense spectacles, and they supplied artificial eyes. They maintained carefully their close and profitable association, and the occasional gift to the Hospital (a barometer here, a set of shelves there) undoubtedly oiled the wheels of business. The other opticians, represented by the Manchester & North of England Optical Society, complained that whereas they frequently directed their clients to MREH to have their problems treated, they never received them back for their spectacles, Armstrongs having appropriated the business. On one occasion an Armstrong's man in the outpatient department had refused to let a patient take his prescription out of the hospital with him. An accusation of monopoly was published in the newspapers. A delegation was received by the Board, and the decision was that the current arrangement with Armstrongs remained the most satisfactory, although two changes were made; firstly, the spectacle prescription sheets (previously bearing Armstrong's heading) were reprinted by the Hospital to make it clear that any optician could supply spectacles; and secondly a renegotiation with Armstrongs led to reduced prices, so that wire-framed glasses with spherical lenses 0.25D–8D were 1s 3d per pair, cylindrical lenses 3s 0d per pair.

The first years of the twentieth century had seen the beginnings of the welfare state, and in 1908 the Old Age Pensions Act had been enacted, enabling those on low wages (less than £21 per annum) who had worked all their lives and were of "good character" to draw the sum of 5 shillings weekly if they were fortunate to reach the age of 70. The second stage was to have a direct effect upon MREH and all hospitals currently dependent upon subscription and donation, and that was the National Insurance Act of 1911. The new system required that all earning under £160 per annum (in other words, the great majority – all those earning more had no trouble paying for their own medical care) were required to contribute 4d weekly to the scheme, their employers and the Government through taxation, supplementing this. The system introduced the concept of sick pay, maternity benefit, free treatment for tuberculosis and access to a "panel doctor" to treat some medical problems. The British Hospitals Association were not amused, and neither were most trade unions, friendly and cooperative societies, who were concerned that the introduction of State insurance would discourage voluntary donation (especially from employers, who were now required to contribute to the new scheme), and the Act did not provide for funding of the charitable hospitals, only for tuberculosis sanatoria. The MREH Board were invited to send a representative to a meeting of the Hospitals Association in London, encouraged strongly by the MRI Board. Mr Gaddum did so, and reported that the Association had been granted an interview with the Chancellor of the Exchequer (Lloyd George) to make their concerns known. At the Annual Meeting of 1912, the Chairman Mr Kessler stated, as reported in the Manchester Guardian:

> A great deal was being done to make hospitals receive something for the work they would do under the Act. Hospitals would have to remain with us, and in the end there might be hospital government. They had been accustomed to have the

management of their institutions free of cost, but changes were probably before them, and hospitals might in the future be run by the authority. He would be sorry to see that day.

Despite these protests at both local and National level, the Act came into force, and its effects would indeed prove fundamental, though perhaps more slowly than anticipated by the perceptive Kessler. The Hospital had been very supportive of its valued staff during any periods of illness or enforced absence in previous years, but it now made clear that after the introduction of the Act (as a result of which it had to contribute 3d weekly for every qualifying staff member) no staff could expect support for board, residence, treatment, nursing or wages during illness. One suspects that at least in the early stages of the Act, the staff were financially less well catered for during illness.

Also in the early part of the twentieth century, the beginnings of an increasingly vigorous movement began to rear its head: Women's Rights and Suffrage. The Royal Eye Hospital had permitted, for the first time in 1906, a female doctor to attend the hospital to observe clinics, but the Royal Infirmary would not permit women doctors to be appointed to their House and this was the currently held attitude; the men were doctors and the women were nurses; the men ran the Boards and the women ran the Ladies' Committees. In 1911 a provocative letter was received at MREH from the executors of Mrs Rose Hyland, a prominent Manchester suffragette, whose last act was to bequeath sums of money to various charitable institutions (£130 to MREH) with the stipulation that:

Such legacy shall not be paid or payable unless there shall be on your governing body at the expiration of twelve calendar months from her death two women and unless this condition is fulfilled such legacy shall fail.

The Board considered, demurred and shifted its collective feet, eventually deciding that their response to the executors should be:

The Board of Management is not competent to accept the conditions attached to the legacy – the Board being elected, and its constitution determined by the Trustees at their Annual Meeting.

It is not known what, if any proportion of Mrs Hyland's estate was actually distributed to the selected targets. The executors were not however to be deflected so easily, and enquired whether the matter could be raised at the next Annual Meeting. It was, and was considered untenable, this stance crucially being supported by the Ladies' Committee (mainly of course, the wives of the Board members and Honorary Surgeons). The matter was laid to rest, but in fact MREH's first female member of the medical staff was appointed as House Surgeon not long afterwards. The Manchester Royal Eye Hospital is of course well-used to the proximity of suffragettes. Emmeline Pankhurst's home from 1898 to 1907 had been just across the road at 62 Nelson Street, next door to Nelson House (later Lister House) and the house is still standing, now the Pankhurst Centre. It was while there in 1903 that she formed the Women's Social and Political Union, the first organisation of suffragettes.

TABLE SHOWING THE PROGRESS OF THE HOSPITAL.

Year	Patients Admitted	In-Patients	Accidents	Operations	Ordinary Income £ s. d.			Expenditure £ s. d.			Subscriptions £ s. d.		
1815	1885	..	..	..	195	0	0	202	19	11	..		
1846	1473	..	202	..	371	6	7	437	11	5	309	6	9
1847	1484	..	187	..	Sept., 1848			⎫			417	11	0
1848	1525	..	198	..	to Dec., 1849			⎬1567 4 7					
1849	1378	..	199	..	1803	1	0	⎭					
1850	1464	..	192	..	602	2	9	837	14	5	339	19	2
1851	1639	..	199	..	569	13	5	535	1	8	402	15	0
1852	1789	..	205	..	763	0	5	775	3	9	503	3	0
1853	1863	..	310	..	725	4	1	697	5	11	525	14	6
1854	1776	..	207	..	630	6	10	682	17	11	533	16	3
1855	1892	..	228	..	696	1	4	694	11	5	556	4	1
1856	2062	..	250	..	1008	13	10	690	4	0	567	7	0
1857	2160	..	271	..	925	18	5	760	19	5	582	14	10
1858	2097	..	216	..	830	18	2	906	9	3	604	13	10
1859	2200	..	161	..	708	8	2	756	12	0	585	3	8
1860	2227	..	203	..	752	13	10	727	5	1	596	16	6
1861	2476	..	227	..	726	9	7	752	11	8	603	12	0
1862	2289	136	367	..	772	4	11	917	15	1	643	8	8
1863	2965	155	470	..	984	9	7	818	12	7	773	3	0
1864	3205	215	602	513	1073	3	9	1058	0	6	790	18	6
1865	3615	260	773	760	1097	5	3	1242	16	8	803	4	0
1866	3812	265	836	634	1145	8	5	1402	19	2	871	0	6
a1867	3872	398	839	574	1502	2	9	1927	11	5	951	14	0
1868	4600	705	987	928	1846	9	6	1838	9	10	1124	5	0
1869	4900	720	921	837	1930	1	7	1966	0	10	1336	9	0
1870	6022	886	1121	996	2016	13	4	1775	8	6	1321	9	0
1871	6359	931	1302	1077	1990	9	8	1867	17	7	1398	4	6
1872	6832	954	1459	982	2323	5	5	1918	11	8	1433	9	0
1873	6770	1013	1283	863	2445	7	5	1889	11	0	1462	1	6
1874	7008	930	1385	790	2406	13	9	2014	11	2	1523	0	0
1875	7508	942	1554	885	2438	18	4	1930	13	7	1497	6	6
1876	7477	1050	1626	982	2479	18	4	2125	5	10	1501	13	0
1877	8325	1061	1976	958	2562	1	9	1997	13	7	1518	10	6
1878	8591	1102	1690	1079	2617	17	10	2063	14	10	1479	17	6
1879	8573	1082	1324	1005	2326	6	11	2638	3	11	1467	16	4
1880	10262	1178	1764	1156	2816	19	1	2344	4	1	1498	16	2
1881	10919	1130	1802	1145	2543	19	1	2537	13	2	1507	1	6
1882	12961	1265	1900	1212	2855	4	7	2524	14	10	1632	3	3
1883	14702	1213	2090	1365	3171	19	10	2486	19	4	1862	9	0
1884	15427	1155	2190	1597	3334	10	4	2265	11	1	1943	12	10
1885	15184	1253	2283	1610	3397	3	10	2223	19	4	2055	18	6
b1886	16251	1402	2272	2021	3667	14	10	2887	17	4	2108	5	6
1887	16695	1396	2301	2036	3775	4	1	c3894	3	7	2052	17	11
1888	17308	1301	2474	1643	3911	17	1	3272	3	8	2146	17	9
1889	18657	1341	2930	1602	4271	11	3	3389	15	9	2217	17	4
1890	18270	1275	3042	1606	4212	15	10	3693	14	6	2228	18	4
1891	17849	1241	3187	1722	4435	1	9	3477	3	2	2222	16	0
1892	18072	1306	2846	1700	4453	15	6	3818	10	0	2199	0	11
1893	18901	1315	3237	1763	4214	17	5	3680	13	0	2148	6	0
1894	21578	1336	3020	1850	4178	10	7	3413	15	7	2148	1	7
1895	20708	1363	3251	2098	4209	7	8	3959	4	8	2134	3	8
1896	22364	1370	3825	2071	4281	16	8	4313	18	1	3120	19	7
1897	22059	1415	3988	2171	4894	6	7	d4531	18	7	2072	9	9
1898	23369	1394	4574	1901	4429	6	5	e6430	19	8	2157	8	2
1899	23616	1433	5051	1990	4707	1	1	f4993	1	5	2142	11	4
1900	24135	1356	5062	1976	4799	12	7	g4819	2	9	2184	2	2
1901	22973	1344	5396	1827	4786	12	5	h4816	9	8	2178	6	7
1902	24478	1465	5529	2745	5310	2	5	j5773	4	5	2190	14	11
1903	26342	1407	5776	1804	5046	18	11	k5275	8	11	2193	2	6
1904	27619	1544	5874	2107	5116	14	5	l5623	1	4	2193	7	7
1905	28273	1500	6932	2217	5303	15	5	m5443	11	9	2139	6	6
1906	30447	1593	9096	2425	5325	10	5	5127	13	11	2138	19	8
1907	32643	1523	9396	2226	5166	1	4	5261	15	3	2191	4	9
1908	31793	1553	9140	2178	4882	14	8	5236	6	4	2135	9	8
1909	33094	1635	7124	1941	5225	6	9	6288	11	3	2225	16	6
1910	34842	1987	8722	2274	6015	14	10	6965	2	0	2206	18	5

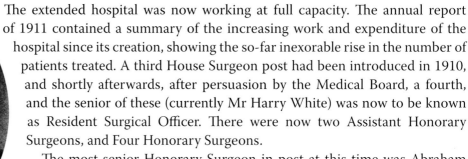

The extended hospital was now working at full capacity. The annual report of 1911 contained a summary of the increasing work and expenditure of the hospital since its creation, showing the so-far inexorable rise in the number of patients treated. A third House Surgeon post had been introduced in 1910, and shortly afterwards, after persuasion by the Medical Board, a fourth, and the senior of these (currently Mr Harry White) was now to be known as Resident Surgical Officer. There were now two Assistant Honorary Surgeons, and Four Honorary Surgeons.

The most senior Honorary Surgeon in post at this time was Abraham Emrys-Jones MD JP. Born in Cardigan in 1852, he graduated in medicine at Edinburgh in 1875. He had joined the Eye Hospital in 1876 as House Surgeon, and as tradition dictated, had risen in the ranks and been appointed Honorary Surgeon in 1882. He was also Honorary Oculist to the Bolton Infirmary, and to the Manchester Industrial Schools. He published actively on ophthalmic subjects, but in addition to his specialist work he was active in the field of public health, publishing on *"Diseases produced by Drink"* and in particular on matters concerning the ever-increasing problem of *"Disposal of the Dead"*, on which he became an authority; it was his intervention that led to the building of the Manchester Crematorium. He was on the Court of Governors of the University of Wales. He became President of the Manchester Medical Society in 1911, when his address was on Lord Lister and his work. Ill-health was to force his retirement from the Eye Hospital in 1914, when he became Consulting Surgeon. He continued to live in St. John Street until his death in 1925.

Abraham Emrys-Jones, Honorary Surgeon to MREH 1882–1914

Alexander Hill Griffith, Honorary Surgeon to MREH 1889–1918

Alexander Hill Griffith MD FRCS was also a long-serving Honorary Surgeon, holding the same post at MRI. Born in Aberdeen in 1859, he graduated from that University. His career seemed well-planned as he came straight to MREH after qualification, remaining on the staff all of his working life, and he had been Honorary Surgeon since 1889. He came from a medical family, his brother holding the post of Professor of Medicine at Leeds University. His main ophthalmological claim to fame was to bring to better prominence the need for cylindrical prescriptions for astigmatism (almost all prescriptions until this time were spherical only), and cylindrical lenses only became a routine part of refraction sets after his multiple presentations on the subject. It was largely for this work that he was awarded in 1897 the Middlemore Prize by the British Medical Association. He was also a keen microscopist, and taught at MREH the skills of histology and pathology (at that time surgeons made and examined their own microscope sections). He was well-known nationally through his prominence in the Ophthalmological Society and BMA (very much a clinical organisation at that time) and was the first President of the North of England Ophthalmological Society on its creation in 1914. He was said to be a wizard with both the ophthalmoscope and the micro-surgical instruments of ophthalmology, and was thought to be a truly inspirational teacher. In the impending Great War he was to become Major RAMC, but he retired in 1918, moving to Surrey where he filled his time with golf, billiards and singing until his death in 1937.

Another Welshman, Edward Roberts MRCS had been on the staff of MREH for 25 years, and Honorary Surgeon since 1895. From Aberystwyth, he qualified at Guy's Hospital and after a brief sojourn in obstetrics there, he moved north both geographically and anatomically, being a stalwart as Honorary Surgeon at MREH since 1895. He was to retire as Consulting Surgeon in this year, 1910, and afterwards moved back to Wales where he was to become President of the Aberystwyth Infirmary until his death in 1935.

John Gray Clegg, Honorary Surgeon to MREH 1902–33

Every so often a giant of a personality appears on the scene, and one such man was John Gray Clegg MD FRCS. Born in Manchester itself, he was described as "from the North and *of* the North, with much of northern ruggedness in his characteristics and outlook on life". He was educated at Manchester Grammar School and then the Victoria University. He was destined for ophthalmology, and he spent every waking hour delivering it, teaching it or writing about it. After a brief time as House Surgeon elsewhere he spent his whole career at MREH, being appointed Honorary Surgeon in 1902, a post he would hold for 31 years. He was a prolific publisher of articles on ophthalmology especially in the field of cornea and glaucoma, and was the first to describe heredity in endothelial dystrophy. His immense experience (and high degree of organisation) were demonstrated in a later paper on penetrating injuries, which began "During my term of office as Honorary Surgeon at the Royal Eye Hospital, Manchester... I have had 12,895 accident cases. Of these 1,448 have been admitted as in-patients under my care, including 859 cases of penetration or rupture of the globe". In the same paper he advised horse-hair for corneal suturing. He was very much an Associations man – founder member and leading light of the North of England Ophthalmological Society, prominent in both Oxford Congress and the Ophthalmological Society of the UK, President of the Ophthalmological Section of the BMA, President of the Manchester Medical Society. He was nationally a very well-known and highly regarded ophthalmologist.

Harry Horsmanm McNabb, Honorary Surgeon to MREH 1908–40

Clegg was blessed with what his obituarist called "that rarer gift, perhaps best described as "flair"". His enormous private practice was the result, but his indomitable workload for MREH was also prodigious. He was regarded as the opinion to be sought, and Treacher Collins said of him "I never met Clegg without learning something from him". He mixed his immense clinical skills with a jovial and thoroughly entertaining character. His early alopecia totalis left him bewigged all of his adult life; whether he knew of his nickname of "wiggy" is unknown (he almost certainly did) but if so he was likely to have laughed uproariously and shared the joke. Always too busy, always late, always rushing. His teaching ability was reflected by his appointment as Lecturer in Ophthalmology at the University, and he also became Honorary Surgeon at the MRI. He married late and perhaps found new reasons to be elsewhere, resigning to become Consulting Surgeon in 1933. He died in 1942.

The last of the Honorary Surgeons at this time was Harry Horsmann McNabb MD. Born in Bolton and graduating from Manchester, he passed through the House at MREH to become Honorary Surgeon in 1908. He was to fill that position for 32 years, but during the latter part of that career was much handicapped by the effects of old pulmonary tuberculosis. He was said to be a superb surgeon, an unflappable clinician, and unendingly helpful to juniors under his wing.

The medical staff of the Hospital grouped together for a formal photograph in 1908, unfortunately one of very few such records to survive. This was presumably taken behind the old dining room, in the position later occupied by the Nelson Street corridor. It is very much a picture of its time, the seated honorary surgeons being a group of confident Edwardian gentlemen in their frock coats, ranging in quality from high to exquisite, probably photographed after a meeting of the Medical Board. The two housemen in their smart suits have been summoned to join them. The lives of all of them were to be very different within only a few years.

The Honorary Surgeons and others in 1908. The three gentlemen in the back row are probably the two House Surgeons, Drs Harrison and Bride, flanking Assistant Surgeon, John Wharton. From the left in the front row: Harry Horsmann McNabb, Edward Roberts, Charles Glascott, Abraham Emrys Jones, Alexander Hill Griffith, John Gray Clegg

CHAPTER EIGHT

World Wars and Welfare State

THE BALKANS, AS BEFORE and after, were the tinder, the over-valued prize bickered over by the Ottomans (rapidly dispelled), the Austro-Hungarians, the Russians and their allies. The Serbs were the spark, and following the unsatisfactory results of the Second Balkan War in 1913, Serbian activists had Austro-Hungary in their sights. Both Germany and Great Britain in the meantime, were inexorably re-arming on land and at sea, in progress towards what to many observers seemed the inevitable wider conflict.

The resulting economic situation in England was unstable, but work continued as usual through 1914, with increased efforts to raise subscriptions. On May 20th, Watson Hartley was appointed as Canvasser for new subscriptions and donations throughout North Wales and Chester, for a commission of 7½%, and Dr Arnold Renshaw was appointed Bacteriologist to the Hospital, with an honorarium of £50pa. On June 10th Dr Emrys-Jones resigned as Honorary Surgeon owing to ill-health, and was made Consulting Surgeon. On June 14th 1914 Archduke Franz Ferdinand was assassinated in Sarajevo. On June 24th Matron requested repairs to the couch in the outpatient department, and Nurse Ledger was off sick owing to swollen glands. On July 15th the Board invested £2,000 in Salford Corporation. On July 28th the Empire of Austro-Hungary declared war on Serbia. On July 29th it was resolved that inpatients could only be visited on Saturdays between two and four o'clock in the afternoon. On August 2nd Germany invaded Belgium and declared war on Russia. On August 4th Britain declared war on Germany. On August 12th Austria invaded Serbia. On August 19th Dr Renshaw informed the Board that he had offered his services to the War Office, and requested leave to depart if necessary. The realities of the outside world began to impinge. One of the House Surgeons, Dr Dixon, left in October to join the Royal Army Medical Corps. His departure (and probably the relative unavailability of male junior doctors at this time) led to a momentous occasion for the Hospital: on October 7th Dr Lily Allen MBChB (Victoria University of Manchester) was the first female doctor to be appointed to the Hospital, just a few days under 100 years after its inauguration. Her salary as House Surgeon was £80pa with board, lodging and washing. The Dispenser had also left to sign up and again, following the interview of two ladies to the post, Miss Angela Emery was appointed at 15s 0d weekly. In due course both Dr Hill Griffith and Dr Wharton, Honorary Surgeons, were appointed officers in the RAMC, with part-time duties at the Western Military Hospital in Rusholme. This, a requisitioned school, was one of many to be taken over for hospital use. These, together with large houses and any other buildings suitable for the purpose, would generate at its peak, 25,000 beds for injured soldiers in Manchester.

The Board of Management of the Manchester Royal Eye Hospital held their regular meeting at Oxford Road on October 21st 1914. Amongst the routine business discussed was an additional item – the proposed offer of beds to the War Office for the treatment of the wounded. Enquiries were to be made, and the minutes of the meeting were signed off as always, by the Chairman. At no stage was there written acknowledgement that it was one hundred years to the very day that the Manchester Institution for Curing Diseases of the Eye had been inaugurated.

At the end of October, 10 beds were offered to the War Office (the University beds), purely for the treatment of eye cases, with board to be charged at 4s 0d per day, and these were accepted on behalf of GOC-in-Chief Northern Command. By the end of the year that number rose to 19. At the Annual Meeting in January 1915 a low-key

British soldiers blinded by mustard gas at Estaire, 1918

acknowledgement of the Hospital's centenary appeared in the Manchester papers, noting that at both inauguration and centenary, there was war in Europe. The first year of operation had seen 1,885 patients treated; 1914 had seen 41,670. The Manchester Evening News opined:

> The hospital began its life in troublous times, in the midst of the greatest European conflict that had ever been known, and it is a curious and sad coincidence that it celebrates its hundred birthday under equally grave conditions

By March 1915, the beds already used for injured soldiers were inadequate, and a separate ward was made available, raising the number of military beds to 49 (and later to a maximum of 50). Captain Edgar Kessler, son of the Chairman of the Hospital Board, was killed at Gallipoli. In typically generous fashion, his parents endowed a hospital bed in his name with a donation of £1,000. More staff volunteered for military service, and the Board were concerned that William Stirling, RSO, planned to do so. The Chairman wrote to the War Emergency Committee to explain the great difficulties that MREH found would find itself under if he were to go. The rebuttal was entirely predictable:

War Emergency Committee

429 Strand

London 7th September 1915

Dear Sir

The Executive Sub-Committee considered your letter of the 3rd instant at its meeting yesterday. The feeling of the meeting was that your Board of Management is undoubtedly carrying on its work under great difficulty but nevertheless it was felt that at a time of emergency such as the present it is the duty of any medical man of military age to enrol himself to come up for service if called upon and clearly explain the difficulty of his position which the Local Emergency Committee, having due regard to the needs of the civil population, would take into consideration when deciding who can be spared and who cannot.

Yours faithfully

N Bishop Harman

This was Nathaniel Bishop Harman, ophthalmic surgeon to the West London Hospital, of the eponymous magnifying spectacles so often used for minor surgery until replaced by telescopic loupes in the 1980s. His devotion to his military cause clearly outweighed any sympathy for fellow ophthalmologists in crisis. There followed a deputation from the Manchester hospitals to London to discuss the matter further, to no effect. The difficulties were compounded by the departure of Matron Miss Sutherland, who had been in post for 14 years. Dr Milnes Bride also applied for a commission in the RAMC, and Dr Stirling departed for the Western front, as predicted. He later served as surgeon in charge of the Calais Ophthalmic Centre. Dr Harry White, House Surgeon, already in the front line in France as Surgeon Captain, was awarded the Military Cross after continuing to operate for 36 hours without respite in a bombed-out dressing station. Back in Manchester, the squeeze on resources was well and truly underway, and an inventive approach to staffing was now required as the number of doctors available for appointment declined progressively. Two senior medical students, Miss Eva Glasier and Miss Dorothy Potts, were appointed as locum house surgeons, and the number of nurses was increased to compensate for the lack of ophthalmologists. Increased salaries were offered, and to the hard-working junior medical staff who cared for far more patients than was normally considered reasonable, a War Bonus was paid. Nevertheless the Hospital could not carry on its civilian work unhindered. The outpatient department at St. John Street had to close on two days per week in late 1915, and then the following year, after Dr Wharton and Dr Milnes Bride departed with the RAMC, it remained open only on two days weekly, and that under considerable stress. Some mitigation was provided by the voluntary return to service of Edward Roberts, retired ophthalmologist. Passing almost unnoticed in 1915 was the first appointment to the Hospital of an anaesthetist, Dr G Barrow, marking the beginning of the end of over 100 years of surgeons administering their own general anaesthetics. The process leading to the total handover of anaesthetic responsibility to specialists was however to be quite slow. In the early 1920s the house surgeons were still required to administer general anaesthetics while their senior colleagues operated, but gradually a system of rota anaesthetists was introduced, paid by the hour, and slowly a safer system evolved.

Gallipoli, Marne, Ypres, Somme, Verdun, Arras, Passchendaele; names all previously unknown to the British soldier, all now permanently engraved on British memory, each generating tens of thousands of casualties which flooded back home, maimed, blinded and disfigured. The military beds at MREH were filled and re-filled, some combatants discharged to a life of handicap, others patched up and returned into the hell of the trenches. Those left behind, mostly women but some Indian male doctors, nurses and medical students, worked many hours to maintain some sort of civilian service in addition to their war duties.

By the spring of 1917 the country's resources were strained to the extent that food rationing was on the agenda. The Matron was requested by the Board to ensure economy in food consumption, in particular ensuring that the resident hospital staff were to be provided with no more than one meat meal per day. At the same time, that other great scourge of wartime reared its head: venereal disease. A memorandum was received by the Board, circulated from the British Medical Association regarding the provision of services during the home-front epidemic, a phenomenon to be magnified substantially during the second war.

The majority of military patients at MREH at this time were injured by blast, burn or bullet. Harrowing descriptions of bilateral blindness exist, and sometimes deaths from accompanying head injury. It was as late as 1917, at Ypres, that mustard gas was

The blinded, in a detail from the painting "Gassed" by John Singer Sargent

first used against British troops. Years of practical experimentation by all sides in Flanders and elsewhere, passing through Chlorine and Phosgene, had settled on this disgusting vesicant as the preferred weapon. For those who did not die in agony from desquamation, or suffocate to death from laryngeal oedema or pulmonary necrosis, in the appalling fashion described by Wilfred Owen (of the Manchester Regiment) in *Dulce et Decorum est,* probably the most powerful anti-war poem ever written, permanent blindness with corneal and conjunctival scarring were the common sequel, and many were so affected, as portrayed so poignantly by John Singer Sargent in his magnum opus, *Gassed,* showing the blinded at Arras in 1918. During 1917, a total of 4355 military outpatients, and 479 military inpatients were treated in MREH. Even in the 1980s this author was seeing a couple of elderly gentlemen, blinded by mustard gas in the Great War, with chronic corneal problems. The greatest irony is that the chemical descendant of nitrogen mustard, cyclophosphamide, is still used at MREH as a sight-saving drug in those with some of the most serious ocular inflammations.

In December 1918 Drs White and Bride were effusively welcomed back after their demobilisation. Bride had served with the RAMC in Mesopotamia and Italy, Dr White in France. Their return allowed some semblance of normality to appear again in staffing arrangements, which had been so affected for 4 years.

Dr John Wharton also returned from distinguished service in France. He had qualified at Cambridge (although his clinical training took place in Manchester) and his first post was as House Surgeon to MREH. He had held the army rank of Captain from 1908, and in the same year was appointed Assistant Surgeon, becoming Honorary Surgeon in 1910. He spent the war treating eye and other injuries in France and elsewhere. He

John Wharton, Honorary
Surgeon to MREH
1910–1942

returned as a redoubtable and long-serving member of staff, also serving at the MRI as Honorary Ophthalmic Surgeon, and as Clinical Lecturer in Ophthalmology at the University. He was a great pioneer for the correct management of ophthalmia neonatorum, setting up an isolation unit at MREH for such babies to be treated. He was said (by OM Duthie in his obituary) to be "superb on a difficult fundus – always with reasons for his opinions, and rarely wrong… As an operator he was first class, making surgery look easy by his dexterity and simplicity of handling". He was plagued however by allergies, and was always recognised by his habit of wearing rubber gloves for all outpatient consultations; not for his patients' protection, but for his own.

The annual report of 1919 recorded that the War Office, via Col. W Coates, Officer Commanding 2nd Western General Hospital Manchester, had relinquished the 50 beds placed at their disposal in MREH. During the war, a total of nearly 16,000 military personnel had received treatment at the Hospital, of which 1,831 had been admitted and 545 had undergone surgery. Captains Milnes Bride and Harry White were released from military service with the RAMC, the latter being promoted Honorary Surgeon, and William Stirling, lately RSO but just returned from France, was appointed Assistant Surgeon in his place. The Board, in that report, paid tribute to the medical students and young doctors, mainly Indian, who had kept the Royal Eye Hospital staffed during the absence of its regular surgeons. During 1918, as the war drew to its fateful conclusion, the Spanish 'Flu began to take its hold (spread widely in Manchester by the large gatherings and celebrations after the armistice), and during the second wave in December 1918 there were substantial problems with sickness amongst the staff, the outpatient service being restricted to accidents and emergencies only. Fortunately there were no deaths amongst the staff, and the work of James Niven, Medical Officer of Health for Manchester, did much to restrict the mortality in the city to a mere 2,000 deaths owing to his insistence that businesses and schools should close, substantially restricting spread.

Gradually the work patterns of the Hospital returned to normal. The soldiers were demobilised and military patients dwindled, their place being inexorably filled by civilians. The Board were concerned in 1919 that there were over 600 waiting for admission yet bed occupancy was poor, and instructed the Medical Board to pull up its socks. During the late nineteenth and early twentieth century, microbiological and pathological techniques had evolved immensely. The surgeons no longer felt able to perform laboratory work themselves. Dr Arnold Renshaw, who had acted in part-time capacity as pathologist, was appointed in 1919 at £100 per annum, and a laboratory assistant was employed at 30s 0d weekly. An up-to-date Baker microscope was purchased at £42 12s 6d, and negotiations with the University were instigated to consider joint pathology services. Facilities were provided for in-house sterilisation of culture media, so that an entirely freestanding bacteriology department was in place.

The function of the "pathologist" in this era should be better defined. Dr Renshaw and his assistants fixed, cut and mounted histological slides from surgical specimens, preserved and bottled gross specimens in formalin, took blood from patients for the Wasserman reaction, other serological tests, albumin and sugar estimations and (manually performed) differential cell counting, took swabs from patients for bacteriological culture and microscopic examination, prepared vaccines, and were the main treatment facility at MREH for the city-wide Venereal Disease system. Within a few years, Renshaw was complaining about the patient throughput; 40–60 patients with syphilis alone on Wednesday afternoons for instance. He requested a "laboratory boy", who was acquired aged 14 at 10s 0d weekly as gopher and bottle-washer (within a somewhat hazardous environment), requested the assistance of one or other House Surgeon on two afternoons per week, and requested a large increase in salary, which was not agreed, but after haranguing over a number of years, rose to £350 per annum.

The war and its aftermath had a major effect on the Nation's wealth, because of the loss of shipping for trade, and the loss of foreign markets for British produce, including cotton (which reduced both employment and financial stability in Manchester). Imports rose in price, and the costs of food and basic provisions rose substantially. In 1919 MREH had a deficit of nearly £4,000, but was unable to attract enough "well-educated young ladies" into the posts of probationer nurse, owing largely to poor wages, but also to the inability to guarantee one day off duty per week; there were 5 posts vacant. The opinion of the Chair, Philip Kessler, was expressed at the annual meeting that "the will for nursing has departed very largely from the people who desire a more free and easy life". At the same time a Conference of Hospital Managers, representing about 50 hospitals in the northwest of England, was held to discuss wage levels and terms of employment with a view to rationalising differences between these autonomous hospitals. The Eye Hospital did not enter into any general agreement, but raised its starting probationer salary to £18, rising to £30 in the third year. Understanding the plight of the voluntary hospitals' finances arising from the war, the National Relief Fund permitted applications for grants from such institutions, and MREH was successful in obtaining £5,000 to alleviate in part its additional expenses.

The end of the Great War marked the beginning of the end of the social structures of nineteenth-century Great Britain; until this time those class distinctions had remained firmly in place in institutions such as MREH. An upper-class figurehead was necessary for all such charities, the status of that aristocrat reflecting his impression of the importance of the institution. At this time the patron of MREH was the 17th Earl of Derby. The relationship was purely nominal, except for major celebratory occasions when the patron would honour the hospital with his presence; it was not necessary, and certainly not desirable, to actually undertake any "work"; that was performed by a Board constituted of the male great-and-good with income from other sources adequate to permit time spent in charitable work. Many of these were self-made men, and in Manchester, overwhelmingly cotton magnates and other industrialists. Almost but not quite their social equals (because they worked, albeit with honorary status, to provide a service) were the Honorary Surgeons. The professional employees of the hospital, the nurses and junior doctors, were of the well-educated middle-class, and the remainder of the employees were generically referred to as "servants". There was a well-ordered hierarchy of wages in these grades. At this time the Resident Surgical Officer was paid £200 per annum, together with board, lodging and laundry (today equivalent to about £14,000). In contrast the Matron earned £125, as did a House Surgeon. A Senior Sister earned about £60, a trained nurse about £36 (all of these, also with free residence and food, which in general added 30–50% to the value of the salary). A dormitory maid was paid £30 for a 10-hour day, six days per week. A charwoman earned 5s 0d per day and no food. The 4th kitchen maid was paid £22 per annum for a 12-hour day, six days per week. Wages were hard-earned.

Before the first war, a successful doctor such as the honorary surgeons at MREH would expect to work hard for eight to twelve hours, six days a week, but would come home to a "household" comprising at the least a cook and housekeeper; a ladies' maid for his wife who may also fulfil the tasks of nursery maid; and a "man" who would act as valet, possibly gardener, stableman and coachman, and who would serve at table. After the war the availability of male servants diminished, financial restrictions began to affect the middle classes, and changes to society hierarchies began. At MREH, the erosion of these historical structures, instigated by the Board itself, began when in 1920 it resolved to amend the Rules of the Hospital to permit a change in its Board; it invited both the Medical Board and the Ladies' Committee to nominate two members each, to sit in future upon the Board of Management. In due course John Gray Clegg served on the Board for the Honorary Surgeons, and the ladies were represented by their President, Mrs Armitage-Bennett, and Lady Donner, who spent much of her time in various voluntary organisations including the Red Cross. She was the wife of Sir Edward Donner Bt, "Grand Old Man of Manchester", who was Chairman of Chamberlain Donner & Co., shipping company, and Chairman of the Manchester & Liverpool District Banking Society. Lady Donner's title was not merely through her husband; she herself had been honoured as DBE for her sterling work in the organisation of the Fairview Auxiliary Hospital in Fallowfield during the war.

In 1920 the question arose of the future of the Hospital branch at St. John Street. The main Hospital in Oxford Road had now been established for 35 years, and extended; all inpatient beds had been housed there since its opening. The Manchester Royal Infirmary had joined it in Stanley Park, and the medical school at the Victoria University close by, was flourishing. The imperative of a branch "in town" was now gone, and indeed, the conurbation of town now extended to their doorstep, with tram lines having been built down Oxford Road some years previously. The numbers of outpatients had actually reduced from the peak of over 39,000 seen in 1914, to a mere 36,000, and would fall further in 1922 to 30,000 before gradually increasing again over several years. This may in part have been due to the reduction in industrial injuries as output had fallen. Since 1885 the ground floor of 24 St. John Street had continued as an outpatient department with its own House Surgeon, and the rest of the building had been rented to a variety of organisations, notably the Manchester Medical Society which had held meetings there for many years. Some doctors had rented rooms for consultation, and the cottages in Span Street had been sold. Until the onset of the war, the outpatient throughput in St. John Street had kept pace with that at Oxford Road, but during the wartime shortage of doctors it had dwindled to a twice-a-week clinic, and although again running smoothly, closure was considered preferable by both Medical Board and management. The property was valued, and notice to quit served on the two current tenants, the Blind Aid Society and the Society for the Care of the Mentally Deficient. By November 1920 outpatient services had stopped in town, and all staff moved to Oxford Road. The building was sold in 1921 for £9,000. It had served the Royal Eye Hospital well for 54 years, but the days of converted dwellings being suitable for medical care were now long gone, and 24 St. John Street passed into the hospital's history without a murmur. It still stands, and is now one of several buildings in the street accommodating legal chambers.

Gordon Renwick, Honorary Surgeon to MREH 1931–48, Consultant 1948–54 (Reproduced with permission of Mrs Barbara Pratt, daughter of GR)

In the meantime the Board had contemplated building a new outpatient department on Oxford Road directly opposite the hospital, and for that purpose had acquired four adjacent properties; 334–338 Oxford Road, and 2 Thorncliffe Grove (a road off Oxford Road, directly opposite the Hospital, now no longer in existence). Despite the regular complaints of the medical staff, the planned new building never materialised, and the properties were rented out for several years before being sold on. The outpatient department at Oxford Road was now predictably getting very overcrowded, and with a feeling of *déjà vu*, the Board recommended (to the disdain of the honorary surgeons) the purchase of a wooden shed in the back yard as an overflow waiting room. In due course an ex-army barrack hut was purchased and reconstructed in the back yard, with a connection breaking through into the side of the outpatient waiting room, at a cost of £530. This ill-lit, cold and draughty shell was to accompany the outpatient department for 16 frustrating years after the sale of 24 St. John Street, before the long-desired new outpatient department was to appear.

In 1918 a young Australian, Dr Gordon Renwick, was appointed House Surgeon, after demobilisation from the RAMC where he was Captain Surgeon. He was one of about 100 Australian doctors who had volunteered for medical service in the war, and he had been wounded in 1917, both legs being broken when the building in which he was working was bombed. In 1920 he became RSO, being given the additional responsibility of curating the new MREH pathological museum, a display cabinet for which was donated by Dr Gray Clegg. From 1931 Renwick would be appointed Honorary Surgeon. We are fortunate to have a rare photograph of an operating theatre setting at MREH, which shows Dr Renwick in 1922 with a child patient, anaesthetist and nursing staff in contemporary theatre garb.

By 1920 the education and training of nurses at MREH was fairly well-structured. Probationers learned their trade on the wards, under the eagle eye of Matron and her Sisters. They learned informally from medical staff when assisting in their duties, but

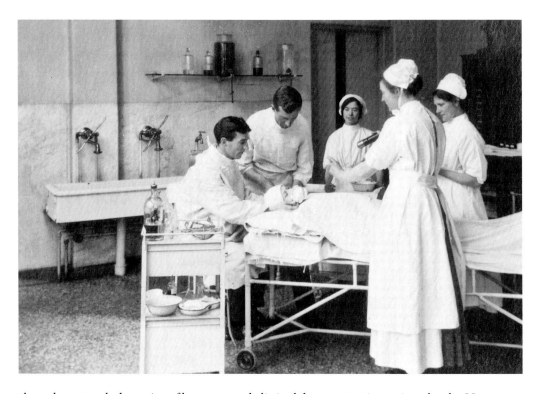

The Manchester Royal Eye Hospital nurse certification badge, issued from the 1920s

they also attended a series of lectures and clinical demonstrations given by the Honorary Surgeons, not completely structured, but nevertheless fairly regular. At the end of the probationer period, an examination was taken, set and marked by the medical staff, and this, together with a good service record and the recommendation of the Matron, led to certification as an Ophthalmic Nurse. In the early 1920s the decision was made to award such successful nurses a badge to mark their achievement. A tear drop shape, bearing the Hospital's name, was thought appropriate, and the successful nurse's name was engraved on the reverse.

Patients were admitted to the Royal Eye Hospital in this era not only with ocular injuries and inflammations, but when substantially unwell in addition, hence a significant mortality rate. These various maladies, and the realisation that a doctor in the twentieth century could no longer be considered a complete generalist, made clear to the Medical Board that a range of expertise should be available. It was decided therefore that for the first time since the resignation of Dr Robinson in 1855, non-ophthalmologists should be appointed to the honorary staff. An Honorary Pathologist already provided opinion on difficult cases, and the current holder was Professor Shaw Dunn, a Scot with what was described as "scrupulous integrity... and awe-inspiring dourness". A more ordered arrangement for anaesthesia was also put into place, with a group of anaesthetists each attending the hospital in rota, for one guinea per attendance. In 1920 Dr Donald Core was appointed Honorary Physician, and would remain so for 14 years until his untimely death. Also a physician at the MRI, he was the son of a

Professor of Physics at the University. He was very widely trained, travelling for tuition under Babinski and at the Pasteur Institute in Paris, and specialised in neurology. He was said to be painstaking, reserved and deeply thoughtful, but when provoked, a thoroughly entertaining teacher. Four years later however, a surgeon joined the medical staff who was to become a giant of Manchester and of the field of neurosurgery: Geoffrey Jefferson was appointed Honorary General Surgeon. He was clearly a brilliant and resourceful man, choosing not to settle into local practice after qualification at Manchester University, but travelling to set up practice in British Columbia, then to St. Petersburg where he worked in the Anglo-Russian Hospital. He repatriated in 1917, immediately signing up as a surgeon in France, where he learned much from severe head and spinal injuries. His appointment at MREH immediately followed a visit to be taught by Harvey Cushing in Boston, one of the great pioneers of brain surgery. Shortly afterwards he was also appointed to the MRI as Honorary Neurosurgeon, and later his post at MREH was re-named similarly. Jefferson was to remain on the staff of MREH until his death in 1951, having been appointed Manchester's first Professor of Neurosurgery, and recognised for his immense contributions to neurosurgery by being both elected FRS and honoured with a knighthood.

In 1923 the House Staff of the Manchester Royal Eye Hospital gathered for a group photograph in the hospital garden (located in the space between MREH and MRI). Matron Miss Barter is at centre, seated with her Sisters. Hospital Secretary Mr Prophet is at left. Resident Surgical Officer Gordon Renwick is standing second from right, House Surgeon Dr Gamm next to him; seated below them is House Surgeon Beatrice Ellison (the future Mrs Renwick) and seated far left below Mr Prophet is House Surgeon Margaret Single. The names of the nursing staff and House Scruff are unknown.

This was still the era of untreatable infectious disease, a matter of great concern to a large hospital. Every transmissible infection was dealt with rapidly, and each reported to the Board. Measles, pertussis and scarlet fever were intermittently reported, each being isolated and then transferred to Monsall Hospital for infectious diseases. Diphtheria was the disease striking most fear into institutions; there were several outbreaks of the potentially lethal infection in MREH through the 1920s, necessitating the immediate removal of patients to Monsall, the closure of wards, the exclusion of visitors to all inpatients in the Hospital, and the disinfection of all walls, ceilings and furniture in rooms occupied by the infected patient. One of the first antimicrobials, arsphenamine (Salvarsan), had been introduced for the treatment of syphilis, and enthusiastically described as a "magic bullet" by its discoverer, Paul Ehrlich, but in fact the potential

Dr Donald Core, Honorary Physician to MREH 1920–34

Sir Geoffrey Jefferson, Honorary General Surgeon (and later Neurosurgeon) to MREH 1924–51

side-effects of its administration were dangerous enough for the Medical Board to insist upon signed consent from parent or guardian to all under 21 years (which was to remain the age of majority for many years to come). The first antibiotics had not yet been introduced; there were deaths in infants from orbital cellulitis, septicaemia in adults following skin infections, and erysipelas could still be fatal. Patients requiring isolation would commandeer the services of a nurse, who was not permitted elsewhere in the hospital, and would enter a separate ward from an external door. Nurses themselves sometimes became infected, requiring the same treatment. Indeed for several years in the 1920s, a section of the Hospital was used as a sick bay for staff.

The medical staff eagerly pursued new instrumentation to enhance patient examination, and in 1924 the first Lister perimeter was purchased, an instrument that was still remaining in use in the 1990s. In the same year a giant technological leap forward occurred at MREH, when it completed the installation of its first slit-lamp. The Henker corneal microscope had already been acquired in the previous year at the recommendation of John Gray Clegg, and the magnification had been a revelation, but the full instrumentation also needed the separately mounted, separately focussed and cumbersome lighting module. Allvar Gullstrand was responsible for the concept of the slit-lamp by combining both illumination and observation system, his "large reflection-free ophthalmoscope" appearing in 1911. In its first form it attracted little attention, but then in 1919 improvements were added by Zeiss (Jena), including a workable dual-mounting system and better incandescent illumination in the form of a Kohler system, which permitted high-intensity diffused beam without a super-imposed image of the bulb filament; in fact, as advertised by Zeiss, "the utmost range of motion and convenience". The system was not confocal and was therefore not easy to use, but its enormous potential was rapidly realised and its use spread throughout Europe and North America. It arrived in Manchester in October 1924. Not long afterwards the Hospital acquired its first giant electromagnet, a cumbersome beast used to remove metallic foreign bodies from injured eyes. It required the patient's head to be placed at the centre of a massive ring magnet, a hand-held steel probe then being applied to the eye within the magnetic field. A later version of this instrument was used in the Hospital until the late 1980s.

The Honorary Surgeons each worked *gratis* at MREH for one or two days of the week, their income coming from their private practices. Until the 1920s, such patients had attended for consultation at rooms, usually in St. John Street or occasionally at the surgeon's home. Operations were performed either at the patient's home, or in a private nursing home. Sometimes arrangements were made for a nurse from MREH to attend a paying patient at their home, by special arrangement with the Honorary Surgeon, the Hospital being reimbursed for her services. However, as specialist technology improved (and accumulated within the Eye Hospital), and as the difference in cleanliness, lighting, staffing and equipment between hospital operating theatre and domestic kitchen table became more stark, the question arose of permitting paying inpatients to MREH, where they would pay the hospital for their board, lodging and nursing care, but their surgeon for their medical care. This was clearly a potential source of income for the Hospital, and in 1927 the decision was made to alter a part of the hospital to accommodate 9 in private wards (5 beds in the female ward, 4 in

A Gullstrand slit-lamp of the type first installed at MREH in 1924 (Reproduced with permission of Mr Richard Keeler, Royal College of Ophthalmologists)

No. 26051   1927.
Manchester Royal Eye Hospital.
_____

Dr. J. GRAY CLEGG'S
OUT-PATIENTS

TUESDAY MORNING,
as directed, before Half-past Ten o'clock.

This card should be carefully preserved and brought to the Hospital on each visit.

An outpatient identity card from 1927, a patient of John Gray Clegg the male). Within 3 months, 29 patients had been treated and there was a waiting list of 50. The Matron however had an occasional dilemma: an overload of inpatients was experienced when a few private beds were free, and she used them, seeking the Board's comments. They agreed that it may be necessary, but "On no account must general patients be mixed with private patients". The Matron requested, and was granted, leave to appoint two more nurses to cope with additional work, but there was no accommodation for them. The solution was to arrange to lodge up to 6 nurses at the Thorncliffe Grove Hotel, near the Hospital, at £175 per annum. Later, one of the Oxford Road houses was also converted for accommodation for domestic staff.

It was in the 1920s that a direct conflict arose between ophthalmologists (supported by the BMA and also by dispensing opticians) and opticians who wished to refract and to some extent, examine the eye. There were vested interests on both sides, and the Joint Council of Qualified Opticians was inaugurated to form a persuasive body to support the notion of independent ophthalmic practice by opticians. The doctors were having none of it, and in 1927 the BMA formed the National Ophthalmic Treatment Board, incorporating ophthalmologists, BMA staff and dispensing opticians, to argue in Westminster that only ophthalmologists should refract. They failed, and the ophthalmic optician (later optometrist) would grow in contribution and importance in the field of ophthalmology. At MREH, there had been a cosy relationship between the Hospital and Armstrong & Bro. Opticians, who had created a monopoly at the Hospital, refracting some outpatients, and dispensing surgeons' refractions. The Hospital decided that the company were profiting more than enough from this informal but well-established relationship, and decided to profit directly from it. They requested a rental of £500 pa from Armstrongs to continue the use of MREH facilities for their purposes, together with the maintenance and provision of spares for all ophthalmoscopes, trial boxes, acuity charts and refraction apparatus. The speed and courtesy with which Armstrongs accepted suggests that they considered it well worthwhile.

In 1928 the Hospital acquired a new piece of equipment which was *de rigeur* at this time, and henceforth opened its new Ultraviolet Ray Department (next door to Pathology). This treatment was applied by nurses two to three times per week, and involved a series of exposures of skin of torso, back and arms to the mercury vapour lamp, the eyes being protected by Crookes glass goggles. The treatment was said to "increase the bactericidal activity of the blood", and was said to be successful in the treatment of chronic iritis, phlyctenular conjunctivitis, recurrent corneal ulceration, trachoma and others. The method was to last a few years longer before attention was diverted to more realistic methods after the introduction of the first potent antibacterials. A Maddox Eye Warmer was also acquired, requiring a transformer to heat a metal plate which, wrapped in gauze, could be applied over an inflamed eye for analgesia and to break adhesions in iritis. This instrument had a far longer lifespan, remaining in use until the 1980s. The Hospital also acquired its first electric ophthalmoscope in 1928.

Managing 30,000 outpatients per year with a single slit-lamp was also proving unsatisfactory, and a second was provided.

The nineteen-twenties saw the growth of the welfare state, and in discussion with the MRI, in 1929 the Hospital decided to enrol its nursing and other staff onto the Federated Superannuation scheme. This required an employee contribution of 5%, and 10% from the employer. Prior to this arrangement, the provision of a pension, or "retirement allowance" as it was described, was entirely discretionary. The scheme would evolve, after 1948, into the NHS Superannuation Scheme. The additional expense to the Hospital was defrayed largely from the additional income generated by paying patients. In the annual report of 1929, the introduction of private beds was described by the Chairman, Alderman Goldschmidt, as "an unqualified success, and have filled a need which has long been felt". As a result, no legacies donated during the previous year had to go into the current account, and the financial state of the Hospital, which had previously remained somewhat unsound owing to the overdraft required for the extension over 12 years previously, was on a firmer footing. Thus began an intrinsic part of the work of MREH which persists to its bicentenary: the Hospital continues to treat both NHS and private patients, the income from the latter continuing to fund facilities which benefit all patients. Alderman Herman Julius Goldschmidt JP had taken the Chairmanship of the Board in 1921, following the death of his predecessor, Philip Kessler. The son of previous chairman Philip Goldschmidt, he was engaged in the family trading business and was to maintain the family link with MREH for a total of 74 years, ably serving as Chairman until 1942.

The funding of the voluntary hospitals had by the nineteen-twenties become complicated. Initially supported by voluntary donation, subscription and bequest, and then by arranged contribution from co-operative societies, other charities, workhouse guardians and others, new methods of funding had gradually appeared. In 1872 the Manchester and Salford Saturday Fund (the first in the country) was formed, with its members working on one additional Saturday per year, the proceeds to be placed into a fund to provide healthcare for its members. Within a few years every city and area in Great Britain had its Saturday or Sunday Fund. The National Insurance Scheme was formed in the early twentieth century, and then hospitals began to amalgamate into consortia in order to negotiate fees for service from a variety of organisations. These schemes catered for those on low earnings, and the well-off paid privately for their medical care. It became necessary to initiate schemes for the middle classes, or for those of "moderate means", as they were described by the Hospital Provident Association when it was set up by the Manchester & Salford Medical Charities Fund. A range of provident associations sprang up throughout the country, some merging together and remaining in force today as private healthcare insurers, including BUPA and WPA.

There were clear regional and local variations in healthcare provision, and this "caprice of charity" as Aneuryn Bevan would later put it, was to become one of the

Herman Julius Goldschmidt, Chairman of the MREH Board 1921–41

driving forces behind the creation of the NHS. The phenomenon was a concern in the nineteen-twenties, with discussions taking place at Town Hall and higher levels, to consider muncipalising the voluntary hospitals. At the Royal Eye Hospital Annual Meeting in 1929, a comprehensive denunciation of this possibility was made, the argument being that the voluntary hospitals such as MREH were efficient and well-run, and would suffer if taken over by central authorities. This view, unsurprisingly, was widely held amongst, and loudly declared by, several of the independent hospitals, and no centralisation occurred at this time.

By the end of the nineteen-twenties the medical staff at MREH considered that the medical residents alone were inadequate for the numbers of patients, and recommended the appointment of a non-resident surgical Registrar. The Board agreed, at a salary of £200. The job description was fairly all-encompassing:

1. *He shall attend the Hospital daily in the mornings*

2. *He shall attend at 9am and shall work in the Outpatients Department if required until the clinic is over*

3. *He shall supervise the work of the Resident Medical Staff under the direction of the Medical Board, and shall instruct the new Residents in their duties*

4. *He shall be in charge of all hospital medical records and notes relating to patients, and shall supervise their proper collation and filing*

5. *He shall instruct the Resident Medical Staff in the preparation of the Annual Medical Report*

6. *He shall supervise the Pathological Museum and Library, and shall see that both be kept in good order and up to date as regards easy reference*

7. *He shall report each month to the Chairman of the Medical Board*

8. *His appointment shall be for one year, but he shall be eligible for reappointment*

In June 1930 the first Registrar, Ogilvie Max Duthie, was promoted from RSO. He was to remain in that post for seven years before being appointed Assistant Surgeon, and would have spent a total of 17 years in junior posts before his future appointment as Honorary Surgeon in 1941. John Gray Clegg had entered a prolonged period of illness, and in 1931 felt unable to continue as Honorary Surgeon. He tendered his resignation having spent 36 years dedicated to the Hospital. The Board were fulsome in their regrets and sympathies. He was appointed Vice-President of the Hospital. An even longer service was brought to an end in the same year when Porter Firby, aged 76, retired after 46 years continuous service to the Hospital. He was granted a pension of £2 per week.

After the closure of the St. John Street branch, all outpatients were now seen at Oxford Road, crammed into an unsatisfactory department supplemented by a cold ex-army wooden shed in the back yard, and the Board were acutely aware of the need for improvement. Following the negotiations with the MRI over space for extension in 1906–8, they were now hemmed into a corner of the hospitals area, the only possibility for expansion being across either Oxford Road or Nelson Street. At one point in 1929 the possibility of moving the whole hospital to another site was briefly considered. The Hospital had acquired properties opposite the Hospital in Oxford Road, but this was now a very busy thoroughfare because of the huge increase in motor car traffic, and the building of a new outpatient department over the road was increasingly unattractive. In fact the Chief Constable was so concerned at the number of injuries to pedestrians near the Hospital, that in 1932 the first signal-controlled pedestrian crossing was installed. Attention was turned instead to Nelson Street.

Nelson Street in 1844 showing Nelson House (later Lister House). To its right is the house later occupied by Emmeline Pankhurst

Prior to the building of the new MREH at the corner of Nelson Street and Oxford Road, the area was well-to-do and residential, with large houses in large grounds. The north side of Nelson Street included two large villas: Oxford House occupying the corner on Oxford Road, and Nelson House centrally, both with very large gardens. On the other side of Nelson House were two large semi-detached villas, one of which was the home of Emmeline Pankhurst, and both of which still exist now as the Pankhurst

The Manchester & District Radium Institute (later the Holt Radium Institute) occupying Nelson House in 1921

Centre. In the 1880s Oxford House was sold and demolished, and its frontage on Oxford Road was built up with terraced houses, which would remain until also demolished in the 1990s. On the space behind was built the Manchester Schiller-Anstalt. This was a cultural centre for German immigrants to Manchester (of which there were many) and included a large library, meeting rooms and a concert hall. It was vacated in the early twentieth century and was converted into a perfumery.

Nelson House in the late nineteenth century was the home of Edward Holt, successful Manchester brewer (later Sir Edward, Lord Mayor of Manchester 1907–8). However, at some stage in the late nineteenth century, it was leased as a nursing home, run by a Miss Stewart. In 1918 the home closed and the house was offered for sale. The Medical Board of MREH recommended that the property be purchased to build a new outpatient department, but their advice went unheeded. In the early twentieth century the Holts became donors to, and sponsors of, the new Manchester and District Radium Institute, opened in 1914 next door to the MRI. In 1921 Nelson House became the new Institute, which then took his name. In 1932 the Cancer Pavilion in Lorne Street amalgamated with the Holt Radium Institute and moved to Withington to form the Christie Hospital. The House was then bought by the University of Manchester to use as a hostel for senior medical students. They had previously, before 1914, been accommodated in houses further along Nelson Street, together named Lister House, and when Nelson House became a hostel, the name transferred and it became Lister House.

In July 1933 the Board seriously addressed the possibility of a substantial new build to house an enlarged outpatient department. The Medical Board were asked to submit their recommendations for space and configuration, and the Ladies' Committee were asked to address future accommodation needs for staff. Enquiries were made as to the possibility of purchasing the three houses opposite MREH on Nelson Street, 66–70, together with the adjacent perfume factory, and in 1934 this proved possible, for £7,100. Demolition work rapidly followed, and Worthington & Sons appointed architects. A building tender was won by Brown & Sons of Wilmslow, for a cost of £39,519.17s 10d, giving a total cost including land, demolition, heating and other installations, of £59,145.19s 3d.

In 1933 the Medical Board recommended the introduction of a Squint Training Department to the Hospital. Worth had created the first amblyoscope over thirty years previously, but assessment was time-consuming. It was Ernest Maddox, Bournemouth ophthalmologist, who took a keen interest in the assessment of strabismus, stereopsis and amblyopia, inventing his own instruments for assessment. His daughter Mary, who worked as his receptionist, was trained by him to perform these tests, becoming the world's first "orthoptist" and opening an orthoptic clinic locally in 1928. She moved to the Royal Westminster Ophthalmic Hospital (later to become the High Holborn branch of Moorfields) to inaugurate an orthoptic clinic there. The MREH RSO was despatched to that hospital to learn the necessary techniques, and the required instrumentation was purchased for about £100. An Orthoptic Director, Miss Edna Stringer, was appointed from Birmingham and the department was running by March 1935, and within two months an assistant orthoptist was necessary. It was the request of Dr Wharton that photography of squint cases be undertaken before and after surgery, and this, the first use of clinical photography on patients at MREH, was initially undertaken at the MRI at a cost of 3s 6d per case. Within a few months, a training syllabus was devised, and two orthoptic students were admitted, fees for twelve months' instruction being £65. The need for the new orthoptic department was demonstrated by over 4,700 children passing through in its first year. Miss Stringer was to remain in post for 32 years, and her matronly care of her trainees was to earn her the affectionate soubriquet of "Auntie Edna". Always dedicated to clinical orthoptics, she found the continual need to teach and train to ensure the increasing supply of qualified orthoptists, somewhat of a strain, but nevertheless she contributed immensely to the development of orthoptics in Manchester. With a familiar refrain, she would later comment "we had wonderful help from the consultants at MREH, but always too many patients and not enough teachers".

By the summer of 1936 the building of the new outpatient department was well-advanced, and the Board turned their mind to the staffing of a much-enlarged facility. Up to this period all paid medical staff were responsible for both outpatients and inpatients, but the increasingly heavy outpatient workload suggested the appointment of Outpatient Medical Officers, and in September, three (Drs Rose, Faulkner and Philipp) were appointed at salaries of £200 per annum. Two of these were previous House Surgeons at the Hospital.

The first 30 years of the twentieth century saw a startling improvement in ophthalmic techniques, and it was the tendency of the surgeons at MREH to pursue such developments as quickly as possible. There are tantalising references to such improvements in care, either by the record of an instrument purchased, or by reference to developments in Board meetings, but the day-to-day changes in patient care remain frustrating elusive. One direct reference was to the new treatment of retinal detachment. Prior to the work of Jules Gonin, many different treatments had been employed since the mid-nineteenth century, with a success rate invariably less than 5% and usually much less; retinal detachment was normally considered untreatable, and with blindness almost inevitable. It was Gonin, working in Lausanne, who firstly identified the presence of a retinal tear in most cases, and who secondly determined (against the opinion of a sceptical ophthalmology profession) that it was the primary cause of the detachment, and needed to be sealed. He did so using "ignipuncture", that is, trans-scleral cautery with a hot needle. In 1931 he reported a success rate of over 50% in a series of over 200 cases, a massive leap forward. The Annual Report of MREH in 1936 declared this "new advance in eye surgery" was now in use, and that the Hospital was the first to employ the technique in Great Britain.

In 1936 the Board learned how much Moorfields Eye Hospital were charging their approved opticians for rent within the hospital, and realised how little by comparison

The new outpatient department
on Nelson Street in 1937, showing
(clockwise from top left) the exterior;
the dispensary; the operating room;
the main waiting room

was paid by their longstanding opticians, Armstrong & Brother. This relationship had been in place for over 50 years, despite challenge by other local opticians who resented the perceived monopoly. As Moorfields were apparently charging £4000 pa, the Board thought it reasonable to ask £2,500 from Armstrongs, and did so. The aghast response led to a prolonged cat-and-mouse game of negotiation against pleas of insolvency combined with examination of revenues, with a final offer from Armstrongs of £1,500. Theodore Hamblin intervened with an offer of £2,000 and Armstrongs were invited to match this if they wished to retain the preferred status. They felt unable to do so and in an exchange of exquisitely polite but bitter correspondence in May 1937, the longstanding arrangement was severed, Hamblin's taking over as Opticians to the Manchester Royal Eye Hospital.

Building of the new outpatient department and nurses' home in Nelson Street had been progressing apace and was finished in June 1937. The furnishings of all residents' rooms was accomplished for £1,700, though at a late stage the modesty of first-floor residents was enhanced by the inclusion of frosted glass in the lower windows. The contract to provide beverages for outpatients from the new buffet was given to Messrs Warings, caterers, for £1 per week. Fourteen shrubs were donated by the Parks & Cemeteries Department of the Manchester Corporation, to be placed on the first floor roof of the new building, and it was opened for business on July 12th. Just prior to opening, a set of photographs of the new building were taken, and they give a flavour of contemporary style, comfort levels and presentation in a pre-war hospital building which the Board were to describe, in their tribute to the architects, "a notable addition to the architecture of the city". The total cost was £65,000, with no debt incurred. The houses on Oxford Road owned by the Hospital and previously used as staff accommodation were now vacated and let out.

The nurses may not have see very much of their new accommodation; in 1938 Matron recorded that the working hours of sisters were 56 hours per week, for staff nurses 62 hours, and for probationers, 67 hours. These hours permitted day staff to have one half day off per week, and one whole day per month. Night nurses were permitted two nights off duty per month. A written protest was received from some nursing auxiliaries. Matron entered into correspondence with several of her colleagues in other eye hospitals, and found that in general they were better provided for. In particular, at the Royal London Ophthalmic Hospital at Moorfields, sisters managed a positively hedonistic one and a half days off weekly. Matron concluded that in order to attract more applicants to MREH, these hours had to be reduced, although her suggestion that a mere 48 hours per week for sisters might be achieved, was ambitious.

If the Board thought that the construction of the new outpatient department would lead to a period of quiet reflection on the part of the medical staff, they were sorely mistaken. The paint was hardly dry before the Medical Board, led by Harry White, constructed a document recommending the "Proposed reconstruction of the existing Hospital in Oxford Road". Their recommendations were numerous, but the main thrust

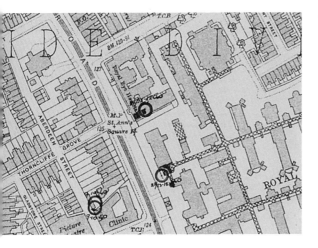

The location of bombs hitting the central hospitals and area during the night of December 22nd; a direct hit on the MREH south wing (Reproduced courtesy of Manchester Libraries Information and Archives, Manchester City Council)

was an increase from the current 177 inpatient beds to 200, with a further 25 for private patients within a self-contained private unit, the provision of two operating theatres, adjacent to each other, and an enlarged orthoptic department. The Board procrastinated.

In the middle 1930s the poorly kept secret of German re-armament became both brazen and increasingly large-scale, aided by the appeasement characterised by the Anglo-German Naval Treaty of 1935, which specifically condoned large-scale German ship-building. The fear of war spread throughout Western Europe and MREH, together with all British hospitals, was asked to consider the response to an emergency situation, permitting a degree of preparation that had not preceded the 1914–18 war. By the time of the inevitable declaration of war in 1939, the Emergency Hospitals Service had already been structured, permitting direct central funding for both staffing and reorganisation during the war. For the first time there was organised direct central control over at least an element of the work of the charitable hospitals, and this would prove to be the next nail in the coffin of locally funded healthcare.

In 1939 the long-serving Matron, Miss Barter, retired after 24 years in post. As for two matrons before her, she had been trained at St. Thomas' Hospital, and had given great service to MREH. She was succeeded by Miss Reilly who was unable to gain the confidence of her nursing staff and left after less than two years. Miss Rimmer came, and went in short order to marry, and the next two matrons managed only 5 years between them. Perhaps their endurance was tested by the circumstances in which they found themselves.

The outbreak of war led to the inevitable pressures on hospital staffing as it had done 25 years previously. Both Drs Smith and Janus left for military service, and the hospital survived for most of the war on a skeleton staff of barely more than one quarter of full complement. As in the first war, 10 beds were reserved for military patients.

Manchester, as one of the important industrial centres, was of course a target for German bombing. The first raids began in August 1940 and would continue intermittently throughout the war, but it was the two nights of bombing on December 22nd/23rd and 23rd/24th 1940 which were to become known as the "Manchester Blitz". On the first night nearly 300 tons of high explosive, and over 1,000 incendiary bombs were dropped by 270 bombers, a little less on the second night. The claims of the Luftwaffe at home that Manchester had been razed to the ground were somewhat over-egged, but nevertheless major and widespread damage occurred, and nearly 700 were killed. The Royal Eye Hospital and MRI were not spared. A stick of bombs fell in the area, two adjacent ones virtually demolishing the south wing of the Eye Hospital, and a substantial section of the MRI frontage. The bomb locations can be seen here on a contemporary War Office map, and the damage was recorded in a photograph on the following day. Astonishingly however, there were only two deaths: Dr Hilda Grinyer, House Surgeon, and Nurse Mabel Holt. Hospital beds were endowed in memory of both. Dr Stewart Scott, House Surgeon, was pulled from the rubble and survived, going on later to become Honorary Surgeon. It was necessary to close the Hospital while the remaining building was rendered safe and habitable, and inpatients were transferred to Withington Hospital for four months, where work continued until April 1941. The damaged wing and adjacent areas were secured but not rebuilt but the rest of the Hospital was then reoccupied. At this stage only 120 beds were available, but the outpatient work continued virtually unabated. The damaged wing would remain closed off but unrepaired until 1947, when approval (and therefore finance) was obtained from the Home Office to rebuild the south wing, and this was not completed until 1949. The partly destroyed façade of the MRI was never rebuilt, hence its current asymmetry.

The Beveridge report of 1942, in proposing substantial initiatives to create a true welfare state, brought central control of the hospitals closer. The Labour party used very well its place in the wartime coalition government to work towards national provision of welfare at a level never previously considered feasible. There were major arguments between and within political parties as to whether hospital control should be local and municipal, or central and governmental, the wartime consensus settling for the former. Clement Atlee, on sweeping to power in 1945, appointed Aneuryn Bevan as his Health Minister, and he was both radical enough and aggressive enough (wanting "the complete extinction of the Tory party") to ensure that the National Health Service Act 1946 was pushed through, reversing the coalition wartime decisions on hospital control and nationalising all hospitals. Most hospital doctors were vehemently opposed to the scheme. Although the structure of society had changed enormously since the Great War, their income still derived from private practice – in other words, as self-employed practitioners. Their contract with the hospitals to which they were attached was entirely honorary, and the relationship between the two was comfortable, lucrative and partly self-serving. Hard-fought negotiations between the Department of Health and the British Medical Association led to the maximum part-time agreement for hospital consultants, a distinction award system and other minor concessions. Aneuryn Bevan may have thought that he had "stuffed their mouths with gold" (and to an ex-miner such as he, it may have seemed so) but he had greatly underestimated both the size of the mouths concerned (and therefore the time that would continue to be spent in private practice), and the influence that those mouths would continue to have in steering healthcare policy.

Four floors of the MREH south wing virtually demolished by a bomb during the Manchester Blitz

For MREH, the end of the war brought with it, partly owing to the strain on hospital resources during the conflict, and partly owing to the generally increasing call upon its services, a substantial appendage; previously referred to only in passing and with minor concern, but now regularly lamented as an increasing problem and a demonstration of the failure of the hospital to cope with the work that it wished to perform; The Waiting List. This paper queue for surgery, long and lengthening, would in future become a constant source of pressure upon hospital managers and surgeons, a weapon with which politicians and press would beat providers around their metaphorical head, but it is important to state that it preceded the formation of the National Health Service and was not created by it; it was merely the demonstration of an infinite demand for medical care pressing on finite resources. In 1948, that demand became clamorous as people realised with astonishment that such care was not merely to be had when donated by charity to the deserving, but as a right for all.

The NHS Act permitted a breathing space for the new arrangements to come into force, so that the 15 Regional Boards could appoint the hundreds of Hospital Management Committees. One profound feature of the Act was to identify teaching hospitals as elite entities which would be responsible directly to the DoH rather than to their Regional Board. In Manchester, the teaching hospitals were to be the central group including MRI, MREH and St. Mary's, which together would now become known as the United Manchester Hospitals. On July 5th 1948 Aneuryn Bevan made a decision to be seen publicly inaugurating the National Health Service not in London, nor in his homeland Welsh valleys, but in Manchester, and so Park Hospital has become forever known as the birthplace of the NHS. The re-named Trafford General Hospital is now a part of the same Central Manchester University Hospitals NHS Foundation Trust which includes MREH. On that day in 1948, at a stroke, the entire healthcare infrastructure built up by myriad charities over two centuries, funded by private donation and subscription, was nationalised; every brick, every roof tile, every door, washbasin, autoclave, knife and fork at the Manchester Royal Eye Hospital became the property of the State.

CHAPTER NINE

1948–1984: Bevan to Griffiths

O N JULY 5ᵀᴴ 1948, in the Boardroom at the Manchester Royal Eye Hospital, the inaugural meeting of the Committee of Management took place. The name of the group had changed, and they were no longer the trustees of a longstanding charitable institution, merely the local representatives of the NHS responsible for the running of the hospital. Nevertheless the business bore a striking similarity to its previous content, with a series of mundane issues discussed. Both the previous Chairman of the Board, Eric Evans, and Herbert North, already Secretary for 22 years, continued in post; the latter would continue until 1960. The Hospital no longer had honorary surgeons working *gratis*; it had *Consultants*; salaried senior doctors paid by contract, and not by item of service. Aneuryn Bevan had secured the formation of the NHS by permitting consultants to work in private practice if they wished, and those who did so were required to work up to a "maximum part-time" contract for slightly less pay. Virtually all established hospital surgeons availed themselves of that opportunity, and would continue to do so until 2003. The surgeons at MREH who were appointed consultant in July 1948 included four who had already retired as consulting surgeons and who were appointed as a courtesy (Harry Horsmann McNabb, John Wharton, Thomas Milnes Bride and Harry White). Several others had already been in post as honorary surgeons for some years. We have already heard of Gordon Renwick, who had been appointed Honorary Surgeon in 1931 and was to continue as Consultant Surgeon until 1954. Ogilvie Maxwell Duthie ("Max") had undertaken all of his medical training, undergraduate and postgraduate, in Manchester, and had been Honorary Surgeon for 7 years before the inception of the NHS, also being Senior Lecturer and in charge of the University beds. He was an inquisitive researcher and would later go on and form the University Department of Ophthalmology in Manchester. William Stirling Jnr was the son of his namesake professor of physiology at the University of Manchester. The others appointed consultant were Sydney Smith, Fred Janus and Alexander Stewart Scott, so that in 1948 there were 6 consultant surgeons at MREH.

Sydney Smith combined his ophthalmology with farming; the proud owner of a pedigree herd on his farm near Bollington, he was naturally an early riser, milking

Frederick Janus,
Consultant Surgeon
1948–75

the herd every morning before coming in to MREH, and regularly being ready in his clinic at 8.00 (reputedly in the same shoes). Looking every inch the farmer, he took up piano playing late in life but gave up because his large farmer's fingers tended to get stuck between the white notes. He was nevertheless remembered as an excellent ophthalmic surgeon, and a cheery but quiet personality. He was a traditionalist, and in company (and it is said also at home!) he always addressed his wife as "Mrs Smith". Fred Janus clearly had some medical genes; born in 1910 in Manchester, the son of a German immigrant draper, his twin brother Oscar also became a doctor, a consultant physician in Oldham. Fred qualified in Manchester, took his MD in 1940, underwent all his ophthalmic training at MREH, and after war service with the RAF Hospital in Egypt, where he rose to become Surgeon Wing Commander, was appointed Assistant Surgeon in 1946. An early paper, one of very few, was on the subject of "heterophoria and neurosis in flying personnel". He was remembered as tall, very courteous, usually smiling, of somewhat unfathomable character, but very supportive to those in training. His approach was announced by his loud and characteristic laugh, which preceded him around the hospital. He remained a true ophthalmic generalist with a busy practice, until his retirement in 1975. He became President of the North of England Ophthalmological Society.

After a succession of four short-term matrons during the war years, Miss Wheatcroft was appointed; a formidable lady who ruled the Hospital with a rod of iron, she was to remain in post for 12 years. The Hospital Secretary Mr North reminisced that she was the only member of staff that he feared.

On one day in September 1948, Max Duthie, Surgeon of the Day, was so concerned at the numbers attending the outpatient department that he called in Mr North to witness that the staff felt it necessary to turn patients away. There were 600 follow-up and 140 new patients registered by 10.30am, and the doors were closed to those who had not yet reached first base. Such problems were to define MREH's reputation as an enormously busy eye hospital for many years. In addition to the 6 consultant surgeons there were 4 house surgeons, 2 RSOs and 12 "ophthalmic first assistants", the forerunners of clinical assistants; yet even with all available doctors working in the outpatient department, such numbers of patients seem astonishing today, and the situation had worsened substantially since NHS creation. In the following month, a memorandum of present and future problems of the Manchester Royal Eye Hospital was sent to FJ Cable, Secretary of United Manchester Hospitals, as follows:

"Since the introduction of the National Health Service Act on July 5th 1948, the Hospital has been overwhelmed by a demand from the public for eye examination in all its forms. It is idle to speculate whether the increased demands on the Hospital are due to publicity or any other factor. The fact remains that for the first time in its history the Hospital is turning away large numbers of patients seeking its service...

It may be suggested that an appointment system should be devised at once. Such a method is condemned to failure in a very short time since, under present conditions of shortage of medical staff, the appointment waiting list would increase by about 300 a week... It would seem quite clear to the Medical Board that every effort should be made to maintain the principles of the Hospital – that no patient should ever be turned away and that a service should be provided sufficient to cope with all demands... The suggestions that the service of the Hospital should, at present, be confined to those patients referred by a general practitioner is not one that commends itself to us... The Faculty of Ophthalmology recognises that two types of medical personnel are required to man the Final Eye Service: firstly, the Consultant who corresponds to the "Honorary Surgeon" of pre-July 5th days and secondly, the "Specialist" who is a medical man with additional training in ophthalmology not up to the rank of "Consultant", but yet sufficiently versed in the knowledge of his subject as to be capable of recognising eye disease in all its forms... The present staff of the Out-patient Department consists of:

One Surgeon of the Day

Dr Dawson Registrar (Senior) Full-time non-resident £850pa

Dr Mitchell   "   "   £850pa

Dr Lees   "   (Junior) Part-time   "   £850pa

Dr Boas OP Medical Officer   "   £500pa

Dr Scully   "   "   "

Dr Hardman   "   "   "

Dr Hoffman   Senior RSO   Full-time resident £700pa

Dr Ashworth Junior RSO   "   "

Under present conditions it is quite impossible for such staff to cope with the mass of patients presenting themselves for examination. One routine OP morning has been analysed; this revealed that:-

170 New patients reported (of whom 60 were refused) excluding all accidents

537 Old patients reported for treatment

180 tests of vision were carried out

Thus obviously an increase of trained medical personnel is required at once.

The numbers requested were, for clinical Purposes: 6 Surgeons, 12 Ophthalmic Medical Officers, 6 Resident Medical Staff (excluding other non-ophthalmic Medical Staff); and for training Purposes: 6 Registrars of different grades. These well-supported arguments for higher levels of medical staffing, and also for higher salaries, fell initially upon deaf ears at UMH, but slow and sustained pressure gradually accumulated junior staff. The perception was that doctors elsewhere were aware of the workload at MREH and that this reduced the numbers willing to apply for posts. Although MREH had lost its independence in matters of appointing staff, the benefits of partial amalgamation with the other hospitals of central Manchester became rapidly apparent, relating to matters as far removed as the provision of anaesthetic registrars to provide general anaesthesia, to the use of the MRI Kosher kitchen when required. An UMH nursing school was inaugurated, and the MREH pathology department became a subsidiary of the MRI department.

The way in which medicine and nursing was practised a mere 60 years ago sometimes provides a stark reminder of the attitudes prevalent at the time, with the presumption that neither patient nor parent contributed to any decision-making. In comparison to the norms of today one particular feature was striking. In relation to parent visits, the Committee of October 1949 declared:

> The Medical Board... were not in favour of children being visited generally, but in certain special circumstances, it was thought that a visit by a parent might be beneficial. Regarding the latter, special permits would be issued.

Until the formation of the NHS, patients at the Royal Eye Hospital had obtained their spectacles by arrangement firstly with Armstrong & Brother, and more recently with Hamblin & Co. However, in 1950 the Hospital made a decision to employ ophthalmic opticians directly, for the first time. In August of that year Mr Stephen Dawson, from Bradford, was appointed the Hospital's first Senior Ophthalmic Optician, and three others together with two trainees were appointed to work within his department. Two dispensing opticians were also appointed. In the meantime, an audit of the quality of artificial eyes supplied by Hamblins, compared with those from the Department of Pensions, was undertaken, revealing no difference in quality but too high a cost from the former, whose services were therefore dispensed with entirely.

Since the end of the First World War, the training and certification of nurses within ophthalmic practice was undertaken within MREH, as was also the case for other specialist hospitals. There was communication between them to achieve some consistency, but centralisation loomed: in 1952 the Ophthalmic Nursing Board was created, a National body to ensure consistency and quality of training, and therefore to introduce a fixed syllabus. Qualification via this route would lead to the award of the Ophthalmic Nursing Diploma. The ONB insisted that units must have 60 or more beds for a complete nursing diploma education to be permissible, and of course MREH applied for and secured teaching status. Shortly afterwards a formal arrangement was also made with the Manchester College of Technology (later UMIST) to teach students of optics at MREH. These, together with medical and orthoptic students, made MREH a busy training centre.

In 1954 a substantial change to the senior medical staff took place. Both Drs Renwick and Stirling retired, after 35 and 42 years at the Hospital, respectively. An opportunity arose to strengthen the University Department of Ophthalmology, which had been officially created in 1952, headed by Max Duthie, but now a new appointment was planned in support. Duthie was now Reader in Ophthalmology and had been in charge of the University beds since 1946, but the creation of a clinical and research team around him now took place. Simultaneously it was decided to dedicate 60 beds (rather than the 10 previously designated University beds) to the department. The University Department was clinically entirely separate from other hospital work; it had its own University Operating Theatre on the ground floor of the South ("New") Wing (which was now to be refurbished), its own ring-fenced beds, its own separate outpatient clinics and even its own entrance to the University Wards, at the rear of the Hospital. It was allocated 3 of the 7 senior registrars at the Hospital, 2 of the 7 registrars, and one senior house officer from 4. It was responsible for the education of medical students at the University, at that time 90 per year. Duthie pointed out that office space for the unit would be inadequate, but in the absence of room in the main building, one of the houses opposite on Oxford Road (still owned by the Hospital) was considered. The possibility was however rapidly dismissed owing to the state of decay of these properties, which would in due course be sold on and later demolished. Attention then turned to a house for sale in Grafton Street, immediately behind the outpatient department. Negotiations had already begun on this property when it was revealed that Lister House was being vacated by the University, having been used as a hall of residence since 1932. Immediately regarded as a better option, it would offer not only rooms for the University Department of Ophthalmology (which took over the first floor and incorporated a new library), but also for a postoperative squint recovery ward, permitting more rapid turnover in the children's ward in the main building (the waiting list for such surgery having swelled enormously to around 2,000). Plans also existed for a Corneal Graft Unit and other developments. However, it was not to be until 1956 that the property was eventually acquired, and after necessary alterations it was opened for business in May 1957. A plan to create a physical link between the house and an extended outpatient department, costed at £65,000, was later abandoned, and clinical work was now being performed in three separate buildings, Nelson Street running between. It was at this stage that the Board first made a request to the Town Council to close Nelson Street at its junction with Oxford Road, in recognition of the volume of pedestrian traffic between hospital buildings, but that suggestion fell on deaf ears, and it was not until the 1990s that such a step was eventually taken.

Duthie gathered around him a succession of Lecturers who would develop .a particular research interest in strabismus and amblyopia. His work was recognised

Max Duthie, Honorary Surgeon 1941–8, Consultant Surgeon and Reader in Ophthalmology 1948–64

Alan Stanworth,
Consultant Surgeon and
Reader in Ophthalmology
1954–61

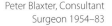

Peter Blaxter, Consultant
Surgeon 1954–83

nationally and he would go on to become Master of the Oxford Ophthalmological Congress in 1959 and 1960. The first Lecturer, Alan Stanworth, ex-RAMC Captain, was appointed in 1953, and became Consultant Senior Lecturer in 1954, later also being appointed Reader. His main interest was in ocular inflammatory disease, and he inaugurated MREH's first specialist Uveitis Clinic (indeed, one of the first anywhere) in 1954, publishing widely on the subject and later reporting on 500 consecutive cases. He was also involved in strabismus research and clinical work, making substantial alterations to improve the major amblyopscope, and being the first to define microstrabismus. He was tempted away to head the Sheffield University Department of Ophthalmology in 1961, and in fact the University Department at MREH became a substantial training ground for Sheffield ophthalmologists at this time, others passing through including AJ Dark and CA Palmer.

As a tribute to Duthie on his retirement in 1964, the departmental history and communications were bound in 3 volumes and presented to him as a gift, with the words "None of their contents would have been possible without his initiative, encouragement and advice". He must be considered the instigator of academic ophthalmology in Manchester, and his reputation internally as a somewhat controlling individual should take into account his high achievements. In a more modern age he would have been awarded a Chair. The Eye Hospital, but its University Department in particular, was now training ophthalmologists who would take up consultancies in the ophthalmic departments of the Northwest, some newly formed by their first incumbent: PR Stevens, AD McKenzie, MJA Britten, W Dugmore and others.

In 1954, Peter Blaxter was appointed consultant at MREH, one of very few to date who had been trained outside the Hospital. A southerner from Kent, he qualified at Cambridge and Guy's, and after service as lieutenant in the RAMC, was trained in ophthalmology at Guy's and Moorfields. Quintessentially an English gentleman with a military background, Blaxter was always impeccably attired in blue pinstripe, never a hair out of place, courteous to a degree, somewhat laid-back in style but with an innate ability to cut to the chase of complex cases. He was a generous and sociable colleague, and described by Alan Ridgway as "a charming, avuncular breath of fresh air". He drove a Bentley, and it is said that he navigated by looking through the steering wheel, rather than over it. His main clinical interest was in ocular motility but he also published significantly on glaucoma. He later became both President of the North of England Ophthalmological Society and Master of the Oxford Congress. On arrival at Manchester he did not find a particularly happy House; there were undercurrents of conflict, and he found OM Duthie a domineering personality. He and his wife Patricia went out of their way to encourage friendship between colleagues, and the gatherings and tennis parties at their house in Fulshaw Park were said to be memorable.

Lister House car park – a 70s
time capsule

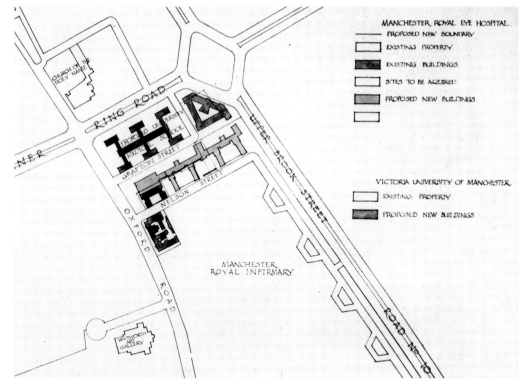

A 1960 plan for MREH
and medical school
expansion which never
left the drawing board

The late 1950s saw an attempt to reappraise the quality, volume and layout of
hospital property. The main building was now over 70 years old and in need of substantial and expensive re-roofing; the main operating theatre, on the first floor at the north
of the building, had originally been built (as had most rooms) with an open fireplace,
and at this time was served by only an extractor fan, so that it filled with steam when

sterilisers were opened, and "air change" was achieved by opening the doors straight onto the adjacent corridor to Russell ward. The installation of a second extractor to improve the situation created in effect a negative-pressure room, the microbiological significance of which was not at the time appreciated. Wards and beds were constantly re-arranged and re-labelled; a two-bed retinal detachment "unit" was created on the first floor, later to be replaced by a 6-bed unit on the second. There was a proposal to extend the old middle wing of the hospital, which was shorter than the others, over all 4 floors to provide additional space for a lecture theatre and other facilities; the plans never came to fruition. In order to de-congest Nelson Street and Oxford Road, it was arranged for the first time that no parking was permitted on either frontage of the Hospital, thus depriving the consultants of their usual convenient spaces. These were recreated by extending the space in front of Lister House, which continued to serve as the consultants' car park until its vacation in 1995. A somewhat grandiose scheme of expansion along Nelson Street, combined with plans for a new medical school next to a proposed inner ring road for Manchester, was drafted, but never came to fruition.

The year 1958 saw the wholescale introduction of written consent for eye surgery for the first time; prior to this, only the parents of minors (up to 21 years old, which remained the age of majority), and those consenting to the removal of an eye, were requested to complete one. There was some reluctance amongst the consultant staff about this, owing to the perceived difficulties in signing for those with very poor sight, but the Medical Defence Union had spoken, and the change took place. A further move towards modernisation was made soon afterwards on the wards: until this time, each type of eye drop had been dispensed to all patients throughput a ward from a single bottle, which was merely replaced when it had run out. Microbiological tests for contamination were carried out fortnightly, with only "occasional" positive results. Nevertheless it was now considered necessary to introduce bottles identified separately for each patient, and the anticipated additional costs of £1,500 per annum, together with necessary alterations to the dispensary, were absorbed.

In 1960, an appraisal of outpatient numbers and mode of attendance was undertaken. Until very recently, the Hospital had used a "first come, first served" system for outpatients, the doors being opened at 8.30, and any patient through the doors by 10.30 being seen. However, for those requiring refraction, orthoptic testing or prosthetic fitting an appointment system had been introduced. New patients could if they wished arrange an appointment time through their general practitioner, but these were given more for reassurance that punctuality. An average of 400 follow-up patients attended per day, and they were now requested to be at the hospital in "blocks" of quarter of an hour. A one-week audit in July showed that in addition to those resident in the Northwest and surrounds, patients attended from Anglesey, Buxton, Chester, Devon, London, Leeds, Liverpool, Newcastle, Southampton and Wrexham. Despite these numbers, most clinics were finished by 1pm, and this was still the era of patience and perseverance, sliding posteriors on the wooden forms of the waiting rooms, "seat-shuffling" gradually closer to the point of initial consultation, for which the patient stood beside the consultant's lectern before being sent, often without words, for investigation or treatment. In the afternoon, some special clinics were held, which did offer appointments. On Friday afternoons, minor operations were performed, under general anaesthesia if necessary in both adults and children, in the outpatients department. Over 100,000 patients were now seen yearly. The Hospital's immense workload, it appeared, was becoming a barrier to the appointment of new medical staff owing to the limited time available for direct teaching; changes were clearly necessary. Following the audit, both structure and function within the department were amended, and this included the construction for the first time, of two visual acuity stations. The rearrangement of outpatient medical staffing, increasing the numbers available for morning work, ameliorated the load to some extent, and led to the practice of senior registrars attending the general clinics of consultants other than their own, which persisted into the 1990s. In 1961 the first GP Clinical Assistant, Dr Alvi, was appointed, and more gradually followed. Nevertheless the numbers rose inexorably, and indeed spectacularly after the formation of the NHS: in the 16 years to 1947 (the last pre-NHS year) outpatients increased by 60% to 45,000; a further 16 years later, in 1963 that number was 135,000 (up 300%).

It is not known when the first corneal transplant was performed at MREH. The operation had first been performed successfully in a human as early as 1906, by Eduard Zirm near Prague, using a 5mm donor button excised by a trephine and kept in place by overlay sutures. However, the operation required considerable development and better-quality sutures before it became more readily accepted as safe by the ophthalmological community, and the particular contributions of Ramon Castroviejo in New York, and Ignacio Barraquer in Barcelona, were crucial. Donor cornea needed to be obtained within two hours of death, was refrigerated and then transplanted within 4 days. MREH, with a significant waiting list of patients, was concerned about the lack of a ready supply of cadaver material. It began a prospective audit combined with a publicity drive directed mainly towards those local hospitals notable for their failure to generate donors, especially by encouraging housemen to approach the bereaved with such requests. In 1960, of 106 donated corneas, the great majority were obtained from MRI, Withington or by private donation. Because eyes were sometimes unsuitable for use either because of corneal quality or bacterial contamination, only 28 corneal grafts took place in this year. It would not be until the late 1980s that the work of David Lucas would bring to fruition the use of tissue culture to prolong corneal life and enhance material usage.

The year 1960 was notable for the hospital's first purchase of a retinal camera, at a cost of £700, together with a cinecamera for £300, with a view to experimenting upon fundal cinemaphotography. Also, two Fison indirect ophthalmoscopes were bought at £35 each. This crucial tool enabling hands-free wide-angle retinal examination was invented by Charles Schepens in Boston, but it was the modifications made in 1959 by Lorimer Fison at Moorfields Eye Hospital which rendered the instrument user-friendly, and it rapidly became an indispensable tool for ophthalmologists at MREH. In the same year Miss Wheatcroft, Matron and stalwart of MREH for 12 years, retired, and her place was taken by Miss Mustard, who would continue the tradition of matronly autocracy in a somewhat less dictatorial style, but with a combination of exquisite courtesy and if needed, a steely glare.

The introduction of orthoptics to ophthalmological practice in the 1930s had been rapidly followed by a realisation that such intervention, either independently or before and after squint surgery, could markedly improve outcomes and reduce amblyopia. The problem of supply therefore outstripped demand. The MREH full complement of orthoptists was in theory 8, 4 being clinical, and 4 for teaching students within the school, led by a Head Orthoptist and Head Teacher, respectively. In practice however, there were at one time in 1962 only 2 in post, and there were at least 40 posts unfilled in England, when schools were only producing 25 qualified orthoptists per year at most. Smaller eye units had virtually surrendered the possibility of appointing an orthoptist at all. There was no shortage of applicants for studentships, but a dearth of available teachers. The clinical throughput of squint cases was severely compromised, and it was decided that owing to the inability to train orthoptists adequately in these circumstances, the MREH Orthoptic School should temporarily close, permitting all orthoptists to deal entirely with clinical cases (the turnover now being in the region of 15,000 per year). No new student intake occurred in 1962, and those in training were transferred to London. The Medical Board, mortified by the problem, attempted (with the complete support of both the United Hospitals Board and the Department of Health) to introduce an Orthoptic Auxiliary post, designed to be trained up to a much less rigorous standard than an orthoptist, but who could absorb some of the workload of the department. However, the British Orthoptic Board, on hearing of this outrageous attack on its profession, roundly condemned the Hospital's policy "which has been conceived with so little forethought" for sullying the name of the specialty, and proposed "to withdraw its recognition from the Orthoptic School at the Manchester Royal Eye Hospital". The posts disappeared, leaving the department in its parlous state. However, in due course a face-to-face meeting with the BOB was arranged, at which an understanding of intent was agreed, such that "Ophthalmic Technicians" (as they were now re-defined) could continue to be trained and they would not be permitted to erode the recently formed profession of Orthoptics; the meeting rose happier and better-informed. However, an opportunity was missed: the concept of the ophthalmic technician could have been further developed at MREH, and if so, the hospital would have led such development in the field of ophthalmology.

In 1962 the bed establishment and staffing levels were reappraised because of nurse grading changes. There were 181 adult beds and 33 child beds and cots (a total of 214, the largest inpatient capacity that MREH would attain) including 20 low-supervision beds in Lister House, but occupancy could be as little as 70% and beds were constantly "closed" owing to shortages of nursing staff. The required complement (including wards, outpatient department and theatres) was stipulated as 21 sisters, 37 staff nurses, 20 SENs and 47 others including pupils (a total including Matron, of 125), and this remained as a constant aspiration, but was never achieved; attempts, only partially successful, were made to increase pupil numbers by the diversion of applicants from MRI and St. Mary's. The quality of nursing accommodation at MREH was considered to be partly at fault, and in an attempt to attract staff the nurses' home above the outpatient department was refurbished, all rooms being fitted with a washbasin and refurnished by Waring & Gillow at some expense. Again, only partial success followed. The creation of a United Manchester Hospitals School of Nursing went some way to formalising and improving nurse training.

Glaucoma clinics had been running since 1953, the first being created by the University Department, but the need for more widespread glaucoma clinics had become apparent, and now all consultants ran one weekly. The measurement of intraocular pressure had not previously been considered a mandatory part of an ocular examination, and was performed only on the basis of perceived clinical need. In the late nineteenth century, the pressure could only be palpated by the surgeon's fingers on the patients' eyelids, the ability to detect the difference between a soft, normal or hard eye being learned with practice. Attempts had been made to mechanise the process beginning with von Graefe in 1862, but it was in 1905 that Hjalmar Schiotz in Oslo first invented a safe and reproducible method. The Schiotz tonometer was to become the standard method of measurement of intraocular pressure for 50 years, and involved placing a concave metal surface onto the patient's anaesthetised cornea, a central rod indenting it and diverting a needle along a measuring rule; the measurement was then compared with a reference scale. The patient, supine on a couch, was asked to look at a large black spot, painted on the ceiling in each room for that purpose. Various other methods had attempted to improve the technique, but the introduction of electrotonometry (requiring both expensive equipment and a trained technician) in 1960 persuaded MREH to go down this route. However, in 1954 Professor Goldmann from Bern had introduced his applanation method, requiring a precisely calculated flattened corneal circle to remove (in theory) the variable of corneal rigidity. Unlike indentation tonometry, the technique could be performed at the slit-lamp with the patient sitting and was therefore much more convenient. However, the expenditure on electrotonometry meant that Goldmann tonometers would not be in use at MREH until 1965. Goldmann tonometry remains the gold standard in 2014, despite the introduction of several new methods of measurement in the intervening 60 years. Although Schiotz tonometers would remain the mechanism of measurement on most wards for at least 10 years more, following the purchase of the electrotonography equipment in 1963 part of Lister House was designated the "Electrotonography Department" where patients were admitted for repeated measurements of intraocular pressure, sometimes for several days. Later renamed the "Glaucoma Unit", it was in this guise that this author found Lister House ground floor on his appointment in 1982, where one of the on-call SHO's duties was the "phasing" of inpatients.

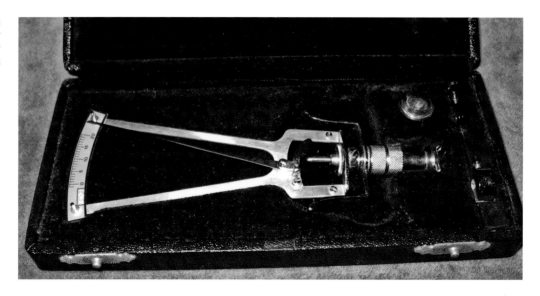

A Schiotz indentation tonometer, as used for measuring intraocular pressure until the 1970s

New technology continued to have an impact on MREH. The first disposable syringes were introduced. Surgery had been performed without any form of magnification, and without artificial light, in the nineteenth century. Although operating loupes (magnifying lenses positioned in front of normal spectacle lenses) had first been used in 1876, most surgeons did not employ them until the twentieth century, the more innovative combining them with a head-mounted light. Modern variants of high quality are still used for extraocular surgery. However, the miniature anatomy of intraocular surgery, particular cataract surgery, and advances in suture manufacturing technique demanded greater magnification, and in 1958 Keelers developed the first

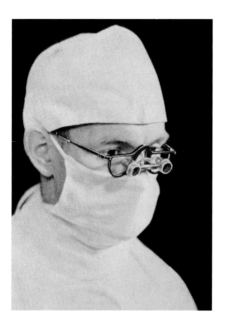

Operating loupes from the 1960s (Reproduced with permission of Mr Richard Keeler, Royal College of Ophthalmologists)

The first Keeler operating microscope, as acquired by MREH in 1962 (Reproduced with permission of Mr Richard Keeler, Royal College of Ophthalmologists)

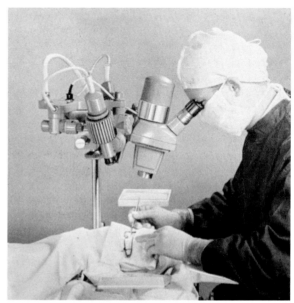

1948–1984: BEVAN TO GRIFFITHS

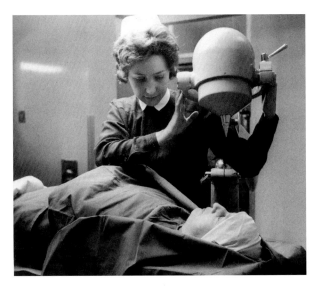

A nurse demonstrates the new giant electromagnet in 1964

The matron, Miss Mustard, in 1964

ophthalmic operating microscope. In 1962 the Hospital acquired its first, at a cost of £500. The more senior surgeons would continue to use operating loupes for cataract surgery until the 1980s, often remaining standing for surgery, but surgical microscopy was here to stay, and the need for foot controls ensured that from this point, all microscopic intraocular surgery was performed with the surgeon sitting.

The Hospital's 150th anniversary occurred in less unhappy times than its 100th, and thus was celebrated rather more prominently. A commemoration service was held in Manchester Cathedral; a Hospital open day was held, including tours of wards and departments, and lectures to the public were given, including "Double Vision" by OM Duthie; a staff dance was held at Bellevue, and a history of the Hospital was commissioned. In the absence of an enthusiast on the staff, Mr Frederick Stancliffe was asked to write the book; he was a solicitor, but also an established author on local history and being previously Chairman of the Salford Group Hospital Management Committee was also involved in healthcare, but had no previous association with the Hospital. His book, suffixed "a short history" filled the bill admirably and for some details has remained useful to this author, as some Hospital archives had been lost. A series of articles celebrating the occasion was written for the Manchester Evening News, and illustrations were published

A drawing of a retinal detachment by Roy Dalgleish at MREH, 1962

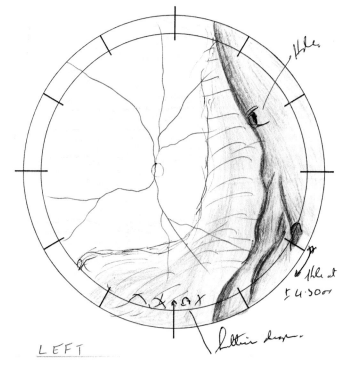

of staff and equipment, including the relatively new giant electromagnet, which had recently replaced the first one obtained by the Hospital in 1907. The most prominent celebration of the 150th anniversary was a University Dinner, held on October 21st, to which a long list of dignitaries were invited, including the civic office-holders of the City of Manchester, the leaders of all ophthalmic and associated professional bodies, Sir Stewart and Lady Duke-Elder, the officers of the prominent Manchester hospitals, together with the medical staff, Board and many staff and alumni of the Hospital, especially those of long service, a total number of 200 or more. The principal guests were presented with souvenir silver spoons adorned with the Hospital badge, and a great time was had by all.

Since the techniques of retinal detachment surgery introduced by Gonin thirty years previously, other developments were taking place. In the late 1940s Charles Schepens, originally Belgian but working in London before emigrating to the United States, invented the binocular indirect ophthalmoscope, and this was later refined by Lorimer Fison. This for the first time permitted well-illuminated, wide-angle and stereoscopic funduscopy. In the meantime the longstanding diathermy technique of Gonin, used to reattach detached retina, was associated with substantial complications. Harvey Lincoff and others developed a retinal cryoprobe which attained adhesion without tissue necrosis, and new methods of scleral indentation began to appear and gradually replace the unsatisfactory Arruga string. Lincoff also developed his "laws" which facilitated the location of the retinal break in rhegmatogenous detachment. The specialty of modern retinal surgery was well and truly underway. In 1961 Roy Dalgleish was appointed Lecturer and Honorary Consultant. A South African, born in Johannesburg and graduating from Witwatersrand, he had a broad surgical experience before choosing ophthalmology, training at Moorfields and MREH. He was initially much involved in retinal detachment surgery. This was the era of meticulous, sometimes artistic depiction of the state of a retina before surgery, as demonstrated here by Dalgleish himself in 1962. The requirement to compile an accurate depiction of the extent of detachment and of the precise clock-hour location of retinal breaks, was a fundamental prelude for juniors wishing to operate themselves; this author remembers well the small pack of coloured pencils that were standard equipment for SHOs and registrars, the slow mapping of a patient's detachment with the retinal chart upside-down beside the patient's head, and the careful scrutiny and either criticism, or a brief nod of approval from the consultant, sometimes followed by the invitation to perform the required cryopexy and plombage. The artistry of retinal drawing, and to a large extent the discipline of retinal topography, has been almost lost since the domination of vitrectomy and internal search for detachment surgery.

In 1965 the wards of the Hospital, since 1885 variously named, reorganised and re-labelled, now went through a formal re-designation. The South wing, bombed in 1940 and rebuilt in 1948, had been designated the "New" wing. The ward numbers allocated in 1965 will still be remembered by many alumni. The designation might be prosaic, but each ward had its own character, instilled mainly by its sister, some of whom would remain in charge of the same ward for many years.

In the same year, an application to the Ministry of Health was made for recognition of the Eye Bank at MREH, which had been functioning for internal usage for several years, to be officially recognised as a Regional service. The Orthoptic School was officially re-opened after its temporary closure, with Miss WA Venables as its Head Teacher. A modern safety measure was introduced into the Hospital pharmacy with the novel instruction that for the first time, "medicines issued to outpatients should be labelled with the name of the contents". Also for the first time, it was arranged that manufacturers of ophthalmic equipment would display their wares to doctors attending the forthcoming North of England Ophthalmological Society meeting, taking place at MREH as it had done on many previous occasions.

```
Re-titling of Wards
It was agreed that the wards should be re-titled as follows:-

           University Ward      - Ward A
           First New Ward       - Ward B.1
           First Centre Ward    - Ward B.2
           Ann Russell Ward     - Ward B.3
           Second New Ward      - Ward C.1
           Second Centre Ward   - Ward C.2
           Second Women's Ward  - Ward C.3
           Third Floor          - Ward D
           Lister House         - To remain "Lister House"


                              .................................
                                      Chairman.
                              13th January 1965.
```

The ward designation system introduced in 1965

Max Duthie had retired in 1964, after placing the University Department of Ophthalmology on a secure footing. His departure prompted the decision to appoint a Chair of Ophthalmology, and in 1965, Professor Calbert Inglis Phillips arrived. A Scot, born in Glasgow and brought up in Aberdeen, he had qualified at that university and after a residency at Moorfields Eye Hospital had taken up a consultancy at Bristol in 1958 before departing for further training at Massachusetts Eye & Ear Hospital. On his return he became consultant at St. George's Hospital, whence he was appointed at Manchester. An ophthalmological polymath, his scientific publications had included work on congenital malformations, but his main interest was in the pathogenesis and treatment of glaucoma, and he led the introduction of beta-blockers into management. He wrote basic ophthalmology texts for both medical students and postgraduates, but also was a keen logician and amateur philosopher. His book "Logic in Medicine", published much later, ran to 10 editions, and was witness to his approach to clinical practice: always logical and methodical, sometimes idiosyncratic, sometimes considered a pedant. His arrival in Manchester was a shock to him. He found in the University Department "a daunting number of beds, and huge clinics", and the balance between research and clinical responsibility was very challenging; his relationship with the other consultants in MREH was not easy, and the University Department did not thrive under his leadership; he was to depart for a more native climate when in 1972 he became Chair of Ophthalmology at the University of Edinburgh and Eye Pavilion.

We return to 1966, when the longstanding and vexed issue of outpatient numbers and appointments reared its head again. The problem was simply that on some days

Calbert Phillips, Professor of Ophthalmology and Honorary Consultant, MREH 1965–72

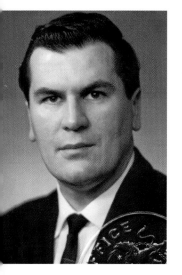

Roy Dalgleish, Consultant Ophthalmic Surgeon 1961–88

far too many patients turned up, as they had done since 1814, without appointments (as they were permitted to do before 10.30) and without prior arrangement (as any follow-up patient was allowed to do). It was too unpredictable and an appointments-only system was mooted. However, the Board were only too aware that similar changes in other hospitals had immediately been followed by a surge in attendances at casualty departments, and that local general practitioners were unhappy with such changes. A halfway-house was agreed in the shape of a partial appointment system. It would only be in 1978, a mere 36 years ago, that all outpatients would be required to obtain an appointment before attendance. The connected problem of archaic outpatient record cards was also addressed. Simple folding cards of 8"×5" had contained brief medical records for many decades, and had been kept by the patients, but now general hospitals were changing to a larger-format system, which was stored within cardboard envelopes and kept at the hospital. Glasgow Eye Infirmary had begun such a system, thus far unique in eye hospitals, and such a change was carefully considered (the clerical burden being substantial) and deferred. It would eventually be introduced in the 1970s.

In 1966, Mr Roy Dalgleish left the University Department and was appointed substantive Consultant at MREH. His main interests were in lacrimal and eyelid surgery. He developed new approaches to both dacryocystorhinostomy and ptosis, but his main impact was to be the first to demonstrate, by radiological analysis of eyelid movement with metallic implants, the pathology of senile entropion, thus steering the previously unsuccessful surgical methods in a different direction. He maintained his interest in extraocular surgery, and although largely self-trained he can be considered the first oculoplastic surgeon to work at the Hospital. A large and daunting man of few words, nevertheless he was clinically very perceptive and had a dry, sardonic sense of humour. He kept a farm, and his Range Rover negotiated both that territory and the Hospital car park. He emerged from it in his Barbour with a lumbering gait and pronounced wheeze, and fitted the paradigm of farmer better than eye surgeon; nevertheless his large hands performed very delicate extraocular surgery. He was of that generation of surgeons who found the new developments in intraocular microsurgery, and the necessary transition from operating loupes to microscope, somewhat difficult.

In 1966 the Board berated the dreadful state of the Hospital's two lifts, the oldest of which (at the North end) was installed in the 1930s. Replacement was recommended, but the daunting cost of £11,000 proved unaffordable, and alumni will remember with amusement that the same lift, with its manually operated steel concertina gate, stayed virtually unchanged, though repeatedly coaxed back into life after breakdowns which imprisoned sundry members of staff and public for an hour or two, until the Hospital was eventually vacated in 2009.

Developments in the technique of cataract surgery had progressed apace, and Manchester surgeons were keen to remain at the forefront of developments. The extracapsular method of extraction, as performed by David Little in 1893, had several drawbacks, not least of which was the inability to guarantee the complete removal of the lens, remnants causing post-operative inflammation and scarring, which sometimes required further surgery. Such complications were rendered much more visible since the introduction of the slit-lamp. The removal of the intact lens and capsule together (intracapsular extraction), facilitated by the introduction of better local anaesthesia in the early twentieth century, was popularised mainly by Hermann Knapp in New York after the second war. A variety of methods had been devised to rupture the connections between the cataractous lens and the suspensory ligament, all at times unsatisfactory and all associated with a significant complication rate, the main problem being vitreous loss. Two recent developments changed all that: firstly Joachin Barraquer in Barcelona in 1958 had the idea of dissolving the fibres of the suspensory ligament by injecting chymotrypsin, a pancreatic enzyme; this made the cataract easier to remove (but had to be washed out after two minutes, to prevent damage to other intraocular structures). Secondly Krwawicz of Poland in 1961, and then Kelman in New York

Intracapsular cataract extraction using the cryoprobe (Reproduced with permission of WHO).

in 1962, developed the cryoextractor, a fine-tipped probe capable of instant freezing when very cold carbon dioxide or nitrogen was passed through it. This permitted the probe to stick to the cataract, allowing it to be pulled from the eye. The two developments together led to a substantial increase in the number of cataract operations performed, and both techniques were rapidly adopted in Manchester. Together they led to the complete demise of extracapsular surgery for adults (but not for children, the Fuchs' two-way syringe remaining the instrument of choice for extracapsular extraction following discission) and this preference remained until the 1980s. This author's first 80 cataract procedures, in the early 1980s, were performed using the intracapsular method; the entrance wound was made limbally *ab externo*, after conjunctival peritomy, either by keratome followed by left-cutting and right-cutting curved scissors, or with razor fragment. Lens extraction was a three-handed technique; the scrub nurse held the corneal flap up, and the surgeon swept aside the iris whilst attaching the cryoprobe to the lens, swinging from side to side whilst gently pulling out. Leave the iceball a moment too long and it attached to cornea or iris and had to be melted and re-started. Failing to notice iris adhesion could lead to complete avulsion. Vitreous loss was uncommon but not rare, because chymotrypsin could also disrupt the anterior hyaloid. If it occurred, crude vitrectomy was performed with swabs and de Wecker scissors, reminding one irresistibly of dipping soldiers into a breakfast boiled egg. In order to ensure the rapid ability to close the eye after lens extraction, the sutures (8/0 blue virgin silk) were pre-placed, and then covered with conjunctiva. Eventually eroding away, such sections often left an upper limbus with multiple depressions, rather like Herbert's pits.

Even in the early 1980s, aphakia remained the result of choice for some surgeons. Patients were therefore required to wear powerful convex lenses post-operatively, and these remained a common sight not only in ophthalmic waiting rooms, but on the street. In the first few weeks after surgery and before post-operative refraction, temporary Fresnel +10D aphakes (colloquially known as "temps") were a common sight on the wards and in outpatient waiting rooms. However, the cosmetic and functional problems associated with these led others to implant intraocular lenses. Since Harold Ridley's experiments with human intraocular lens impantation in the early 1950s, a wide variety of designs, all partly unsatisfactory, had been introduced. At this time all those used in Manchester were iris-fixated, the top loop being sutured to iris; Binkhorst 4-loop, Boberg-Ans and Severin were all used, all suffered from not infrequent post-operative complications including dislocation, and the retinal surgeon's task, if required later, was a nightmare because the pupil could not be fully dilated for retinal examination without iatrogenic lens dislocation. Although *de rigeur* elsewhere for a time, anterior-chamber angle-fixated lenses were little-used in Manchester; a brief foray by one surgeon into the world of the Novoflex led to a whole series of corneal grafts after lens-induced decompensation. The rigid Choyce IX lens, with problems all its own, was hardly used at MREH. These were the early days of intraocular lens implantation; at best a pseudophakic patient was given excellent visual acuity without distance glasses; at worst, eyes were blinded by retinal detachment, corneal decompensation or the appropriately named UGH (Uveitis/Glaucoma/Hyphaema) syndrome. It would not be until the reintroduction of the new extracapsular surgery that a transformation would take place.

In 1967 Miss Edna Stringer, Principal Orthoptist, retired from MREH. She was the first to lead the new department and had been in post for 32 years. At the outset she was seeing a few patients; when she left the department was dealing with thousands of patients every year. She was replaced by Margaret Fitton, who would serve for only 8 years before tragically dying in a road accident in 1975, whereupon Ann Dayson took over, until her retirement in 1983.

The mid-1960s brought with it increasing financial strains on revenue, and a virtual inability to fund capital projects; in 1967 the clear feeling amongst the Board was that 19 years of association with the United Manchester Hospitals had not been to the benefit of MREH or its patients. Previously independently governed and self-financing, it had gradually become victim to the limitations on funding controlled by the Department of Health, in combination with internal financial decision-making at UMH which left MREH feeling marginalised. In September 1967 a major audit of expenditure was performed, and compared firstly with per capita spending within UMH and at similar hospitals, and secondly between major eye hospitals throughout the country including Moorfields, Birmingham, Bristol and Glasgow. The nursing budget was "over-spent" despite the staff head count being considerably under-establishment (82 compared to 90). The total hospital expenditure was £95,000, an over-spend of £3,300. A major series of modernisation projects and upgrading necessities were listed, all of which proved to be impossible to fund. The cost per in-patient week at MRI was £51, at St. Mary's £53, and at MREH £32, with a national eye hospital average of £37 (including both teaching and non-teaching institutions) whereas costs at other prominent teaching eye hospitals included Birmingham £38, Bristol £39 and Moorfields (always well-endowed!) £57, and these differences were represented across all aspects of expenditure, including staff payments, provisions and maintenance. Manchester Royal Eye Hospital could therefore legitimately claim an extremely careful and frugal approach to expenditure, and yet unsuccessfully remonstrated with the UMH Board at the calculation of funding levels between UMH hospitals.

The main building was now 81 years old. The ground floor University Ward and theatre were in need of major upgrading. Lister House was planned for demolition in 1972 as part of MRI rebuilding plans, with no clear plan for the replacement of MREH or University Department accommodation. Major changes were needed to operating theatre sterilising equipment. The outpatient throughput of the Hospital had risen that year by almost 10% to 113,000. The attitude of the UMH Board to the plight of the Eye Hospital was made clear however, in their Capital Expenditure Budget for 1968–9, which totalled £414,000, the allocation to MREH being the round figure of £0. The MREH Board expressed the reasonable view that "this hospital had suffered far too long from an inadequate financial allocation". Following further vigorous negotiations, UMH allocated an additional £10,000 to MREH for 1968–9, but since this was barely adequate to cover the increasing overspend, it could not facilitate any development. Further economies were forced upon the MREH Board, notwithstanding their prior demonstration of parsimony in patient care. The Hospital stagnated.

The impact of these years (between 1948 and 1968, but particularly the last few of these) on the relationship between MREH and UMH, and on the perception of the MREH consultants as to the treatment of the Hospital compared both with other hospitals in the group, and with eye hospitals elsewhere, cannot be over-stressed, because it tainted future relationships with UMH and its successor organisations. Always attempting to improve patient care with new technology, better space and facilities, and attempting to lead research, they felt hamstrung by a perceived attitude of irritation and mild disdain from their much larger neighbour, in their minds entirely unjustified by the relative quality of care provided. Manchester Royal Eye Hospital had over 134 years until 1948, worked hard, deservedly to acquire a reputation as the premier provincial eye hospital in Great Britain, and this reputation had been progressively eroded by what was perceived to be the ignorance and possible bias of the UMH Board. For many years the UMH would in practice be referred to both internally and externally as "MRI", a complacent misnomer that the senior staff at MRI did nothing to correct. The under-funding of MREH perpetuated and magnified the (to some extent justified) perception elsewhere in British ophthalmology that it was merely a medical

Aphakic lenticular spectacles, the end result of cataract surgery for tens of thousands of patients up to the 1980s

Temporary Fresnel aphakes ("Temps") worn by aphakic post-cataract patients before refraction

sweatshop, with enormous clinical workload (and therefore it should be said, unsurpassed clinical experience) but inadequate facilities, inadequate space, and inadequate time for study, research and career development. That reputation persisted for many years longer than was justified, and only in the twenty-first century have decades of work finally dispelled the long-held impression. Nevertheless, looking back now to 50 years ago, it is difficult to avoid the opinion that the development of this great Hospital was chronically handicapped by the very people at UMH who were meant to represent its interests.

The world's first contact lens to be fitted successfully to a human eye was manufactured by German ophthalmologist Adolf Fick in 1888, was made from glass, and was of haptic type (covering both cornea and conjunctiva). However, being cumbersome and heavy, it could be worn only for short periods. Developments progressed, and in 1936 William Feinbloom, American optometrist, manufactured a light plastic scleral lens. By 1949 a much smaller rigid plastic lens had been manufactured, which could sit on cornea alone. Hamblins had set up a Contact Lens Centre in Deansgate in 1949, and for some years one of their opticians, Mr SP Gordon, had been fitting contact lenses to MREH patients, a room being provided within the outpatient department for him. However, both he and the retired MREH Senior Optometrist Mr Fraser now offered to provide a cheaper service directly to the Hospital, and Gordon resigned from Hamblins in order to do so. This arrangement marks 1967 as the origin of the MREH contact lens service. The cost of lenses was high, at about £38 for a pair (substantially more than an average week's wage at this time, and this cost had decreased by over 50% in the previous 6 years).

In 1968, following the sideways move of Roy Dalgleish, Professor Phillips persuaded the University of Manchester to appoint to a new post of Senior Lecturer in Ophthalmology. The Hospital agreed to grant honorary consultant status, and in due course Mr TG Ramsell was appointed from Oxford where he had been Lecturer in the

Nuffield laboratory. However, he was to stay for less than a year, moving then to be consultant to Arrowe Park Hospital.

Since its creation in 1814 the Hospital had accepted patients attending as emergencies without appointment, and these were dealt with amongst all other outpatients, priority being given as deemed necessary. In the 1960s, emergency attendances were seen in the outpatient department in Nelson Street. However, pressure on space there (described by the then Hospital Secretary, Edwin Bell, as "market day in Old Baghdad") suggested in 1968 the possibility of creating a separate Accident & Emergency Department, to be sited in the main building in the rooms occupied by the orthoptists. Alterations were undertaken in 1970 at a cost of £13,000, and the new department, occupying rooms originally designed as the outpatient department of 1885, became active in January 1971.The number of A&E patients attending had increased from 14,000 to 18,000 between 1967 and 1968 (following the imposition of a partial appointments system in OPD), and by 1971 the figure would be nearly 30,000. There were four whole-time equivalent SHOs at the time (3 full-time and two shared half-time with the University Department of Anatomy – the so-called "twin" posts) and their workload had been criticised by the Faculty of Ophthalmologists; a request for a further mid-grade junior post was made to UMH (the previous RSO post having ceased to exist).

In October 1971 Mr Emanuel Rosen was appointed to the consultant staff of MREH. He had undertaken his training there, but was a very keen and expert photographer, and had been proactive as a senior registrar in pursuing retinal photography, and in particular the new technique of fluorescein angiography. Fluorescein was not a new substance in human medicine, and had been injected intravascularly for observation of gut and skin circulation in the 1940s. Direct observation of retinal intravascular flow in a human was first made by MacLean and Maumenee in the USA in 1960,

Emanuel Rosen, Consultant Ophthalmic Surgeon 1971–93

Emanuel Rosen performs retinal detachment surgery, with an enthralled audience

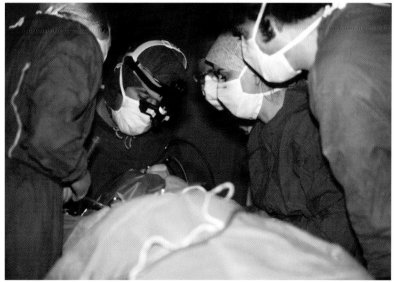

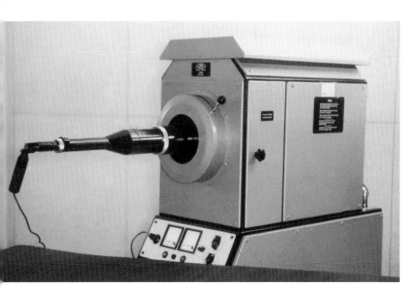

The "Jumbo" Xenon arc photocoagulator in the 1960s

and shortly afterwards, the addition of still-frame retinal photography to the technique by Novotny and Alvis created the technique still used today. Rosen persuaded MREH to purchase its first fundus camera, the Nikon F, in 1967, and pioneered the technique in the UK; in 1969, still a junior doctor, he published *A Short Handook of Fluorescein Photography of the Ocular Fundus*, the first major text on the subject in English. He led the introduction of retinal photography to MREH and as a result obtained a grant to pump-prime the salary of the first retinal photographer, Ernest Young, who was appointed in 1972. For this and other photographic work, Emanuel Rosen was elected a Fellow of the Royal Photographic Society. This author undertook his undergraduate elective within the Retinal Photography Department in 1980, studying diabetic retinopathy and ophthalmic photography under the supervision of Emanuel Rosen. Ernest Young was a fine photographer, and the quality of images taken by him in the early 1970s has not been bettered by all the digital technology available today. He carried an air of superiority and was initially somewhat intimidating, but I found him a generous teacher who, together with "ESR", began my career-long admiration of high-quality ophthalmic photography, and an extensive collection of clinical images. Rosen was also one of the first in MREH to undertake vitrectomy, using the John Scott technique with indirect ophthalmoscopy.

The enhanced diagnosis of diabetic retinopathy and other pathology provided by the new fluorescein angiography led inexorably to more widespread retinal ablation in its treatment. The ability of very bright light to cause retinal damage had been understood well before artificial attempts to induce damage were pioneered, firstly by a carbon arc lamp, and later by xenon arc, the first instrument being introduced by Zeiss in 1956 (being affectionately known as the "jumbo"). The lamp was aimed via an ophthalmoscopic attachment and fired by a trigger, producing a large and deep chorioretinal burn. The development of lasers was however not far behind, the first true laser being patented in 1958, and the first (ruby) laser being used to treat the retina in 1963. The argon gas laser arrived in 1964 and by 1968 had been declared superior clinically. In 1972 MREH acquired its first, at a cost of £11,000. In some other eye hospitals however, the Xenon arc continued in use until the 1980s.

Late in 1972 Professor Phillips departed for Edinburgh. The consultants supported a chair in ophthalmology, and requests to reappoint were made. Unfortunately the enthusiasm expressed by senior staff of MREH was not shared by the Dean of the Medical School, rheumatologist Professor Kellgren. It is unfortunate that the department so assiduously planted and watered by Max Duthie was allowed to wither by Kellgren's refusal to fund a successor. His intention was clear – he requested that the University staff at MREH be dispersed between other firms. Later in 1972, consultant Sydney Smith retired. Mr David Leighton, MREH Senior Registrar, was promoted to replace him and he also became part-time Senior Lecturer, thus administering the dormant University Unit. However, this lasted for only a few months, as he then moved to take up a consultancy at Stepping Hill Hospital. His departure was followed rapidly by communication from Kellgren that "there was no hope of a senior appointment being made in the University Department of Ophthalmology in the near future". The door had been firmly closed. The reasons for Kellgren's opposition are unclear; his antipathy may have been to ophthalmology in general, to MREH in particular, or merely to individual members of staff; in contrast he was proactive in ensuring the development of his own rheumatology department, which would subsequently be named after him. It would be 15 years before the situation at MREH was rectified, and the academic drought during those years did substantial damage to the standing of MREH in the context of a rapidly developing UK ophthalmological research community; it took a determined and resourceful man to retrieve that situation in 1987, and we shall arrive there in due course.

The fabric of the MREH main building (1885) and of the MRI next door (1908) was by the 1960s beginning to age badly, with frequent and expensive remedial work. A plan for rebuilding was required, and as early as 1962 the Board of UMH had submitted to the Ministry of Health a proposal for the rebuilding of both, MREH to be accommodated in principle in "Phase 2" of this process. The bid had been to retain 200 beds for MREH, but only 150 were agreed by the Regional Health Board (RHB). However, support for the retention of a single eye hospital in Manchester was patchy. The RHB now in 1972 proposed a different solution: the fragmentation of Manchester eye services into 3 separate sites (the other two being Salford and South Manchester), reducing MREH to 80 beds. Thus began a battle for integrity which was both chronic and painful, the staff of MREH arguing the necessity of a large teaching unit in order to maintain specialist clinical services, teaching and research of adequate quality. The arguments were eventually successful for MREH on this occasion, but MREH was in the end excluded from Phase 2. Cosmetically, perhaps that was a blessing. The longstanding lack of support for ophthalmological medicine and surgery, apparent ignorance of its necessity, and occasionally frank antipathy to MREH amongst those leading regional and area healthcare, was to continue for three decades, to the continued frustration and bemusement of senior medical staff at MREH, such battles being repeated on a number of occasions (most recently an attempt to delete MREH from the new building plans which finally came to fruition in 2009).

The Hospital had existed with two operating theatres for many decades, but in 1971, plans were first mooted to extend to five, two of which would incorporate two operating tables to be used simultaneously (a practice that had been common in eye hospitals, and had been regularly the case in the MREH University Theatre). The plan was over-ambitious and unnecessary, and had to be scaled back to 4 theatres, but it was clear that the University Department on the ground floor of the New Wing was the best location for new theatres, and plans were initially drawn up with a maximum budget of £75,000. Capital from UMH being unobtainable, a direct application to the Department of Health was eventually successful, a budget of £115,000 being awarded. The new operating theatres would eventually open in 1975, but the nursing support required to staff the additional operating lists was simply not available; often only two theatres could be operated simultaneously, and in 1976 four theatres were in operation only occasionally.

The operating theatres were not the only part of the hospital under-staffed by nurses: in the face of a surgical waiting list increasing to nearly 2,000, wards too had been closed; in particular, ward B3 would remain unused for over 4 years, despite regular appeals to UMH for an increased allocation of nurses. Amidst this frustration, in 1977 UMH informed MREH that it was considering the appropriation of ward B3 and the adjacent, now vacated operating theatre, to provide a free-standing renal transplantation service for Manchester. The MREH consultants were incandescent; not only was the Hospital perceived as being starved of finance, but the areas of the building out of use as a result were now under threat of invasion by an entirely unrelated branch of medicine which they stated, would lead to the integrity of MREH being either "lost or debased". In language rarely used in such official communications, the Division of Ophthalmology informed UMT:

> "The proper channels had been used to submit proposals for an expanded ophthalmic service. Members were somewhat aggrieved that their patience had been rewarded by the suggested introduction of an alternative service"

It is not known whether this was ever a serious suggestion; if so, it was foolhardy to consider housing a renal unit in a building separated from a range of essential support services at the MRI and merely provoked an entirely predictable reaction by the senior staff at MREH; the invasion was repulsed. Instead, in 1977 a proposal was made to create a Regional Retinal Medical Service, with a specialist 5-day ward, retinal laser unit, and a retinal imaging service housed within the old operating theatre. The District Management Team would not support the required nurse staffing for such a suggestion, and a more realistic suggestion that the proposed ward become a retinal outpatient clinic, was taken forward. The area remained with that function until the Hospital was vacated in 2009.

Consultant expansion was in the air, and early in 1973, with the Departure of Mr Leighton, and with the retirement of Mr Janus approaching, the MREH consultants suggested that three be appointed: one to be jointly between MREH and west Manchester including Park and Stretford Memorial Hospitals; one to be jointly between MREH and Crumpsall, and the third to be a predominantly paediatric appointment between MREH and the children's units at Booth Hall, Pendlebury and

St. Mary's. These suggestions seem today to be eminently forward-looking, the beginnings of a potentially effective hub-and-spoke model of care. The third suggestion was facilitated by a request from the Paediatric Medical Division at Salford Hospitals to provide a paediatric ophthalmic service in that locality. However, negotiations with the Regional Board produced, at their insistence, an unattractive job plan with only 3 sessions at MREH, the residue being peripatetic between Crumpsall, Booth Hall and community clinics – effectively an unappointable post. Modification was eventually forced by MREH, with a slight improvement to 4 sessions at the Hospital.

In 1974 Mr Alan Ridgway was appointed consultant to replace Mr Leighton. After qualifying from Cambridge, his ophthalmological training had taken place at Oxford, Cardiff and Birmingham. Dynamic, forceful, sometimes irascible, sometimes volatile, but immensely hardworking, his arrival brought modern glaucoma expertise (he had been an early author on the success of the new glaucoma operation called trabeculectomy) and he went on to become a leading anterior segment surgeon, developing a comprehensive and research-active corneal service, and also taking on paediatric cataract and glaucoma. In 1975 Fred Janus took retirement after 27 years a consultant, and was replaced by Satish Bhargava, senior registrar at MREH. Born in Lahore, he qualified in Delhi but emigrated, undertaking his ophthalmology training at the West of England Eye Infirmary, Glasgow and Manchester. He had taken a close interest in electrophysiology and its application to retinal dystrophies, an interest which he would pursue both clinically and in research, during his consultant tenure. He would die tragically young, in post in 1991. Also in 1975, Mr Christopher Dodd was appointed from a senior registrar position at MREH to the new consultant post at MREH and North Manchester/community. He would develop a major interest in community and paediatric ophthalmology, initiated community orthoptic services in Manchester, and set up the ophthalmology consultation service at Booth Hall Hospital. Shortly following this began the first of the 6-month registrar rotations to other ophthalmological units, Stepping Hill Hospital inaugurating a system which would later become formalised as a regional rotation.

By 1974 the advantages of fluorescein angiography were becoming clear. The resulting increase in throughput in the photography department was

Alan Ridgway, Consultant Ophthalmic Surgeon 1973–2001

Below left Satish Bhargava, Consultant Ophthalmic Surgeon 1975–91

Below Christopher Dodd, Consultant Ophthalmic Surgeon 1975–2003

impossible for the single photographer Mr Young to maintain, and he was financed only from research money. Formalisation of his appointment was arranged, together with the appointment of a second photographer and darkroom technician; the department was beginning to burgeon.

After the Second World War, experienced nurses in ophthalmic hospitals would actively participate in minor treatments, especially of emergencies. One unfortunate side-effect of the formalisation of nurse training and accreditation during the twentieth century was the erosion of these skills, acquired during long experience, to the point of non-existence. However, in 1975 the Medical Committee suggested that training in the performance of some minor procedures should be reintroduced, the particular suggestions being removal of corneal foreign bodies, excision of eyelid cysts, sub-conjunctival injections and carbolisation (the application of carbolic acid by wooden applicator to herpetic corneal ulcers, a treatment then *de rigeur*, and which would remain so until the early 1980s). Unfortunately the UMT senior nurses were not supportive and so the reintroduction of the nurse "practitioner" (as they would later become known) would be delayed by 15 years.

The provision of contact lenses for patients had for some years been contracted to an external optician who would work sessions at MREH. However, the increasing numbers of patients involved led the Committee to set up an internal Contact Lens Service for the first time in 1976, to be led by Mr John Bullock, MREH ophthalmic optician. Ocular ultrasonography was also now possible, a service being provided by Dr John Storey, MREH ophthalmic optician, and in 1976 a new "echo-ophthalmograph" was purchased. Also on the expenditure list for this year was the first slit-lamp camera, at a cost of £8,000.

In 1977 MREH bought its first vitrectomy apparatus. The vitreous humour, scourge of the eye surgeon, cause of many intraocular complications and generally unhelpful phylogenetic detritus, had required partial removal, with difficulty, by cataract surgeons since Daviel. Removal in full had been performed since 1960 via an "open-sky" approach which required the removal and replacement of the cornea. However, in 1971 Robert Machemer, working in Miami, developed a combined vitreous cutting device which also aspirated and replaced fluid via coaxial tubes. This "closed" pars plana vitrectomy technique was in its initial manifestation (the VISC: vitreous infusion suction cutter) cumbersome and difficult to use, with illumination initially only through the cornea and a somewhat "bouncy" cut-rate of only 1Hz. The Kloti cutter, developed soon afterwards by a Zurich ophthalmologist, was the first acquired at MREH. It did in due course permit endo-illumination, but the early devices, according to Chris Dodd, were rather "like searching a cave with a candle". The small-gauge, disposable, rapid-cutting (>1200Hz) instruments used today with their high-efficiency fibreoptic endo-illumination bear little resemblance to these pioneer instruments, which were often used with indirect ophthalmoscopy (thus adding optical image inversion and reversal to the technical difficulty) rather than with the operating microscope. Chris Dodd led the new technique at

MREH, becoming the Hospital's primary retinal and vitreoretinal surgeon for a decade.

Other developments in 1977 included the inauguration of a Corneal Eye Bank. Research into the viability and storage requirements of donated corneas had been undertaken by Dr David Lucas, Consultant Ophthalmic Pathologist appointed to MREH in 1972. An intensely quiet and private man, and in his spare time an expert horologist, he was nevertheless the driving force behind the development of corneal storage in Manchester, and his work on tissue culture was later to be recognised when the David Lucas Manchester Eye Bank was named after him. He was also an accomplished writer, taking on the authorship of the venerable standard textbook, *Greer's Ocular Pathology*.

In June 1978 the workload of doctors in the outpatient department again reared its head. All general clinics were held in the morning. Patients passed through medical "triage" by consultant or senior registrar, being briefly assessed at the lectern by torch or direct ophthalmoscope, being sent for tests or minor surgery if necessary, and having a coloured disc attached to their notes (green = to return to consultant, red = return to another doctor). Once the triage had been completed the consultant and others would complete consultations deeper within the clinic. Those bearing green discs would complete their bottom-shuffling wait *within* the consultant's room, where a bench contained three or four waiting patients who would be party to the current patient's consultation, while waiting their turn. The consultant of the day would depart to rooms at a variable time, but inevitably before the clinic had finished. Most went on past "lunchtime", and Mr Stewart-Scott's, notoriously, until 3.30–4.30. Medical staff today may reconsider their lot when reading of the opinion of the Division:

It was thought that the recommendation of the Faculty of Ophthalmology (sic) of one doctor to see 14 patients per session was not possible to achieve in this Hospital at the present time. As a rough guide, the following has been suggested to achieve a throughput of 190-200 patients per eight doctors per morning clinic.

Consultant:		30-35
Senior Registrar	(3)	25
Registrar	(2)	20
Senior House Officer		12-15
Clinical Assistant		20-25

The opinion followed that if clinics so small were to be imposed, a greater length between outpatient visits would have to be enforced. The outcome was to be observed, and of course the inevitable rise in accident and emergency attendances followed. Further pressure on outpatient numbers was to follow in 1981, when national guidelines on the availability of study for senior registrars led to the withdrawal of all 6 at

MREH from one clinic each, weekly. There was never a greater need for clinical assistance. Those part-time general practitioners and other doctors who have perennially provided clinical assistance at MREH are largely unsung, and are a dying breed, but their contribution to the provision of general outpatient ophthalmology and glaucoma in particular has been essential from the 1970s to the twenty-first century. The names of Dr Atta, Dr Dunn, Dr Soman, Dr Bhatt, Dr Joshi, Dr Gadd, Dr Doyle, Dr Narayan and others will be well-remembered by those who worked alongside them.

Later in 1978 the DHSS, which organised the National Artificial Eye Service from its headquarters in Blackpool, informed MREH that in order to "rationalise" the provision of such services in the Manchester area, it intended to close its department in MREH (the largest provincial eye hospital in the country, with the greatest concentration of patients with eye problems outside London) and re-site it at Withington Hospital (which had no ophthalmology service) on the basis that Withington was to house the new Artificial Limb & Appliance Centre. The administrative convenience that this would generate for the DHSS was clearly felt to be more important than the practical disadvantages that it would impose on almost all involved patients. The "horror" expressed by the medical staff at MREH seems entirely justified. Prolonged discussion followed, involving Mr James Hudson, HM Government Advisor in Ophthalmology. It was only in 1980 that the overwhelming case for retention of a service at MREH was recognised. However, the deteriorating quality of care, with waiting times of up to 40 weeks for a prosthesis, was an increasing source of dissatisfaction to MREH staff, who referred to it in 1981 as offering a "virtually non-existent service". It was eventually realised (during a lecture by the then Northern Regional Manager of the Artificial Eye Service, Mr Robin Brammar) that in order to offer a reasonable facility it would be necessary for the Hospital to create its own Ocular Prosthetics Department and appoint staff to it. As a result, Mr Brammar himself was approached by MREH consultants, and was appointed to a new post in 1982. He was to develop and expand the service over a period of 26 years, also making oculofacial and aural prostheses, and in particular undertaking training in Gothenberg in the manufacture and fitting of osseointegrated implants, which came into its own after the introduction of an expert orbital surgical service in the 1990s.

In 1979 Mr Stewart Scott, consultant of 32 years, staff member for 40 years, and survivor of the Hospital bombing in 1940, retired. He was one of the last of the old-school ophthalmology generalists, dealing with each and every eye condition from cornea to orbit, from cradle to grave, usually without recourse to discussion with, and certainly not referral to, colleagues. Remembered as a pleasant and benign gentleman, but somewhat jealous of his practice, and having no truck with the concept of trainee rotation between firms, he had become an anachronism in an era of developing specialist interests, and although having an immense NHS practice, he did not contribute to the development of his specialty in Manchester. He was replaced by Mr Chris Dodd, who preferred a substantive MREH contract to the peripatetic consultant post which he had occupied for four years. The vacated post was renegotiated as 4 sessions at MREH, 4 at Booth Hall and Crumpsall, and one in the community. It was filled by Mrs Joan Noble, lately senior registrar at MREH; she was the first female consultant to be appointed at MREH, in its 165th year. Her external commitments were predominantly paediatric and she would be the mainstay of ophthalmological expertise at the Manchester paediatric hospitals until the end of the twentieth century. She developed the ultrasound service and her main surgical interest was in orbital surgery. In July 1980 the consultant numbers were expanded by the appointment of Miss Maeve McDermott as Honorary Consultant. Previously Lecturer and senior registrar, she had an interest in medical retinal disease. After her appointment she spent time in a fellowship in the USA and returned to MREH only briefly before moving back to practice in Eire. Also in the summer of 1980, Dr John Storey was appointed Principal Ophthalmic Optician; already working in the department for several years, he would continue in post until his untimely death in 1993.

Joan Noble, Consultant Ophthalmic Surgeon 1979–2007

The decade of the 1970s had been one of tremendous political and social upheaval, and it left the Manchester Royal Eye Hospital a very different organisation than it had been in the 1960s. Within the decade 5 consultants had left and 7 had been appointed; the hospital ophthalmic opticians had moved from merely a support role in refraction to an active department pursuing new developments and specialisation; corneal and paediatric services were in their infancy; there was a freestanding ophthalmological A&E Department; and the Hospital had moved into the era of intraocular lens implantation. Modernisation in education, both undergraduate and postgraduate had taken place, with formal rotations becoming established. However, the Hospital still lacked academic leadership in the absence of a chair of ophthalmology, and those of the consultants who were proactive in research were also too busy clinically to provide the necessary political support at the University. Consultants at MREH continued to negotiate for a replacement chair, to no avail. The decade had also seen the increasing financial strain of NHS funding, and in some areas MREH had been unable to acquire the staff or resources to provide the quality of care aspired to. Much expenditure on items normally considered to be basic, was provided by endowment funds, and this established a pattern that was to continue until the present. The same decade had seen a rapid alternation of Conservative and Labour Governments. It was a decade of national poverty, with abject requests for bailouts from the International Monetary Fund, devaluation of the pound, and a three-day week. The NHS could not be properly supported, and political change had been demanded. Keith Joseph's unfortunate NHS Reorganisation Act of 1973 added layers of administrative control, bringing hospitals, GPs and community services under the control of Area Health Authorities (created to match local government boundaries), overseen by Regional Health Authorities.

In 1980 Dr David Lucas, Consultant Ophthalmic Pathologist, presented a paper to the Division proposing the formal establishment of a Cornea Service. Until this time, all corneas were obtained from donors soon after death by the on-call team (only medical practitioners were at that time allowed to obtain donor eyes), and were either used as donor material within a short time, or discarded. Safe storage had not been possible, but Dr Lucas' team had exhaustively tested a tissue culture method for storage of donor material for up to one week, and had visited centres including Oslo where such methods were already established. He proposed the appointment of a corneal scientist to prepare and maintain material, costed necessary equipment and proposed the development of a regional service. The proposal was met with approval but ultimately development occurred as part of a National service; in 1983 the Corneal Transplant Service was launched by the UK Transplant centre in Bristol. That city acquired its Eye Bank in 1986, and Manchester followed in 1988. The Corneal Tissue Act 1986 changed the law to permit trained non-medical staff to obtain donor eyes, and developments in tissue culture permitted storage for up to 30 days, thus enhancing numbers available, confirming sterility, moving transplantation from an urgent to an elective procedure and permitting the movement of corneal tissue between centres. In cooperation with the local corneal banks at Moorfields and East Grinstead, the two eye banks in Bristol and Manchester became the National Eye Bank Centres, the Manchester branch obtaining and providing donor material for use both at MREH and throughout the North of England.

In the 1970s an intellectual giant from just next door at the MRI (Sir Douglas Black, Professor of Medicine) became involved in healthcare policy and was invited, when President of the Royal College of Physicians, by the Government of James Callaghan to investigate inequalities in healthcare and their cause. A tall, dour and somewhat intimidating Scot, fortunately his bone-dry sardonic humour mitigated his terrifyingly incisive mind. He felt a longstanding dismay at the clear social inequalities in both access to, and quality of healthcare. His team produced in 1980 the now-revered *Black Report*, which through careful statistical analysis of geographic and socioeconomic disparities, quietly screamed the truths of inequality based upon household income. The report was published not by its Labour instigators, but by the recently elected Conservative government which had unwillingly inherited its results, and which shared few of its sentiments; a small number of copies were quietly circulated without fanfare, but the passage of time and greater appreciation by healthcare commentators and policy-makers internationally has rendered this one of the great healthcare publications of the twentieth century. Although ophthalmology was not specifically included in his report, it is interesting to witness local and regional expressions of such disparity within this field. The North Western Regional Health Authority issued in 1981 its revised Strategic Guidelines on Ophthalmic Services. The document included statistics on the provision of services in the Northwest compared to that of England in general, and this provides illuminating reading considering the Black report and its subsequent lack of effect on domestic healthcare policy. The average daily available beds per 100,000 population (and MREH provided a substantial majority of these in the Northwest) was greater at 8.8 than the figure of 8.5 for England as a whole, and this statistic provided the basis for political efforts to reduce those beds (especially at MREH of course). However, a further analysis of those figures provides rather greater detail: In the Northwest, compared to England, the patient turnover per bed was greater, the waiting list for treatment per discharge was greater, the average inpatient stay and turnover intervals were shorter, and the percentage occupancy was higher; in other words, the Region may have been better-bedded for ophthalmology than England in general, but it made significantly better use of those beds, and yet still had more waiting for treatment. Despite this unequivocal evidence of high turnover and efficiency, reduction in central funding to force bed closures had already been politically decided. The figures for outpatient services in 1981 were even more striking: the 30 consultants in the Northwest provided far fewer outpatient clinics per 100,000 population (at 135 compared to 204 on average for England). However, they dealt with almost as many new patients during those sessions, and each saw 37 patients per session, compared to 27 on average for England. In other words, the consultants of the northwest worked far faster. The one statistic that the NWRHA did not dare to divulge (because the contrast would have been too stark) was the number of consultants per 100,000 population, compared to England in general: the Northwest had less than one third of the England average (and yet were providing two thirds of the number of outpatient clinics, and during them, were seeing almost as many patients as elsewhere). The reputation of MREH (if representative of the Northwest) as a hard-working hospital was very much borne out by these figures.

In 1981 a thinly veiled threat was received by the consultants of MREH, from Dr WP Povey, Area Medical Officer for the Manchester Area Health Authority (an ephemeral organisation, created during NHS reorganisation in 1974 and due to be abolished in 1982). The provision of ophthalmology for the residents of Salford had always been less than satisfactory. At this time an outreach outpatient service was provided by Mr Roddie, consultant at Bolton, but it was the strong desire of both Salford and Manchester AHAs that the service should be provided by MREH. The consultant staff had perennially resisted such a move, for several reasons; firstly, some thought that the city of Salford was large enough to create its own eye unit; secondly Hope Hospital, Salford's main hospital at which outreach clinics would be based, was an inconvenient journey from MREH; and thirdly was the never-to-be-directly spoken effect on private practice (a phenomenon seen nationwide): consultants were in general very happy to accept an outreach clinic (and therefore to develop a professional relationship with a group of GPs) in an affluent area, but a clinic in a chronically deprived area such as Salford was unwanted. Dr Povey's gambit was to threaten the future of the Eye Hospital by stating his support for a substantial reduction in beds at MREH, to be actioned by withdrawal of funds. Although he mooted that such a change would be "tragic" his message was clear. It was not ultimately successful, however. Although an outreach clinic from MREH to Hope would exist for several years, it would not persist, and at the time of writing, consultants from Bolton continue to offer outreach clinics in Salford, whereas MREH provides almost all emergency and A&E care for its residents. The failure to develop a more robust connection with Salford was one of MREH's most important strategic failures of the last 50 years; had such a link been strengthened, it is highly likely that a satellite unit of MREH would now exist in Salford, offering both surgery and outpatient care, conveniently adjacent to the Greater Manchester Neuroscience Centre at Salford Royal (previously Hope) Hospital. *Sic transit...*

The MREH A&E Department had been sited within the main building since 1971. However, during the following decade the number of patients had risen from 27,000 to 37,000 per annum, the space was becoming unfit for purpose, and two doctors still worked side by side in a single consulting space. The preferred option was to invade further the residual orthoptic space, providing a new build on the rear of the outpatient department to house a new orthoptic department and school, together with a diabetic eye centre, an extension to the opticians' department, and a new ophthalmic pathology department. However, these pipe-dreams proved unfundable; financial constraints led instead to the conversion of the then-empty old laundry building in the Hospital's back yard. The highly unsatisfactory long, thin building was converted at low cost to supply reception, waiting area, 3 consulting rooms, treatment room and minor operations room, the un-salubrious entrance being on Nelson Street opposite the outpatient department. Despite later re-naming the building was to serve as the doctor-led emergency service for many years.

The MREH A&E Department entrance in about 1985

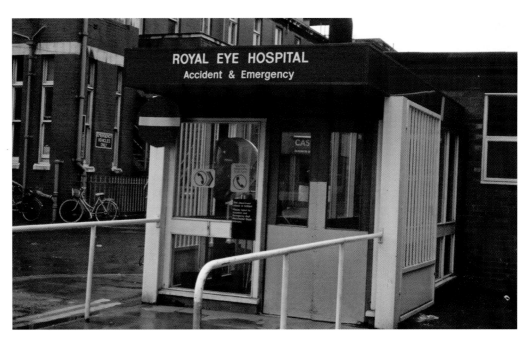

From the 1960s to the early 1980s, management decisions within hospitals were made largely by consensus between the "triumvirate" of three key figures: the Chairman of the Medical Committee (usually rotated between senior consultants) who oversaw all medical staff and medical matters; the Matron, who oversaw all nursing and domestic matters; and the Hospital Secretary who oversaw all other staff, administrative and non-clinical matters. In 1983 Roy Griffiths was commissioned by Margaret Thatcher and the then Health Secretary, Norman Fowler, to investigate and comment upon manpower issues within the NHS. However, he chose unilaterally to enlarge his brief and made recommendations on changes to the whole structure of management of the NHS (based on his stated opinion that all ultimately depended upon the management structure, and manpower decisions would flow naturally; how wrong he has been proven). Griffiths, a vice-chairman of Sainsbury's (a successful grocery chain) and Fellow of the Institute of Grocery Distribution, brought in to help him three business acquaintances, amongst whom the combined healthcare expertise included a background in TV Southwest, British Telecom, and United Biscuits. At no stage during the investigation process were any health economists, public health experts, Royal colleges, primary care or hospital doctors, members of the nursing organisations, hospital committee members, hospital scientists or technicians, or any patient representative, involved in the decision-making process. The results of that process were announced by a letter (unaccompanied by any data, any statement of logic, any glossary of background information) which rapidly and flatteringly became known as the "Griffiths Report". The brief document became best known for its catchy sound-bite "if Florence Nightingale were carrying her lamp through the corridors of the NHS today, she would almost certainly be looking for the people in charge". The events which followed have established very clearly that policy-making by sound-bite, by the ill-informed with pre-conceived agendas, is both shallow and expensive. Manfred Davidmann, renowned sociologist, rapidly offered a critique of the report, its content and mode of production:

> One cannot over-emphasize the importance of the changes put forward in the Inquiry's report. They amount to a fundamental and far-reaching reorganisation which, working from the top downwards, would completely alter the style of control and management in our NHS, in what is perhaps the biggest organisation and employer in the United Kingdom and one of the largest in Western Europe, on which depends the health and welfare of the whole population. Hence one would expect fully documented conclusions and recommendations backed by comprehensive investigations and findings... But the Inquiry report does not provide details about what was done and how it was done, what facts were established and the conclusions drawn from them, so that it seems to me that what is missing from the report is much of the basis for their consequent recommendations.

Notwithstanding the complete lack of either evidence base or healthcare expertise within the panel, the Conservative Government decided to implement the recommendations in full: the institution of a corporate management structure requiring executive responsibility, from Elephant & Castle to every ward and outpatient department. An entire tree of managers grew downwards from the Department of Health to take control of the organisation of healthcare, and at hospital level this introduced the General Hospital Manager. At every hospital including MREH, both matron and consultants (those senior professionals directly responsible for patient care) were effectively deprived of executive input into hospital policy and strategy. The post of Hospital Secretary, occupied for precisely one hundred years at MREH by 6 incumbents, ceased to exist, and the present occupier, Edwin Bell, left to work elsewhere in hospital administration.

CHAPTER TEN

Purchasers, Providers, Politics and Perennial Re-disorganisation

THE GRIFFITHS REPORT OF 1983 coincided with the beginning of a new era for the NHS; an era when medical and technological developments produced new and improved treatments at increasing pace, when access to information about these methods became increasingly easy, and when politicians were at pains to inform their constituents that nothing was too good for them. The result was that despite vastly improving medical science, improved timeliness and quality of care, improving outcomes and improving healthcare access, nothing that the NHS could do was considered adequate by the media, by polemic "healthcare commentators", by patient groups with progressively higher expectations, or by the successive governments who were required to fund the NHS from taxation. The result was a series of interventions either to change the organisational structure of the NHS, or to force changes in healthcare prioritisation for political, not medical reasons. These changes, each in itself disruptive to healthcare delivery (with the Griffiths Report in the vanguard) were all different, but all had much in common; there was little evidence base for each; they were not proactive, but reactive, usually to ill-informed media pressure and therefore decided on-the-hoof; medical involvement in planning was either superficial or specifically prevented; none were piloted; none were properly audited; and mistakes went unlearned. The result has been aptly called "perennial re-disorganisation". It has been the task of healthcare purchasing and delivery organisations, the trusts and hospitals, to attempt to continue and develop healthcare despite, rather than aided by, these changes. Ophthalmology at the Manchester Royal Eye Hospital has been no exception. Almost all real developments have been led by technology and medicine.

The next episode in the evolution of cataract surgery is a prime example: intracapsular cataract surgery had been the method of choice for 30 years or more but in the early 1980s, the introduction of high-quality coaxially illuminated microscopes (giving for the first time a hands-free red reflex), and the realisation that a retained posterior capsule enhanced surgical safety (markedly reducing the incidence of vitreous loss and therefore retinal detachment) together with the introduction of posterior chamber intraocular lens implants (IOLs), marked a move back to extracapsular surgery (the method first used in the eighteenth century) although now with substantially superior equipment, and reliable anaesthesia. In the meantime, very small-calibre (10/0) monofilament nylon sutures had become available, replacing 8/0 virgin silk, and the majority of surgeons therefore moved over to corneal incisions (buried nylon being entirely satisfactory for this, but virgin silk unacceptable). The change from intracapsular to extracapsular surgery at MREH had been led not only by the innovative consultants but also by senior registrars, especially by Messrs Ridgway, Mills, Marsh, Rosen and Tullo, and by the mid-1980s most cataract surgery at MREH was carried out by this method. The days of the iris-supported lens implant were over. Other technical developments had facilitated anterior segment surgery: the introduction of hyaluronidase permitted a single retrobulbar injection of anaesthetic to percolate through tissue planes, providing all four of the preferred parameters for surgery (anaesthesia, akinesia, a paralysed orbicularis and temporary loss of vision). Prior to this, local anaesthesia for cataract surgery had been more complex and much more unpleasant for the patient. A paralysed orbicularis had been achieved by facial nerve block (the O'Brien method being into its main trunk anterior to the parotid, the van Lint method being into its branches in upper and lower eyelids) and many surgeons used both methods. The old-fashioned method of lid retraction sutures was still used by some surgeons into the early 1980s, being a hangover from the reluctance to use a lid speculum owing to the perceived greater risk of vitreous loss, and this also necessitated infiltration of anaesthetic under the lid margins. A retrobulbar block to work properly had to be intraconal (within the extraocular muscle cone) and lastly, the superior rectus tendon (which would be impaled by a traction suture) was also anaesthetised. The complexity and discomfort of local anaesthesia was one of the main reasons for the predominance of general anaesthesia at MREH for cataract surgery at this time, and hyaluronidase was one of the great changes that moved cataract surgery back towards local anaesthesia.

Together with microscope improvements, fine sutures, posterior chamber lenses and hyaluronidase, the most important development during the 1980s was sodium hyaluronate, a viscous gel extracted initially from cockscombs, but later synthesised. Prior to this a collapsed anterior chamber, with consequent corneal endothelial damage, was a regular feature of cataract surgery; the only reliable methods of preventing this were either an attempt to perform intraocular manoeuvres through a small wound, or by the injection of air and the reliance on the bubble's surface tension to maintain a space. Both techniques were difficult, and corneal oedema after cataract surgery was not uncommon. Hyaluronate was little short of a miracle for anterior segment surgeons: here was a substance which could be injected intraocularly through a narrow-gauge cannula, which was transparent and which would occupy space safely while still permitting surgical manoeuvres well clear of the corneal endothelium. Surgery was transformed, and for those surgeons very adept at the new form of extracapsular surgery with posterior chamber IOLs, the whole procedure was often performed in 10–15 minutes, a significant improvement on previous operation time. A new era was here, we thought, as we gradually became used to the post-operative high astigmatism caused by tight corneal sutures, and spent many a happy hour removing said sutures from patients at the slit-lamp, 8–12 weeks after surgery. We also became used to posterior capsule opacification, a complication affecting the majority of those with early posterior chamber IOLs, but the introduction of the Neodymium-YAG laser in the mid-1980s changed its treatment from an operating microscope surgical procedure to an outpatient visit. Nevertheless, visual results after final refraction had never been better, and having learned the new technique, a period of stability was apparently well-deserved. However, already new developments were afoot...

During the 1980s the MREH Consultants' Committee continued its regular meetings, but as the Chair was effectively no longer an executive post, it effectively reverted to a medical committee as was seen in the latter nineteenth century. Hospital Managers, including Mrs Rosemary Knights and Mr John Foster, were the conduit for medical advice to UMH, and the period was effectively one of medical disenfranchisement, the disadvantages of which would be realised by Government after approaching a decade of the "Griffiths" method of organisation.

The year 1988 marked the beginning of an important new era for MREH. Since the departure of Calbert Phillips in 1972 the Chair of Ophthalmology had sat gathering dust, the vacancy firstly being caused by the opposition of the Dean, and secondly by a lack of vigour in the construction of a job description both by University and Hospital staff. However, the post was duly recreated, and the two highly reputed candidates were Mr Emanuel Rosen, longstanding consultant surgeon at MREH, and Mr David McLeod, highly successful vitreoretinal surgeon at Moorfields Eye Hospital. The latter was successful.

David McLeod was a Northerner, born and bred in Burnley, but genetically of Viking descent which may explain some aspects of his character. He qualified at Edinburgh with the Leslie Gold Medal as the most distinguished medical graduate of his year. He entered ophthalmology immediately after registration, firstly at the Edinburgh Eye Pavilion, and then at Moorfields Eye Hospital, where he became its youngest-ever consultant in 1977, rapidly establishing with his mentor, Peter Leaver, a vitreoretinal surgery unit of high repute. After a decade of professional success in London he was invited to consider the Chair in Manchester, and was clearly a man to meet the considerable challenge.

There is no disguising the fact that by 1988 the quality of postgraduate training at MREH was embarrassingly low, simply because national improvements in junior rotas and formal education provision had overtaken MREH and left it standing; indeed the Hospital was not far from de-recognition as a training centre by the College of Ophthalmologists (a step which may have been terminal for the Hospital). The MREH Junior Doctors' Association, only recently created as a formal body as a result of shared problems with training, had been moved as a result of proposed changes to junior staffing pending the arrival of Professor McLeod, to audit in detail the workload of

David McLeod, Professor of Ophthalmology and Consultant Ophthalmic Surgeon 1988–2006

junior staff, the teaching provided to them, and more contentiously, the input of some consultants to both training and NHS clinical work. A report compiled by the JDA President (this author) comprised a polite but detailed demolition of the contemporary state of affairs and of the proposed changes, suggesting alternative plans for junior allocation, outpatient clinic timetabling and doctor sessions per clinic, operating theatre timetables, A&E rota and on-call rota. It was sent to all consultants and to Professor McLeod, who met its author in a corridor at MREH on his arrival, saying "you have taken this just as far as you could have done – now leave it to me".

He was as good as his word, and character traits became rapidly apparent; careful analysis so that he was always perfectly briefed, very detailed preparation so that arguments could be demolished at the time, not later; a polite but very direct approach, delivered in his unmistakable Burnley brogue, which suffered no condescension or suave rebuff; great tenacity and drive, sometimes bluntness, sometimes stubbornness, but always with clarity and a careful strategy. These attributes were combined with an appetite for hard work that even within the medical community, was notable: after a normal hard-working week, much of this preparation (and work for his many external commitments) were dealt with on Sunday mornings, when he could work undisturbed in his office. Sentiment played little part in decision-making, so that whilst always

Mr Frank Bruno opens the David Lucas Manchester Eye Bank in 1989, together with (from left) Mr Borys Marciniuk, Eye Bank Manager; Mr Alan Ridgway; Dr David Lucas

PURCHASERS, PROVIDERS, POLITICS AND PERENNIAL RE-DISORGANISATION

being very supportive of genuine talent, mediocrity was unwanted and if necessary, summarily disposed of. It was only half in jest that the juniors, during one memorable Christmas Show, gave him the soubriquet of "The Terminator".

Professor McLeod immediately took on the role of STC Chair and Training Programme Director for the Northwestern Deanery, initiating sweeping changes. A regular weekly postgraduate teaching session was instituted on Wednesday afternoons at MREH, replacing the previous ad hoc system, and this continues successfully after 25 years. The training programmes of juniors in the region were rationalised and improved, and it is no exaggeration to say that from an untenable position, over a period of a few years MREH was transformed into a centre of excellence for training, so that when he retired from the STC chairmanship in 2001 the rotation was described by the College as "exemplary".

Within a year of his arrival at MREH Professor McLeod sought to appoint a Clinical Lecturer in Ophthalmology and secured HEFCE funding for the post. Two MREH senior registrars were interviewed, and this author was appointed in 1989. Clinical research into uveitis and ocular trauma followed, with honorary consultant status being granted in 1991, at which time the Manchester Uveitis Clinic was inaugurated; a specialist service being reintroduced in the Northwest of England after a gap of 30 years (following Alan Stanworth's departure for Sheffield). Clinical lectureships have continued to be a possibility for MREH trainees, enabling combined clinical training and research with several doctorates ensuing.

David Lucas, Ophthalmic Pathologist, had retired in 1987. His work both in the development of tissue culture methods, and in forming links with Bristol to enhance the UK Corneal Transplant Service, was recognised when the David Lucas Manchester Eye Bank was formally opened in January 1989. Mr Frank Bruno, patient and friend of Professor McLeod, kindly agreed to perform the honours. Initially sited in the ground floor corridor of the main building, the bank moved successively to the basement, Lister Centre, and now the 4th floor in our new building, where excellent facilities were designed to receive it. Dr Richard Bonshek was appointed Consultant Ophthalmic Pathologist in his place and continues to provide that service.

Andrew Tullo, Consultant Ophthalmic Surgeon 1989–2004

Later in 1989 Mr Andrew Tullo was appointed Consultant Ophthalmic Surgeon at MREH with a special interest in corneal diseases and ocular infection. He had joined as senior registrar in 1985 having undertaken his doctorate in herpetic corneal disease under Professor David Easty at Bristol. Taking over the management of the Manchester Eye Bank, he formed an active research group concentrating on ocular infection, and enhanced the diagnosis of herpetic, chlamydial and bacterial conjunctival and corneal disease using novel investigative methods. Following the publication of the 1989 Government papers *Working for Patients*, he was asked, together with this author, to lead the introduction of medical audit into MREH, and did so for several years. A deeply thoughtful and careful doctor, and a fine surgeon, he was also a stalwart of postgraduate education at MREH. He co-wrote with Senior Nursing Officer John

Perry the popular manual *Care of the Ophthalmic Patient*. He was appointed Visiting Professor of Ophthalmology at UMIST. Unfortunately he retired early due to ill health in 2006, and is much missed.

In the late 1980s and 1990s, medical students of the University of Manchester each undertook one week's clinical attachment in ophthalmology, as their entire undergraduate exposure to ophthalmology. The largest medical undergraduate class in the country (over 300 at this time) therefore rotated in groups of 12 through MREH during the academic year as part of a teaching block called "specials" (also incorporating ENT, maxillofacial surgery, dermatology and orthopaedics). Most undergraduate clinical teaching in Manchester was split between the three major teaching hospital groups, but only MREH was able to provide ophthalmology teaching within the city. This author, as Senior Lecturer, organised this superficial exposure for a decade, attempting to enhance it, with marginal success, by forcing access to the BISC lecture course and arranging for ophthalmologists in the Northwestern and Welsh DGHs to teach some ophthalmology to Manchester students during their 4th year residential clerkships. It was however a forlorn task, and as the class enlarged, the Faculty of Medicine experimented with a variety of changed timetables until at the end of the 1990s, with the introduction of themed semesters and problem-based learning, clinical exposure to ophthalmology disappeared from the mandatory curriculum, so that only student-selected optional attachments (available to perhaps 40–50 per year) remained. Now, in our bicentenary year, we hear of a reversal with mixed views – once more all undergraduates are to attend for one week each. Rather like old clothes, teaching methods seem to come back into fashion eventually. The Hospital also had a responsibility for the clinical teaching of undergraduate optometrists from UMIST (as it then was), and regular clinical attachments, together with an examined lecture course in clinical ophthalmology, have been a perennial commitment. For several years, optometry students from the University of Aston also undertook clinical attachments at MREH.

The years 1990–91 saw a flurry of activity after the *NHS & Community Care Act 1990* introduced the schism of healthcare purchasers from providers, which in Kafkaesque fashion introduced competition for business (described as an "internal market") into a system which was already incapable of providing the necessary volume as a whole; an interesting but fundamentally flawed business model. Hospital Trusts were set up soon afterwards, and UMH became the Central Manchester Healthcare NHS Trust. The decision on healthcare purchases was now made by local health authorities on the basis of perceived local need. The immediate concern of large teaching hospitals including MREH, was the likely inability of local decision-making bodies to identify (indeed, to be aware of) and adequately remunerate care for highly specialised conditions, and so perennially it has proved, despite political tinkering with the structure of such purchasing authorities. The National Specialised Commissioning Advisory Group, concentrating as it did only on very rare diseases, did not adequately mitigate this problem. Clinical Directorates were added to the trusts' management structure, reversing several years of the exclusion of consultants from executive decisions. Professor McLeod was appointed this Hospital's first Clinical Director in 1991. At the same time, GP Fundholding was inaugurated: the ability of a single practice or group of GP practices to ring-fence their funding and arrange their own healthcare. As a result, in addition to substantial contractual administration imposed by the purchaser-provider split, individual negotiation with small groups of GPs became necessary, and the inevitable result was preferential treatment (mainly in terms of waiting times) of those GPs' patients (to the disadvantage of the patients of others, because there was no extra capacity). There were medical ethical issues involved here, to the discomfiture of those consultants involved at MREH, but the retention of funds from those practices was considered essential. A further inevitability of the system was that other GPs, perceiving the imposed disadvantage to their patients from *en bloc* contracts and being aware of the computer systems provided *gratis* by Government when enrolled, also sought to become fundholding, and during the next seven years, 57% of practices had taken this step. The incoming Labour government rapidly abolished the scheme in 1998, but had it been retained, most advantage from becoming a fundholding practice would have been neutralised, simply because the ability to negotiate preferential treatment would have disappeared as almost all practices would have succumbed to the system. Contracting at MREH was thereafter somewhat simplified for a time.

In 1991, this author was asked by the Clinical Director to lead a working party investigating the working practices of the A&E department. Several conclusions were drawn, the most important being the recommendation of a nurse-delivered walk-in service staffed by trained nurse practitioners. Such changes rapidly took place, the first incumbent being Sister (now Professor) Janet Marsden and the second, Sr Liz Revington. Shortly afterwards, the nurse-delivered Emergency Eye Centre (EEC) was physically separated from the Acute Referral Centre (ARC) and re-sited within the A&E department of the MRI next door. The ARC was staffed by junior ophthalmologists and saw patients referred by EEC practitioners or directly from GPs. This pattern of acute care provision was continued for nearly two decades, before EEC and ARC were reunited within our new hospital.

The Manchester Uveitis Clinic began as a small-scale affair in March 1991, directed by this author. An unmet need was rapidly identified so that referrals grew over a period of years. A prospective database was used from the outset which has permitted a considerable clinical research output. In its 23rd year, a report on the first 3000 patients (the largest uveitis epidemiological survey in the world literature) has been published. The author's experience led to the publication of the popular textbooks *Uveitis: an Illustrated Manual* in 1998 and subsequently *Uveitis: Second Edition* in 2012. The clinic now deals with over 150 child and adult patients weekly, and provides subspecialist teaching for fellows in uveitis and medical retina.

David McLeod had seen the enormous clinical workload at MREH on his arrival and had been considering ways to ameliorate it. One partial solution was the development of a hub-and-spoke model of care in which staff undertook outreach clinics. Consultant-delivered care was not always necessary, and the plan was to appoint non-consultant career-grade doctors to posts which would combine outreach service and in-house specialist work. In due course three doctors were appointed as Community Eye Physicians (CEP), firstly on the Senior Clinical Medical Officer grade, and subsequently as Associate Specialists. A series of ophthalmology clinics were inaugurated at a variety of general practices and health centres, and the CEPs also provided support for the consultant-led hospital outreach clinics. Internally these doctors have been involved in anterior segment and extraocular surgery, laser work, botulinum toxin clinics, uveitis and inflammatory disease, glaucoma and many other forms of ophthalmology, and they remain stalwarts at MREH: Rod McKenzie, Khalid Aziz and Chad Deka.

In 1967 Charles Kelman, New York ophthalmologist, had invented the intraocular phakoemulsifier. The instrument was initially crude and provided no advantage over contemporary surgical methods. However, gradual refinement led to increasing safety and a realisation throughout the world by the late 1980s, that the single great advantage of the technique was the ability to remove a cataract through a very small incision (3.5–4.0mm at this time). That advantage was largely neutralised by the need, having removed the cataract, to enlarge the section to 7mm to implant a rigid polymethylmethcrylate IOL. That problem delayed the acceptance of phacoemulsification by many, including those at MREH, but the ongoing tedium of outpatient corneal suture removal, and occasional residual postoperative high astigmatism, led a few enthusiasts at MREH, notably senior registrar Alan Watson, to provoke the introduction of the instrumentation, which arrived at MREH in 1991. In this early stage, the first-generation phako machines were ultrasonically inefficient and the fluidics somewhat untrustworthy in maintaining anterior chamber depth; posterior capsule rupture with vitreous loss was a concern, and a substantial proportion of attempted phakoemulsifications were converted to standard extracapsular extractions. Surgeons were initially wary. Nevertheless the advantages of rapid postoperative recovery became obvious. This author began conversion to the technique (initially via scleral tunnels) in early 1993, after only 8 years of extracapsular surgery. Many UK surgeons remained unconvinced that this was going to be a long-lasting change. However, two further developments completely altered the perspective; the next-generation phako machines in the later 1990s were an order of magnitude better, with high efficiency and reliability, rendering extracapsular extraction obsolete except for brunescent cataract, and the first folding IOLs ensured that true small-incision surgery could be used. Cataract surgery was transformed: the days of inpatient stay were largely over, bed numbers in eye hospitals including MREH would collapse, day-case units would become universal, and "alternative providers" were now able to provide freestanding daycase-only surgery in small surgical units, permitting free-market competition (but only, of course, for straightforward cases;

the established eye hospitals would continue to operate on all-comers with their far higher incidence of ocular and systemic co-morbidity). Before long even the ritual of first-postoperative-day examination was proven unnecessary after routine phaco-emulsification, repair of occasional post-operative wound leaks and iris prolapses disappeared entirely from the agenda, and outpatient suture removal became a thing of the past.

In 1994 it was necessary to make preparations to evacuate Lister House which was finally due for demolition, its rear elevation being braced by timber flying buttresses to prevent disaster. Redundant ward space was increasingly available owing to the move towards day-case cataract surgery, and it was decided that Wards C3 and C4 were to be refurbished to provide much of that accommodation. A very pleasant area was created on C4 (previously an adult female ward), to house the University Department and ophthalmic pathology offices, junior mess, on-call SHO bedroom, hospital library and librarian's office. Ward C3, previously the children's ward, was reconfigured to create a clinical research area with consulting and laboratory space, renamed the Hardy-Heywood Suite.

Other spaces within Lister House found new homes: the seminar room had housed all large-group teaching for many years, but recently the CMHT Postgraduate Centre had been updated luxuriously, and the weekly ophthalmology postgraduate meetings moved over into the 200-seat lecture theatre there, where they have remained. Internal seminar room space was however still required, and an area within the basement of the main building was refurbished to provide two connectable teaching rooms, together with a wet lab to facilitate surgical training. The first floor of the Nelson Street outpatient department, originally built as a nurses' home for MREH but latterly used as sundry staff accommodation for CMHT, was now co-opted as a space for consultant and secretarial offices, being inevitably re-named the Lister Centre. All of Lister House was now vacated, and the building, which had served healthcare well in various guises for a century, was demolished to provide car parking space.

In 1994, David McLeod resigned as Clinical Director (CD) and the post was taken up by Barry Mills. A consultant at MREH since 1981 with a special interest in glaucoma, he was eventually to serve two long periods as CD (or Clinical Head of Division as it was later to be called), 1994–98 and 2005–12. A natural and astute medical politician with an acute eye for potential service development and an almost prescient feel for political change, he proved to be an outstanding CD who led MREH successfully through what would prove to be very stressful financial times, apparently dealing with each new political incentive, each urgent demand for applications for funding from the Department of Health, and each new internal crisis, with complete equanimity. A steady head, a calm approach, an urbane and productive consultation method, a ready laugh and a winning smile were the character traits. His complete grasp of healthcare economics and vast experience of contracting and funding issues made him as highly respected by the Trust board as by colleague consultants, so that his frequent changes

Barry Mills, Consultant
Ophthalmic Surgeon
1981–2012

of strategic direction, occasional forgotten promises and "light touch" on internal detail were repeatedly forgiven.

The early and mid-1990s saw the appointment of several new consultants. In 1990 Michael Lavin was appointed Consultant Vitreoretinal Surgeon after training at Moorfields, and in 1991 this author was appointed Honorary Consultant. Later in the same year Alec Ansons, strabismus expert, was appointed Consultant and went on also to develop a specialist neuro-ophthalmology service. His standing in the strabismus world led to him taking over the authorship of the standard text *Diagnosis and Management of Ocular Motility Disorders*. In 1992 Brian Leatherbarrow was appointed consultant with a special interest in orbital, lacrimal and oculoplastic surgery. Trained at MREH, he had undergone fellowships at Moorfields and in Iowa, and returned to inaugurate what would become a highly respected specialist unit which has now swelled to require 5 consultants and which deals with the whole range of facio-orbital work including periocular cancer, Mohs' surgery, and complex combined orbit/neurosurgery. Working with Robin Brammar, Ocular Prosthetist, oculofacial and osseointegrated prosthetics expertise was developed. Fellows were rapidly attracted to train in the unit, and Mr Leatherbarrow's popular textbook *Oculoplastic Surgery* is now in its second edition. George Turner, Moorfields-trained, joined the retinal team in 1993 having previously been consultant in Taunton. In 1995, Christopher Lloyd was the first MREH consultant to be specifically appointed paediatric ophthalmologist; he and future colleagues have gone on to develop a renowned service especially for neonatal and paediatric cataract, and his research work has recently been recognised with a personal Chair.

Mike Lavin, Consultant
Ophthalmic Surgeon 1990–

Alec Ansons, Consultant
Ophthalmic Surgeon 1991–

Brian Leatherbarrow, Consultant
Ophthalmic Surgeon 1992–

George Turner, Consultant
Ophthalmic Surgeon 1993–

Chris Lloyd, Consultant
Ophthalmic Surgeon 1995–

Dr Cindy Tromans, Principal (now Consultant)
Optometrist 1993–

Dr Robert Harper, Principal (now Consultant)
Optometrist 1993–

In the meantime, organisational changes were underway. The private wing of the Hospital, for the previous few years outside the Directorate, was reunited with MREH. Ground floor renovation permitted the opening of a Vision Science Centre incorporating electrophysiology facilities, and the new daycase facility was opened near to the operating theatres. Dr John Storey, much-respected Principal Optometrist since 1980, died tragically young in 1993 and a replacement was needed. Two strong internal candidates presented, and ultimately both were appointed: Dr Cindy Tromans specialised in the medical and paediatric contact lens services, and Dr Robert Harper's interest was in low vision and visual rehabilitation. Both remain on the staff, now consultant optometrists, leading strong research into their respective fields. Dr Tromans has recently served a term as President of the College of Optometrists.

In 1994 the British Orthoptic Society took the decision that qualification in orthoptics would change from a diploma to a degree course. Applications for such a course were made by the universities of Sheffield and Liverpool, but for reasons unclear, not from the University of Manchester. This led inevitably to the closure of the MREH Orthoptic School, one of the oldest and busiest in the country, which had been in existence for over 60 years. Ironically, the only two degree courses to be created in the UK were both immediately headed by orthoptic teachers departing from MREH; Helen Davis at Sheffield, and Gail Stephenson at Liverpool, both still in post and both now professors of orthoptics. The longstanding Head of Orthoptic School at MREH, Mo Hill, continued to work clinically but retired in 1998. Orthoptic students continue to be taught in clinical attachments at MREH as part of their degree courses.

The NHS contractual environment of the 1990s saw further political changes:

the number of Regional Health Authorities was reduced in 1996, and subsequently, reflecting their increasing redundancy they changed from "Authorities" to "Offices". The incoming Labour Government of 1997, champing at the bit after 16 years in opposition, almost immediately abolished GP fundholding, and in 1999 an alternative local purchaser arrangement was inaugurated in the form of Primary Care Groups (PCG). Those organisations had barely ordered the office furniture, and provider hospitals barely made the acquaintance of its members, when the PCGs were dissolved, it having been decided that they were too small, and in 2000 larger Primary Care Trusts (PCTs) were created. The officers of the pre-existing authorities, as before and since, took re-employment at the new body, alongside many of the same faces as before. The management staff of CMHT and MREH once more began renegotiating contracts with a different set of administrative bodies. However, patient care at MREH seemed to go on uninterrupted. In 2002, the largely redundant Regional Offices faded into non-existence, and 28 Strategic Health Authorities were created.

During the NHS contractual upheavals of the mid-to-late 1990s, the management team at MREH were approached by a variety of purchasers outside the traditional catchment area, and requested to provide outreach care, on the basis of dissatisfaction with their local service. Again, ethical issues arose, but they were overcome by a combination of poikilothermic pragmatism and a shortage of resources (in particular, an inability to replace expensive equipment without recourse to charitable funds). As a result, clinics were set up in Stoke-on-Trent, Rossendale valley, Lancaster and elsewhere, and a constant stream of cataract patients on long waiting lists either came to MREH for surgery on all-day weekend operating lists, or surgeons from MREH went to operate on them locally. Several thousand patients were thus dealt with, to the apparent satisfaction of their local funding authorities, and to the sometimes furious objection of their local consultants, who argued that they too were starved of resources and that such predatory action by a neighbour was not only unhelpful, but further weakened their negotiating position. To an extent therefore, the purchaser-provider split had worked beautifully – it had become dog-eat-dog in a battle for scarce resources (which was presumably the aim of the Government that had initiated the system). The period did lasting damage to a previously amicable relationship between ophthalmology units in the Northwest, and the longstanding Regional Specialty Committee (which met biannually with a representative from each unit to discuss common strategic ophthalmology interests) ceased to exist. Politically, perhaps amicable relationships between neighbour units had been interpreted as complacency. The price paid for any worthwhile change should be weighed in the balance.

In 1997 Mr Stephen Charles was appointed Consultant Vitreoretinal Surgeon at MREH, at that time becoming the fourth in a strong vitreoretinal team. Having worked with John Scott at Cambridge and then undertaken a VR fellowship at MREH, he had taken a consultant post in Oslo for two years before returning to the fold, where he remains now as Clinical Lead for Medical and Surgical Retina.

The late 1990s saw the appearance of BSE and variant Creutzfelt-Jacob disease (vCJD), and fears over the potential transmission of prions between humans by surgical instruments, reared its head. This concern was accompanied by changes to sterile supplies units within CMHT and as a cost-saving measure, the subsequent loss of the MREH Theatre Sterile Supplies Unit. The removal of surgical instrument sterilisation to a larger off-site CSSD was followed by increasing concerns at MREH about damaged instruments and high replacement costs, and this together with the vCJD fears led to the rise of the disposable surgical instrument. For over 150 years a relatively small number of long-established surgical instrument manufacturers had been the traditional suppliers of re-usable instruments for ophthalmic use. These were expensive to purchase, cared for carefully in-house, repaired when necessary and strictly supervised by senior ophthalmic theatre sisters. Now, with elements of that supervision removed, surgeons were increasingly frustrated by instrument failures. In the early 2000s, low-cost disposable instruments, manufactured largely in the Far East, were becoming available and a succession was trialled. They were initially crude and with poor quality control, with resultant stress and dissatisfaction amongst the surgeons, but incrementally quality improved and price reduced so that several ophthalmic surgical procedures are now performed entirely using disposable instruments, and all outpatient clinic procedures are thus equipped, using instruments virtually indistinguishable in quality from those bought 20 years previously, often at less than 5% of the cost.

The years around the turn of the century saw further consultant appointments: in 1998 Fiona Spencer was appointed with a special interest in glaucoma. After training in Glasgow she had studied glaucoma with Steve Vernon in Nottingham and Paul Roux in Pretoria. In addition to a busy clinical practice she would go on to lead postgraduate training in the Division and the Deanery for several years, and to play a major part in College educational activities. Paul Bishop, an MREH trainee, had occupied a Wellcome Research Fellowship examining vitreous ultrastructure and also in 1998 was appointed Honorary Consultant Ophthalmologist with a special interest in medical retina. In 1999, Ahmed Sadiq was appointed after training in Nottingham, to join Brian Leatherbarrow in oculoplastic surgery. Arun Brahma, an MREH trainee who had undergone corneal fellowships in Manchester with Alan Ridgway and in Dundee with Charles McGhee, was appointed in the millennium and the following year would open the Refractive Surgery Suite at MREH. In 2001 Alan Ridgway retired having seen both corneal and paediatric ophthalmic surgery develop under his influence. His departure was rightly marked by a Festschrift. Paediatric ophthalmology was reinforced by the appointment of Sus Biswas in 2002, an MREH trainee with fellowship experience with David Taylor and others at Great Ormond Street. Also in 2002, Saj Ataullah joined the orbital and oculoplastic team having trained at MREH, and Cecilia Fenerty joined the glaucoma team from Liverpool.

During the early years of the twenty-first century, there was considerable political

Steve Charles, Consultant
Ophthalmic Surgeon
1997–

focus on the amount of work performed by doctors, and a few high-profile news stories followed a consultant or two driving to his private clinic when he should have been in his NHS hospital, or enjoying a round of golf when not on leave. A scandal had apparently been unearthed; ergo, hospital consultants were greedy and lazy and should be brought to heel. The tabloids were furious, and the Government forced the introduction of a new consultant contract in 2003, which was an hours-based method intended to detail where an individual should be at any time during the working week. Despite this being declared by many consultants as a contract not for professionals, but for tradesmen, one step short of clocking in and out, the great majority signed up to it because for the first time since 1948 it provided what most considered to be adequate remuneration for their NHS time. Contracts were signed at MREH, job plans were negotiated and recorded and lo, it came to pass that most consultants had actually been working substantially more hours than they had previously been paid for and, these hours now being mandatorily identified, were now more often paid 12 PAs than a standard full-time 10 PAs (no more than 12 being payable no matter what hours were worked over 48 per week). There had been "no efficiency gains" from the new contract, consultants were "working no harder than before" etc. The new contract had been "a complete waste of money". The tabloids were furious...

In 2003 a new method of glaucoma referral and monitoring was introduced at MREH, led by recently appointed consultant Cecilia Fenerty. Trained in ophthalmology at the St. Paul's Eye Hospital in Liverpool and MREH, she had undertaken a glaucoma fellowship with Peng Khaw at Moorfields and had been appointed in 2002 with a host of innovative ideas for service development which has characterised her tenure as

Fiona Spencer,
Consultant Ophthalmic
Surgeon 1998–

Ahmed Sadiq, Consultant
Ophthalmic Surgeon 1999–

Arun Brahma, Consultant
Ophthalmic Surgeon 2000–

Sus Biswas, Consultant Ophthalmic
Surgeon 2002–

Saj Ataullah, Consultant Ophthalmic
Surgeon 2002–

Cecilia Fenerty, Consultant Ophthalmic
Surgeon 2002–

consultant. The Optician-led Glaucoma Assessment (OLGA) scheme had new glaucoma referrals seen by trained MREH optometrists with special expertise in glaucoma
(later recognised by a diploma), and in due course they also took on the continued
monitoring of those with stable controlled glaucoma and ocular hypertension. This
was one of several novel models of glaucoma care tried throughout the UK, but this
method in particular has become popular and widespread. In tandem with OLGA
was developed the Glaucoma Referral Refinement Scheme: interested optometrists
throughout Greater Manchester were invited to undergo further training in glaucoma
initial assessment, and to streamline referrals to MREH consultants with a proforma
including standardised information including proper optic disc assessment and field
analysis. This permitted more accurate assessment for prioritisation which had become
necessary in the context of (what was by now) virtually universal intraocular pressure
measurement by community optometrists, and very frequent asymptomatic visual
field screening; referral numbers with suspected glaucoma had enormously increased
and methods to streamline care were clearly necessary. The false-positive referral rate
was reduced by 40%. Later developments in glaucoma management were to increase
this pressure further.

Paulo Stanga, Consultant
Ophthalmic Surgeon
2003- and Professor in
Ophthalmology & Retinal
Regeneration 2010–

In 2003 Chris Dodd retired having worked at MREH for well over 30 years. He had
led the development of community orthoptics in Manchester, and had been the first to
introduce vitrectomy to MREH, for some years practising single-handed in this area;
by the time he left there were 5 vitreoretinal surgeons providing a regional service. His
replacement was Paulo Stanga. A graduate of Buenos Aires who undertook ophthalmological training there, he also undertook a series of research, retinal and vitreoretinal

fellowships including Cornell, New York with Harvey Lincoff, Moorfields with Alan Bird, and in Liverpool with David Wong. A strong academic interest in the development of innovative imaging techniques, including the clinical introduction of optical coherence tomography to the UK, has been reflected in the wide range of cameras now available at MREH. Other major projects include research into pattern-scan argon laser treatment for retinal disease, and the use of a digital epiretinal prosthetic implant for those with very poor vision. Stanga's strong research profile has now been recognised with a personal chair.

In 2006 Professor David Mcleod retired. He had spent 18 years at MREH, and during his tenure had transformed it in several ways. Postgraduate training had been enormously improved, working practices had been modernised; the period, not least because of his presence and influence, had seen sub-specialty expertise both broaden and deepen; he had inaugurated in 1995 the world's first MSc Course in Ophthalmology and Vision Science, which continues to be popular especially amongst doctors, optometrists and orthoptists; and he had re-inaugurated a University Department and strengthened ophthalmic research in Manchester. He had brought with him as Senior Lecturer Dr Mike Boulton, cell biologist from the Institute of Ophthalmology, who built a strong laboratory team over a decade before departing to take the Chair of Optometry at Cardiff University. Dr John Flanagan, postgraduate optometrist with a strong visual field research background, joined the team for a time before appointment to a Chair in Toronto. Dr David Henson, renowned visual field researcher and inventor of the Henson field analyser, joined the team in 1996 from Cardiff and in due course attained a personal Chair. He has been a prolific researcher and publisher, particularly in the field of visual fields technology, and remains a stalwart of University ophthalmology in Manchester. His textbook *Visual Fields* is a standard for many courses. In the meantime, McLeod encouraged and supported local talent so that in particular, Paul Bishop and Graeme Black, researching into vitreous biochemistry and architecture, and ophthalmic genetics respectively, both attained Senior Wellcome Trust Research Fellow status (at one time the only two in UK ophthalmology, and the only Senior Wellcome Fellows in Manchester) and both have gone on to be professors at the University of Manchester. Bishop, appointed Consultant Ophthalmologist in 1998, is now Professor of Ophthalmology and Matrix Biology. His initial research interest was in the ultrastructural biochemistry of vitreous, but this has broadened, and spans laboratory science and clinical trials with a focus on age-related macular degeneration, diabetic retinopathy and vitreoretinal disorders. He is Academic Lead for the Hearing and Vision Research Centre at the University of Manchester, Co-Director of the Centre for Advanced Discovery and Experimental Therapeutics and Lead for Special Senses Research at Manchester Biomedical Research Centre. Black is now Professor of Genetics and Ophthalmology, was Director of the NIHR Biomedical Research Centre in Manchester 2009–12 and is now Director of the Manchester Institute of Human Development. His major research interest is in genetic disorders causing

David Henson, Professor of Ophthalmology & Vision Science 2002–

visual disability, and the characterisation of genes and proteins underlying inherited disorders such as anophthalmia, cataract and retinal degenerative disorders has substantially improved understanding of these diseases. His scientific team provides genetic testing for retinoblastoma and has developed a national genetic testing service for inherited retinal diseases.

The Clinical Lecturer system reintroduced by McLeod permitted trainees at MREH to take time out for academic research, and a string of doctorates resulted. Several hundred research papers were the result of the combined efforts of David McLeod and his research teams, and his departure was marked with a well-attended Festschrift. By the end of his tenure, owing to University reorganisation the Department of Ophthalmology had ceased to exist, such structures to be replaced by Schools and Research Themes, but this did not detract from the very strong position in which ophthalmic research in Manchester was left, and from which it has continued to build.

These academic developments were all undertaken in tandem with David McLeod's clinical work as an internationally renowned vitreoretinal surgeon. Originally training and working with his mentor Peter Leaver, retinal and VR surgery had been substantially developed under his direction, and he established around him in Manchester a strong team including Messrs Lavin, Turner, Charles and Stanga who provided a regional and supra-regional service which has been further expanded. The contributions of Professor David McLeod to MREH are difficult to exaggerate, and no attempt should be made to moderate them; he should be remembered as one of a small handful of MREH staff who will be considered essential landmarks in its history and development.

The last 6 or 7 years has witnessed startling developments in the field of vitreoretinal surgery. The field had already grown almost exponentially over the previous decade owing mainly to the demonstrable superiority over traditional methods of internal tamponade using silicone oils or gases including SF_6 and C_3F_8, but also with the development of new techniques including epiretinal peel for macular disease, and intraoperative retinal manipulation with perfluorocarbon liquids. To these have now been added vastly improved wide-angle operative microscopy systems, and narrow-gauge (23G and 25G) instrumentation which has shortened procedure times, virtually eliminated scleral suturing and enhanced post-operative recovery. These fine portals can now support excellent endo-illumination, forceps, picks and chandeliers to permit subtle retinal manipulation, and very high vitreous cutting rates (from 1,200 to 5,000 cpm) have facilitated safe peri-retinal vitrectomy. Internal limiting membrane peel has changed from experimental to routine surgery, retinal translocation and surgical removal of choroidal neovascular membranes have appeared, proliferative vitreoretinopathy is markedly reduced, and success rates for retinal reattachment have never been better. These new techniques have also contributed to a marked reduction in post-operative head positioning, previously the bane of the patient, sometimes for weeks,

Paul Bishop, Consultant Ophthalmologist 1998- and Professor of Ophthalmology & Matrix Biology 2006–

Graeme Black, Professor of Ophthalmology & Genetics 2002–

Fiona Carley, Consultant Ophthalmic Surgeon 2006–

Jane Ashworth, Consultant Paediatric Ophthalmologist 2007–

Anne Cook, Consultant Ophthalmic Surgeon 2007–

Niall Patton, Consultant Ophthalmic Surgeon 2008–

and thus inpatient beds for ophthalmology have reduced even further. Jules Gonin, if reincarnated, would be astonished and delighted.

In 2006 Fiona Carley was appointed corneal and anterior segment surgeon following the early retirement of Andrew Tullo. Trained at MREH, she underwent corneal fellowships both in Manchester and in Leeds. Initially appointed consultant in Oldham in 2003, she returned to MREH where she has taken over management of the Manchester Eye Bank. In 2007 Joan Noble retired and Jane Ashworth was appointed paediatric ophthalmologist, having undertaken fellowships in Manchester and Liverpool. She took over the North Manchester paediatric outreach service until it amalgamated with CMFT, and she now leads the Paediatric Uveitis Service in addition to subspecialist work on mucopolysaccharidoses. Anne Cook, MREH-trained, was appointed to make a team of 4 dealing with oculoplastic and orbital disease, and developed a subspecialist clinic for thyroid eye disease. Two new consultant posts were appointed in 2008: Niall Patton, trained in Edinburgh and at MREH, also undertook vitreoretinal surgical fellowships in Perth, Western Australia, and in Glasgow, Edinburgh and at Moorfields, and was appointed vitreoretinal surgeon; Saj Mahmood was appointed medical retina specialist after training at MREH and a clinical/research fellowship at Liverpool. He leads research into macular disease at MREH and is Clinical Lead of the Macular Treatment Centre. Mandagere Vishwanath, trained in Mysore followed by fellowships in paediatric ophthalmology at Great Ormond Street, and strabismus and neuro-ophthalmology in Liverpool and Manchester, was appointed in 2009 and has formed a neuro-ophthalmological unit with Alec Ansons and Dr Adam Zermansky, Honorary Consultant Neurologist. Bruno Zuberbuhler joined the team in 2009 to lead the outreach cataract service at Withington, but departed in 2012 to work at St. Thomas' Hospital.

Significant challenges have arisen for ocular pathology at MREH during the first decade of the twenty-first century. Our longstanding and highly respected Ocular Pathologist, Richard Bonshek, has contributed significantly to national improvements in the quality of ocular pathology (most of which, except in the largest centres, has been traditionally provided by neuro-pathologists) and in 1991 inaugurated (and for several years supervised) the National Ophthalmic Pathology External Quality Assurance (EQA) Scheme, establishing quality control nationwide in this area. These initiatives took place for a number of years in the context of a University Department of Pathology whose head did not recognise the need for ocular pathology as a separate sub-specialty even within the second-largest eye hospital in Europe. Manchester has also been disadvantaged in ocular pathology because of the geographical anomaly that permitted both Liverpool and Sheffield (smaller cities with much smaller eye departments, on either side of Manchester) to become NSCAG-funded centres for intraocular oncology. Notwithstanding the very large extraocular oncology service provided at MREH, the preferential funding acquired by Sheffield and Liverpool on the basis of intraocular cancer, has threatened the fragmentation of MREH-based ocular pathology. It was into this environment that in 2011 Dr Lucianne Irion was appointed Consultant Ocular Pathologist at MREH; she now works split-site between Manchester and Liverpool. The future of ocular pathology as a clinical service at MREH, this very large and busy eye hospital, seems, bizarrely, to be under threat in the face of clear evidence for its continuing requirement.

Three consultant appointments were made in 2010: Felipe Dhawahir-Scala qualified in Madrid but trained in England and undertook the MREH vitreoretinal surgical fellowship, bringing the VR team back up to 5 following the decision of Mike Lavin

Saj Mahmood, Consultant Ophthalmic Surgeon 2008–

Mandagere Vishwanath, Consultant Ophthalmologist 2009–

Felipe Dhawahir-Scala, Consultant Ophthalmic Surgeon 2010–

Tariq Aslam, Consultant Ophthalmologist 2010- and Professor of Vision Science and Interface Technologies

to discontinue VR surgery. He has also taken over the management of the urgency services at MREH and has substantially re-modelled patterns of care, with more consultant-delivered sessions, and enhanced training. Tariq Aslam graduated from Oxford and trained in ophthalmology at MREH and in Edinburgh. He was appointed with an interest in medical retina but has also become the NIHR Special Senses Research Lead for Ophthalmology, Greater Manchester. His work in innovative technology has earned him an Honorary Chair in Visual Science and Interface Technologies at Heriot-Watt University. Leon Au trained in Nottingham and at MREH including fellowships in cornea and glaucoma, and was appointed with a dual interest in both of these areas. He is pioneering minimally invasive glaucoma surgery and stenting. In 2011 Yvonne D'Souza returned to MREH to lead the diabetic eye service. For 25 years, Associate Specialist Lorna Young, working nominally with Mike Lavin but essentially autonomously, had led a diabetic eye service at MREH. During that time the service had been substantially improved, surveillance for retinopathy in the region had been transformed from ad hoc to automatic, communication between community optometrists and hospital ophthalmologists had been vigorously developed and more recently automated via a diabetic eye disease electronic patient record, and laser training and management had been enhanced and made adherent to the evidence base. Too much for one person at such a large hospital, it was necessary to appoint a consultant lead. Dr Young continued until her well-earned retirement in 2013. Miss D'Souza was trained at MREH and also underwent medical retina fellowships at Moorfields and the Western Eye Hospital. Tomas Cudrnak from Slovakia also joined the medical retinal team in 2011 but departed for pastures new in 2012. The most recent consultant appointments at MREH are: Dan Nolan (2012, oculoplastics); Eleni Nikita (2014, glaucoma);

Leon Au, Consultant Ophthalmic Surgeon 2010–

Yvonne D'Souza, Consultant Medical Ophthalmologist 2011–

Dan Nolan, Consultant Ophthalmic Surgeon 2012–

Eleni Nikita, Consultant Ophthalmic Surgeon 2014–

Konstantinos Balaskas (2014, medical retina); and Timothy de Klerk (2014, cataract services). In early 2014 there is a likelihood that up to 5 more new consultants may be in post within the year.

It is interesting to observe the almost exponential growth in ophthalmic consultant numbers at MREH in the last two decades, reflecting the increasing expectation of senior expertise, the narrowing of that expertise, the reducing input of junior doctors into routine care, and the political pressure for a consultant-delivered rather than a consultant-led system. In 1970 there were 6 consultants at MREH; during the following decade, 6 were appointed, but five left, so that in 1980 there were still only 7 in post; in the 1980s, only 4 were appointed and two left; in the 1990s however, there were 11 new consultants but only two left (leaving 16); in 2000–2009, 13 were appointed and 5 left (leaving 24); and from 2010 to date, 10 have been appointed and 2 have left, giving a current senior medical staff of 32 consultant ophthalmologists at MREH, together with two consultant ocular pathologists, one consultant neurologist and one consultant geneticist.

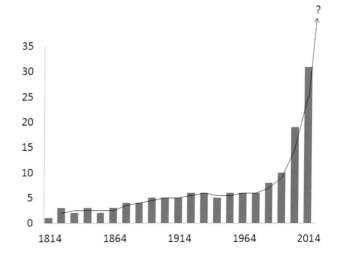

The number of senior ophthalmologists (honorary surgeons until 1948, consultants thereafter) at MREH so far during its 200 years' existence

During the past 20 years one feature of ophthalmic care is striking in a large teaching hospital such as MREH: the rise of subspecialisation and the disappearance of the generalist. This change has occurred in tandem with increasing expectations of speed of access, management by senior staff, and high-quality outcomes. In such a climate of rapid medical developments, the death of the generalist (at consultant level) was inevitable, and successive consultant retirements have been followed by the appointment of those with narrower (but hopefully higher) expertise, in larger numbers. A necessary accompaniment to subspecialisation (and sometimes an apparent barrier to efficient care which is poorly understood by patients, general practitioners and politicians alike) is the increasing time needed for investigation, planning and medical care when working at such high levels of skill and patient expectation. A further development is the increasing need for multi-consultant input into the care of a single patient with either complex or rare disease, in which this Hospital has particular strengths. The paradox is that higher-quality care and enhanced outcomes come at the price of longer pathways, increased cost, and often more visits for an individual patient. The need to maintain adequate communication in multi-specialist care has seen the rise of the multidisciplinary team meeting. At the end of this spectrum is the ultra-specialist combined consultant clinic which can in practice only occur at large hospital complexes but which of necessity provides supra-regional care: paediatric ophthalmic genetics; paediatric uveitis & rheumatology; complex macular disease; thyroid eye disease, Behçet's disease etc. The wide variety of subspecialist and ultra-specialist clinics now available at MREH is discussed in the final chapter.

The rise of subspecialisation has been naturally accompanied by increasing numbers of ophthalmic trainees who wish to complete their postgraduate education by an in-depth clinical and/or research fellowship, and MREH now offers such posts, usually for one year, in all areas of its expertise (there being usually 16–18 fellows in post at one time). All major teaching centres such as MREH have seen a gradual increase in the proportion of clinical care provided by fellows under consultant supervision, in tandem with the gradual conversion of junior training from clinical apprenticeship to an increasingly structured and supervised pattern. An ageing ex-generalist such as this author foresees a degree of anti-educationalist reaction in due course which may reintroduce a better balance in postgraduate education than is currently permitted by piecemeal subspecialty training. Nevertheless, subspecialism is here to stay and further develop, forcing trainees into narrower career choices at an earlier stage.

In 2011 the Conservative Government of David Cameron introduced the Health and Social Care Bill, which in 2013 dissolved Primary Care Trusts and introduced Clinical Commissioning groups (CCGs), also permitting healthcare to be purchased from "Any Qualified Provider". Previous experience nationally has taught us that such profit-making alternative providers attempt to attract straightforward, high-revenue surgical cases while discouraging the multifactorial, the complex, the comorbid, the infirm, and the time-consuming, leaving all of these unprofitable patients (and also often leaving their postoperative complications, including all emergencies) to the local eye hospitals. The contractual and revenue implications of these new arrangements for large hospitals such as MREH remain to be seen over the succeeding years, but this Hospital has acquired, by two centuries of hard work and demonstrable quality, a long-standing informal "preferred provider" status amongst patients in Greater Manchester and well beyond; if the CCGs truly place the patient at the heart of their own care, as claimed in the Act, then the Manchester Royal Eye Hospital has nothing to fear.

CHAPTER ELEVEN

A New Eye Hospital for the Twenty-first Century

T HE CLOCK MARKING TIME on the deterioration of NHS building stock started
ticking in July 1948; until that date the boards of management who had raised
money for, and diligently cared for their source of pride, their own local hospital,
ensured as far as possible that maintenance work was budgeted for and carried out

The Manchester Royal
Eye Hospital on Oxford
Road in 2002, after
117 years of service
(Courtesy of Mr AB Tullo)

regularly. When all such stock was nationalised and the reality of central government finance had become so glaringly obvious, routine maintenance at the level previously provided, gradually petered out to be replaced by the antithesis of airline-industry attitudes, and probably at greater cost: wait until it breaks or fails, and then replace it, often after a substantial delay. Many of the hospital buildings inherited by the NHS were Victorian or pre-Victorian, and often well-built, but as medicine developed and time eroded both fabric and relevance, they became less and less well-suited to their tasks. The Manchester Royal Eye Hospital buildings were perfect examples: the main building on Oxford Road was built before the advent of electricity, lifts, central heating, circulating hot water, ventilation or fire safety; all these had been installed piecemeal over decades, sometimes incorporating asbestos, and yet the pattern of patient care had changed beyond recognition and the design and function of the building was no longer adequate. The outpatient department on Nelson Street, up-to-the-minute in 1937, had also been built without a lift, had been altered internally several times, and had many internal steps, hampering wheeled movement. Lister House had been built as domestic accommodation in the 1880s, and was by the 1980s almost unfit for human habitation. By the 1990s, back in the main building, rotten window-frames (unpainted for 20–30 years) needed replacement, but only handmade at £2,500 each (being on the frontage of a grade-II listed building); perennially leaking roofs required reconstruction; rusting, unsafe ugly fire-escapes were replaced by bright, clean, new, galvanised, safe ugly fire-escapes. The Victorian interior style, with its oak dados, broad open staircases and corridors, was destroyed by the building of compartmentalised internal fire-protection walls to meet new standards. Air supply units for operating theatres were intermittently condemned and then repaired. The two lifts (the first installed in 1920) broke down regularly. The basement seminar rooms, wet lab and corridors were characterised by blistering, damp walls and a characteristic odour. Eventually the main building was allocated a "schedule D" building quality, indicating very poor, one step away from "E" (uninhabitable).

The Conservative Government of John Major was aware that the NHS buildings stock was crumbling more with each passing year, and knew that all previous governments since 1948 had failed to find adequate capital for a rolling programme of replacement, because the revenue consequences of nationalised healthcare had become a shocking burden. Major was of the view that Government should not directly fund the massive rebuilding process necessary, being unable to afford it from the current account, and unwilling to finance it from national debt. The Private Finance Initiative scheme was therefore introduced, permitting private investment into public building contracts, structured so as to provide high initiatives for those investors. There was no shortage of interested parties, and Alistair Darling, shadow Treasury spokesman, was not alone in predicting at the time that "apparent savings now could be countered by the formidable commitment on revenue expenditure in years to come". Richard Smith, Editor of the British Medical Journal, was more forthright in his translation of PFI as "Perfidious

Financial Idiocy". Nevertheless, a Health Authority wishing to rebuild a hospital in the 1990s had no real choice but to use the PFI as its method of finance.

In 1995 the Central Manchester Healthcare Trust (as it then was) undertook a comprehensive survey of estates, and found that there was a major problem at MREH. It also concluded that the repair of existing MREH buildings during continued usage would prove too costly and disruptive, and that for MREH, either a complete move, or fragmentation would be necessary. The consultant body were in uproar, opining that the current location of MREH was well-known, prominent and accessible, and that extension and repair (as had been proposed by the Trust as recently as 1991) was much preferable. That argument was not only lost, but it became felt by many internally that the retention of MREH as a self-contained entity within CMHT was a low priority for both Trust and purchasers, and therefore a battle for survival.

The Manchester Royal Eye Hospital in the 1960s had required up to 214 beds to deal with surgical and non-surgical admissions. However, developments in ophthalmology had progressively reduced this need. The move from intracapsular to extracapsular cataract surgery, with its accompanying developments in microscopic surgery and more reliable, fine suturing, had progressively reduced inpatient stays, from an average of 5 days or more for cataract surgery in the 1980s for instance, to overnight stay in the early 1990s, and by the mid-1990s, when phacoemulsification had become the norm, it was increasingly accepted that daycase surgery was safe for routine cases. Glaucoma surgery inpatient stays followed the trend, more cautiously but also progressively decreasing. By this time the routine admission of blunt ocular injuries had also ceased, penetrating injuries were becoming very uncommon because of better safety when driving and at work, and advancing retinal surgery techniques had also reduced the need for prolonged post-operative positioning. Gradually, led by these medical developments but encouraged further by management pressure, bed numbers were reduced to save costs. The Hospital was gradually and substantially reconfigured to reflect these developments (within the constraints of Victorian architecture which left every internal wall weight-bearing). The whole of the 4th floor was reconfigured to provide a bespoke private patient consulting suite and inpatient facilities, and a 5th operating theatre was built together with daycase facilities, the whole being known as the Manchester Cataract Centre, and later the Manchester Centre for Vision. Also moved to the fourth floor was the children's ward. The orthoptic department underwent considerable extension and redesign, incorporating for the first time, a Vision Science Centre specifically for electrophysiology and related investigation. The staff canteen and nursing space behind was closed and refurbished as a day-case unit, providing chairs for surgery and permitting the closure of wards. Ward C4 was refurbished to provide the University Department of Ophthalmology, the Hospital library, a junior mess and resident on-call room, the whole being occupied in 1995. This permitted the vacation of Lister House which was rapidly demolished to provide further car parking. The main dining room was closed and refurbished as the David

Little Clinic, a preadmission service including biometry which facilitated daycase surgery, in particular cataract surgery. Dining facilities re-opened on the first floor, occupying a vacated ward. Finally a major reconfiguration and amalgamation of the only remaining adult wards, B1 and B2, took place, being re-opened as the Nightingale Suite, the only adult inpatient facility at MREH, providing 26 beds to support the then 18 consultants who continued to provide tertiary and quaternary surgical and medical ophthalmology referred from a wide geographical area.

In the meantime, the number of outpatient appointments continued to increase so that there was inadequate consulting room accommodation. Each closed ward had been adapted to a new function, sometimes with considerable refurbishment. Ward C3 (previously the children's ward) had become the Hardy-Heywood Suite, a research clinic also dealing with macular cases. Ward B3 became an extension to the retinal unit. Ward C1 was converted to clerical space. By the end of the 1990s, in addition to a full Nelson Street outpatient department, outpatients were also being seen in a further 5 separate outpatient clinical areas within the main building, each with its own reception and clerical support. The staff of Manchester Royal Eye Hospital had achieved what was humanly possible within buildings designed for a very different style of medicine and nursing, and could go no further. What remained was as efficient as possible (but still costly and inefficient), as "joined-up" as possible (but fragmented, and still divided by a road between the two buildings) and as pleasant an environment as possible (but inside buildings disintegrating from old age).

Running parallel with the negotiations on the future of ophthalmology in Manchester were discussions both national and local, about children's eye services. In 1994 the Royal College of Ophthalmologists, together with the British Paediatric Association, published a report on *Ophthalmic Services for Children*, which called for a greater degree of separation for children in outpatient departments. In Manchester a simultaneous discussion was underway about the organisation of children's medicine in general. Manchester at that time had 4 hospitals for children: Booth Hall Hospital, Royal Manchester Children's Hospital at Pendlebury, St. Mary's Hospital and the Duchess of York Hospital, together with specialised children's services being provided in at least 5 others, including MREH. This perceived "fragmentation" of services was considered unsuitable for the future, and amalgamation of hospitals into a single large paediatric centre was proposed, with a preference for a site adjacent to, or integrated with, one of the three main university hospital campuses in central or south Manchester, or Salford. The resultant Manchester report however, completely forgot to consider ophthalmic services, which were only added to the equation after reasonable protests from MREH staff. It was at this stage, in 1996, that this author took on the role as MREH design lead during the marathon leading to a new hospital, a process which would take 13 long years.

In 1997 MREH produced its *Healthcare in Partnership: Ophthalmic Service Group Report*, in response to proposals for a new central Manchester hospital build. The

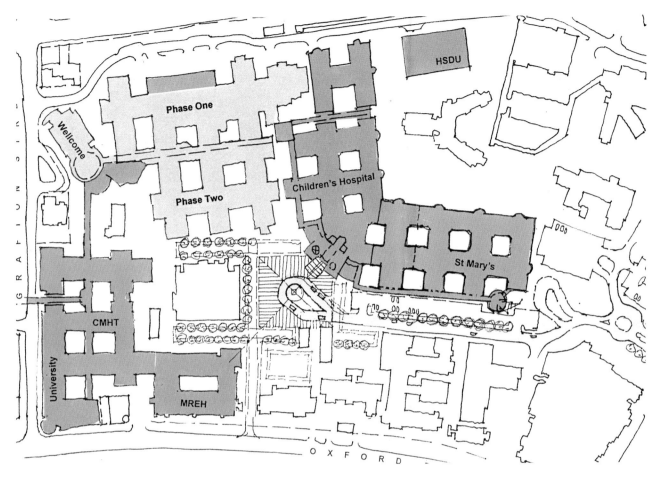

Strategic Outline Case
Plan B (one of two) 1998

report was an attempt firstly to justify the continued existence of a single ophthalmic centre within the city (a feeling of déjà vu here), and secondly to make clear to those intent on the managerial tidiness of cross-specialty integrated services including operating theatres, elective treatment centre, outpatient and children's services, that internal integration within ophthalmology, its various sub-specialties and investigative areas, was of far greater practical importance for patients than the efficient-sounding but potentially destructive suggestions that ophthalmology might become fragmented within all-specialty areas. This proved to be MREH's hardest battle in the 1990s, a battle for existence which had to be fought on several occasions during a very disturbing few years for the Hospital.

The Central Manchester Healthcare Trust and Manchester Health Authority had now reached the conclusion that only a substantial hospital rebuild of the central hospitals could achieve the desired ends, and the multi-stage PFI process began. The first stage was to prove to Government that the project was clinically needed and basically sound, via the *Strategic Outline Case*, which was put together in 1997. A key feature of the political control of costs during PFI processes was the stipulation that every SOC had to reflect current needs and no more (notwithstanding any evidence of inexorable increases in the need for staff and space up to that point). One 2014 problem resulting from that is the inability to identify adequate working space for 31 consultants, their teams and support staff, when the SOC only permitted a claim for office and consulting space for 14. This ban on predictions of future need left MREH fighting to gain space (the need for which seemed entirely predictable and which has proven correct) whilst being actively curtailed by the limitations of the process. By the SOC stage a decision had been made by the Secretary of State that a new children's hospital, amalgamating all Manchester children's hospital services, would be sited in central Manchester, and the SOC was therefore a combined document issued by both the Central Manchester and the Manchester Children's Hospitals NHS Trusts. Interestingly both geographic options provided by the SOC left MREH where it was, with plans to extend, redevelop, and connect to an enlarged MRI. The SOC was accepted by the Secretary of State, following which the *Outline Business Case* (a very detailed statement of needs for space, clinical liaison and configuration to be supplied to potential PFI consortia) was begun.

At the commencement of the OBC process, very vigorous steps were taken by the MREH Lead and colleagues to force adequate space requirement for MREH into the process. The Hospital had been subjected at the SOC stage to an inexpert assessment of future space requirement by an external consultancy acting without internal consultation. The old MREH on Oxford Road provided, together with its Nelson Street Outpatient Department (after the closure of Lister House), 7,500 sqm of space, and as a result of the space survey a mere 6,750 was proposed for a new build going 40 years into the future, despite clear evidence of progressively increasing workload and inventive re-use of space up to that point. Ongoing space negotiations became protracted, sometimes combative and not entirely successful. The Department of Health's own *Hospital Building Notes* (HBN: detailed recommendations for space requirement in clinical areas including ophthalmology) became a powerful tool in ensuring that individual rooms sizes and defined patient care areas provided adequate space. The MREH team was also inventive in ensuring that any HBN-identified rooms were retained even though known to be unnecessary for ophthalmic use; that strategy has proved crucial as such space has been re-designated after occupancy.

In September 1999 the OBC was submitted, and included three options, one of which was the "Do Minimum" incorporating the retention and refurbishment of the Victorian buildings of both MREH and MRI. The "Integrated Service Option" reconfigured MRI and brought the Children's Hospital on site, but left MREH to decay. The "Enhanced Strategic Option" provided MREH with an entirely new, freestanding build on Nelson Street, which was its own preference. An economic appraisal of the three options for MREH was performed, showing a clear preference for a new build. Hopes were high.

It was organisationally necessary for the two Trusts (CMHT and Children's) undertaking the PFI process to merge, to prevent the process from becoming too complex. That merger was not entirely amicable, the Children's Trust leaders being concerned that their needs would be subsumed within a much larger organisation. Nevertheless after a troublesome pregnancy the laboriously named chimera was born in April 2001: Central Manchester and Manchester Children's University Hospitals NHS Trust. The hard negotiating of the real PFI process could now begin.

The crucial document which began the PFI process proper was the *Final Intention to Negotiate*; a detailed list of space, technology and adjacency requirements, available to bidders for the process. Even at this late stage, MREH representatives were fighting to retain space and facilities which had been removed from the specification. The main battle was over the number of outpatient consulting rooms (a battle which was lost to the tune of 8 rooms, to our current detriment) but also included the very strong wish to retain a separate MREH postgraduate library, which was eventually won after a staff petition, only to be lost again at the last hurdle for the most prosaic of reasons: the PFI costs were dependent upon the assumption that by the date of planned occupancy (2007) the patient care process would be electronic, therefore there would be no paper clinical records, and therefore firstly no need for notes storage (at that time 3,600 sqm for the Trust, storing 1.4M records), and no need for on-site clerical staff. All clinicians within MREH regarded this assumption with high suspicion, describing it in written argument at the time as "short-sighted and foolhardy", and fought repeatedly against it, to no effect. In 2003, the Department of Health instructed Trusts that all future EPRs were required to be compatible with its forthcoming all-encompassing healthcare IT system, *Connecting for Health* which was in the process of development; this edict essentially hamstrung any local attempts to develop new EPRs in time for occupancy. In due course, plans for that NHS IT scheme were to collapse spectacularly, at enormous cost and having delayed bottom-up IT development by several years. Late in the new hospitals construction process it was acknowledged that paper records would be very much still in existence after occupancy (and they remain so still, over 4 years later), and the Trust arranged for all clinical notes to be stored in a warehouse in Gorton, whence they are now ferried back and forth by lorry for outpatient clinics. A few months before the planned move, MREH was informed that space for clerical teams (compulsorily omitted from the design) was necessary after all, and MREH was instructed to find that working space (for 43 staff) somewhere within the design. Several hard-fought-for rooms were therefore lost to clerical usage, including the MREH library, the content of which was merged into the Central Trust library.

But we return to 2000. Applications were invited for consortia to bid for the PFI scheme, and a short-listing process identified three preferred bidders, which would then compete over a year-long selection process. This required all design teams, including ours from MREH, to hold detailed meetings separately with all three bidders so that they were given enough information to submit final bids.

Any protracted process such as this will be complicated by events running

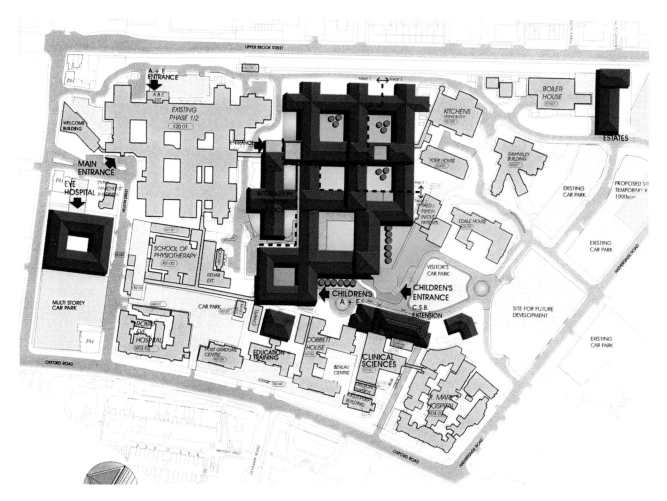

concurrently. In 2000 the Government published *Action on Cataracts,* demanding reduced waiting times for cataract surgery, and steps were required to establish better high-throughput surgical services for cataract, amending the PFI design process. In 2001 the *National Beds Enquiry* required a massive data collection process to support the necessary provision of inpatient facilities for all areas, and MREH had to fight to defend beds for ophthalmology. In 2002, partly as a result of Action on Cataracts, directly Government-funded *Diagnostic & Treatment Centres* (DTCs) were contracted to be built around the UK to create competition with local NHS surgical (including eye) units, and such a centre was planned for South Manchester on the site of Withington Hospital, to open in 2004 (the contrast with the lengthy PFI process for NHS rebuilding could not have been more stark). The management team at MREH were contacted by the leaders of the DTC project, who requested assistance with the design of an ophthalmic treatment suite (which might in due course provide facilities for another provider to compete directly with MREH). A strategy of cooperation was adopted by MREH, and the DTC ophthalmic treatment unit was made practicable by the input of MREH staff. In June 2002 MREH made a formal bid for the cataract surgery component of the DTC and in due course was appointed provider. The creation of a single operating theatre with supporting outpatient and day-case facilities at the DTC (named the Withington Community Hospital) led to the removal of one of the 6 theatres from the PFI plans for the reconstructed MREH.

In March 2002 a detailed scoring process appointed the consortium named *Catalyst* as the successful PFI provider. This group comprised Bovis as builders, Charterhouse Project Equity Investment Ltd as financers, Sodexho as services provider, and Anshen Dyer as architects. Final terse negotiations on necessary clinical space at the 1:200 scale were partly successful (as witnessed now by the ground-floor outpatient rooms which were created out of redundant space within the enormous entrance atrium of the new hospital). Having fixed the space requirement, the build commenced in 2005, while simultaneously a design process at the 1:50 scale was undertaken, finalising all details of room function and departmental layout. The complexity of the design process over such a huge site, together with building delays, set back the planned opening until mid-2009. An MREH Steering Group made all arrangements for changes in service delivery and commissioning teams made other preparations for the move into the new Hospital.

The foundations of the new Manchester Royal Eye Hospital are laid, 2005

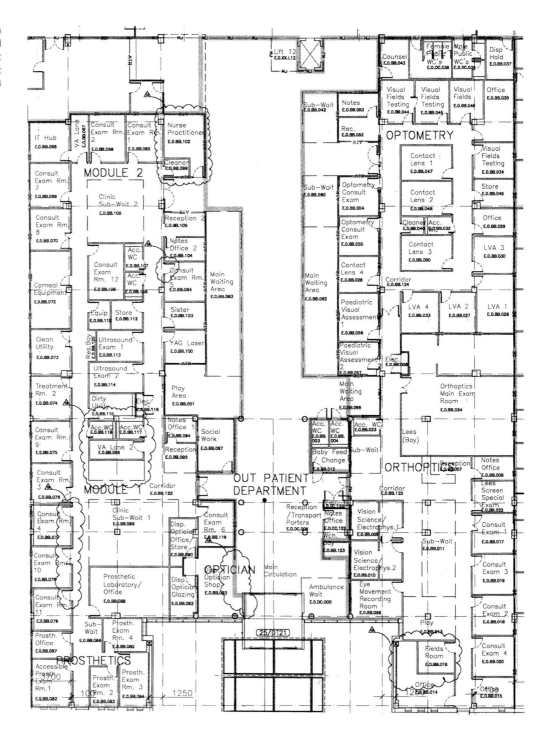

The 1:200 plan for the ground floor outpatient department, front half 2004

It was in 2006–7 that the enormous implications of the newly successful treatments of age-related macular degeneration began to impinge upon plans for the new hospital. A Macular Treatment Centre was proposed. After abortive attempts to have it housed firstly in the smallest of the six ground floor outpatient clinic modules (rejected because other outpatient clinics could not then be accommodated) and secondly within unused ("shelled") ground floor space adjacent to that clinic (rejected on the grounds of unaffordable cost), the first-floor preadmission clinic, adjacent to day-case unit and operating theatres, was invaded for this purpose. In due course, in 2012 the preadmission clinic moved into reclaimed ward space, leaving the entire first-floor clinic for MTC purposes.

It is difficult to remember precisely when it was revealed, after repeated questioning by MREH staff, that the PFI process was intended to provide new buildings, but not any equipment to house within them. This jaw-dropping moment was accompanied by an image of a splendid, clean, bright and completely empty new hospital. A rigorous appraisal of current MREH furnishings and equipment was therefore undertaken, concreting the suspicions that very little of the clinic examination equipment would be fit for purpose if transferred, and essentially none of the furnishings in most departments. The overall budgetary shortfall for Trust equipment was in excess of £20M, and henceforth a charitable appeal was commenced. The MREH team calculated that £5M would be required to equip itself properly; the Trust demanded that this sum be reduced to £3.5M, which internally was believed unachievable. After prolonged negotiation, CMHT agreed that MREH was permitted to add its £750,000 positive revenue

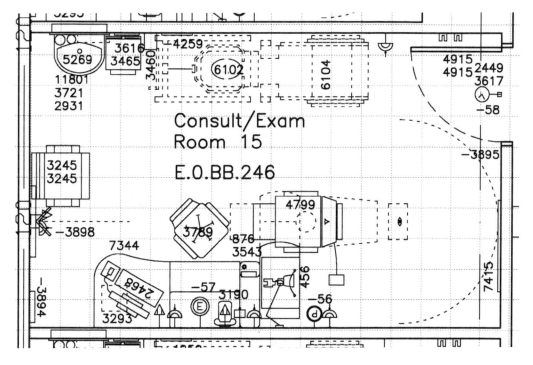

A typical 1:50 design plan; an outpatient consulting room 2005

balance for the previous financial year (such balances usually being reclaimed into the central Trust budget), to make up the shortfall.

A 1:50 planning process for a large hospital is an immensely protracted and complex process. Every mains point, every light switch, every telephone, intranet and ethernet socket, every basin have to be positioned conveniently but to permit safe movement about furniture when introduced. Every floor surface must be ratified for weight-bearing, durability and slip-resistance. Every room must have temperature range minima and maxima to inform the air conditioning plant, and standards of wall sound-proofing are dependent upon function. The ambient lighting range for rooms of variable function has to be provided by the newly designed dimmable fluorescent strips, which have to be tested and improved. A choice of outpatient examination consoles and slit-lamp modules have to be tried, tested and ordered, as does the portable equipment. Each powered patient chair has to be positioned to permit correct distance to LogMAR chart of choice, to

The author, New MREH Clinical Design Lead, together with Patrick Kershaw, MREH Planner, atop the new building 2008

The frontage of the new Manchester Royal Eye Hospital after opening, 2009

A NEW EYE HOSPITAL FOR THE TWENTY-FIRST CENTURY

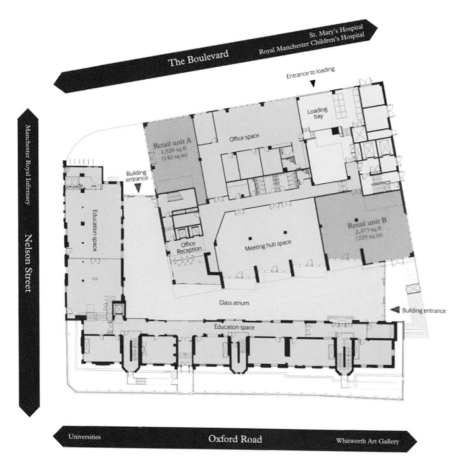

The Boulevard — St. Mary's Hospital — Royal Manchester Children's Hospital

Entrance to loading

Loading bay

Office space

Retail unit A
1,528 sq ft
(142 sq m)

Building entrance

Manchester Royal Infirmary

Nelson Street

Education space

Office Reception

Meeting hub space

Retail unit B
2,373 sq ft
(220 sq m)

Glass atrium

Building entrance

Education space

Universities — Oxford Road — Whitworth Art Gallery

Plans for the ground floor of the new Citylabs building, incorporating the frontages of the old MREH on Oxford Road and Nelson Street. The buildings are linked by an open atrium

permit reclination whilst still allowing indirect ophthalmoscopy through an arc behind, to permit wheelchair access, and the room must still provide space for accompanying persons, and some also for trolley access. The colour palette for hospital-themed decoration must be chosen. The signage for every entrance, every corridor, every lift lobby, every department and every door must be dictated, perused, and errors corrected. All furniture and equipment must be selected and ordered. There are over 300 distinct rooms or spaces within the new MREH. Every aspect must be *Disability Discrimination Act*-compliant and meet accepted (but occasionally changing) standards of fire safety, personnel health and safety, and security. When this author looks back today from a safe distance, and peruses the 11 lever-arch files representing the personal input required during the hospitals design process, one wonders quite how the MREH team managed to achieve what has been done.

The long-awaited move took place in August 2009; the old Hospital building on Oxford Road had been used for 124 years, and was professional (and sometimes literal) home for so many staff, yet had become unfit for purpose many years previously. It was vacated with a mixture of regret and affection for the old, and anticipation of the new. The old outpatient department in contrast, used for 72 years, held few attractions and was left by most without a backward glance. It was rapidly demolished to extend the Trust car parks.

The new Manchester Royal Eye Hospital was officially opened by Her Majesty The Queen on March 23rd 2012. Both she and the Duke of Edinburgh met many members of staff while passing through the atrium, after which the official opening took place on a dais erected outside the main entrance. A commemorative plaque marks the event and stands proud within the Hospital.

Developments in medical technology and healthcare do not wait politely while new hospitals are designed and built; in fact they accelerate remorselessly, and a process lasting for nearly 13 years has seen substantial changes within the field of ophthalmology, arguably more than in any comparative period in ophthalmological history. The most important of these has been the appearance of anti-VEGF monoclonal antibody treatment for wet age-related macular degeneration, transforming the prognosis for the commonest cause of vision impairment in the Western world. The technique has necessitated massive increases in patient throughput, substantially increased need for ophthalmic imaging, and an intraocular injection "factory", all put together as a Macular Treatment Centre and squeezed into existing space. The elderly are living longer, and their associated eye diseases including the above, glaucoma, cataract and diabetes, also require more time and space. The cumbersome and restrictive format of the PFI process permitted only minor on-track modifications, and its duration has allowed significant potential amendments to pass frustratingly by. For future developments, should it be possible, the message is clear: a much leaner process, and much more bottom-up early involvement, would save both time and money, leading to more appropriate, timely and durable facilities.

The new MREH, embedded within a group of new hospitals, would have been a rather different entity had design been led by its users. However, the PFI project was amongst the largest ever undertaken in the UK and MREH was only one of four hospitals involved in that. In retrospect the MREH team was successful firstly in preserving MREH as a separately identifiable Hospital; in ensuring that its operating theatres were reserved as ophthalmic and located adjacent to its own ward and day-case unit (rather than being removed into a multi-specialty elective treatment centre) and in ensuring that clinical space was, as far as possible, adaptable to multi-purpose usage within the specialty of ophthalmology. A reasonable period of complacent satisfaction with surroundings would seem to have been in order. Yet, a mere four years after occupancy a strong feeling of *déjà vu* again appears; many rooms have already been re-designated, new senior staff share several to an office, new clinical processes are sometimes accommodated piecemeal, waiting list initiative clinics are regularly held at weekends and in evenings, and discussions are afoot to increase inadequate outpatient consulting space, not by a shed in the back yard as in 1838, or by an ex-army barrack hut as in 1920, but by portakabins. It seems that the creation of the perfect Manchester Royal Eye Hospital is still an ongoing project.

The frontage of the old Eye Hospital now takes on a new lease of life, via a rebuilding project led by Bruntwood. A grade-II listed building, the Oxford Road and Nelson Street façades are preserved, the remainder having been demolished to permit the creation of a new multi-functional building incorporating biomedical research facilities, educational and office space, named Citylabs (with funding from the European Regional Development Fund). The building is due for completion in the summer of 2014, and occupiers will include the Manchester College, ICON Development

Citylabs during construction, 2013 showing the retained frontage of MREH

Solutions (specialising in early drug development), TRUSTECH (the Norwest NHS Innovation Service, dealing mainly with innovative products), relocated Trust functions including the Charities Office, and others. The new building combines tradition with modernity, and to passers-by will continue to bear witness to its previous manifestation as our eye hospital. Long may it remain.

A NEW EYE HOSPITAL FOR THE TWENTY-FIRST CENTURY

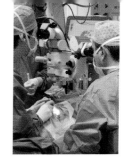

CHAPTER TWELVE

Manchester Royal Eye Hospital in its Bicentenary Year

THE YEAR 2014 FINDS the Manchester Royal Eye Hospital in its 200th year, and in its 7th home. One of the oldest and currently one of the busiest eye hospitals in the world, it has become transformed out of all recognition from the small venture that began on Trafalgar Day 1814. Its history has witnessed, mirrored and sometimes led those developments in science, technology, medicine and surgery that have transformed the outlook for so many eye diseases, and its staff continue to lead research for further development.

The Hospital in 1815, a few rooms on the ground floor of a house, provided outpatient services from a single surgeon two mornings per week, but no beds. By 1965 a total of 216 beds served 7 consultant surgeons (31 beds per consultant) who dealt with 135,000 outpatients in a year. By 2014 those beds have reduced almost 90% to 24, and the number of consultants has more than quadrupled to 32 (0.75 beds per consultant). These figures alone attest to the massive changes in medical care over this period, with safer and more effective surgery being performed almost exclusively as day-case procedures, where 50 years ago patients stayed in hospital for an average of 7 days, and one hundred and fifty years ago, 23 days. In addition to its consultants, the hospital now has an average of 30 ophthalmologists in training, and together with non-consultant

career doctors, a total of 70 ophthalmologists work here. The nursing complement is now 196, there are 27 optometrists, 11 orthoptists, 5 ophthalmic technicians, 3 ocular prosthetists, 6 in the Eye Bank, and together with clerical, administrative and managerial staff the Hospital employs 425 in total.

In the year 2012–13, the most recent for which full figures are available, the Hospital staff undertook a total of 160,000 elective outpatient consultations. Surgery was performed on 11,000, including 4,000 cataract operations and 1,000 emergency procedures. Laser treatment was applied to a total of 2,700 patients. In the Macular Treatment Centre, 11,000 patients underwent intravitreal injections. In the Emergency Eye Centre and Acute Referral Centre, 35,000 urgent visits were made. The Hospital is a veritable hive of activity. Sub-specialisation of eye care has been the inevitable result of increasing technological development, and staff work within specialist teams. The work of these teams, themes and departments is described below:

Academic and Research Ophthalmology

Staff of the Manchester Royal Eye Hospital are engaged in a broad research field, from laboratory studies, through original development of new technology, diagnostics and treatments to a role in global clinical trials on new treatments for ocular disease. There is a particularly strong ophthalmic genetics unit, longstanding research into vitreous biochemistry and there are particular strengths in glaucoma research, all facilitated by close links with the University of Manchester. In addition to developing new technologies, Manchester has a strong background in assessing the latest global devices that have been unleashed into the world of ophthalmology. Clinical research is performed to a high standard by consultants in several specialties and by allied professions including optometry, vision science and orthoptics. The research office currently supports over 15 open portfolio studies and therefore is rich in depth, breadth and quality of output. Ophthalmology has won recent awards for the most rapidly expanding research portfolio across all medical and surgical sub-specialites in Greater Manchester. Recently closed major studies include:

GMAN: A 23-month randomised, masked, prospective phase IV study assessing the safety and efficacy of two alternative treatment regimes using bevacizumab (Avastin™) to treat sub-foveal and juxta-foveal choroidal neovascularisation in age-related macular degeneration (Principal Investigator: Professor Paul Bishop)

IVAN: An RCT of alternative treatments to inhibit VEGF in age-related choroidal neovascularisation (PI: Professor Paul Bishop)

RETAIN: A 2-year randomized, single-masked, multicentre controlled phase IIIb trial assessing the safety and efficacy of 0.5 mg ranibizumab in two "treat and extend" treatment algorithms, versus 0.5 mg ranibizumab as needed in patients with macular oedema and visual impairment secondary to diabetes mellitus. (PI: Mr Sajjad Mahmood)

COMRADE (B17 & C18): A 6-month multicentre, randomized, double-masked phase IIIb-study comparing the safety and efficacy of Lucentis (ranibizumab) intravitreal injections versus Ozurdex (dexamethasone intravitreal implant) in patients with visual impairment due to macular oedema following retinal vein occlusion (PI: Professor Tariq Aslam)

The currently open portfolio studies include:

CIRTED: Combined immunosuppression and radiotherapy in thyroid eye disease (PI: Miss Anne Cook)

Crazy Castle 2: Development of an interactive game-based visual fields test for children using both computer software and electronics hardware (PI: Professor Tariq Aslam)

Eccentric viewing rehabilitative techniques for people with macular degeneration – A community model (PI: Dr Robert Harper)

ENDEAVOUR: A multicentre open-label study of low-voltage stereotactic radiotherapy for choroidal neovascularization in age-related macular degeneration (PI: Professor Tariq Aslam)

Genetic Basis of Glaucoma: 500 DNA samples to be collected from patients with glaucoma, for gene identification. (PI: Dr Forbes Manson)

HYDRUS IV: Prospective multicentre RCT to investigate the safety and efficacy of the Hydus aqueous implant for lowering IOP in glaucoma patients undergoing cataract surgery (PI: Mr Leon Au)

INJECT: Investigation of ocriplasmin in patients with confirmed vitreomacular traction (PI: Mr Niall Patton)

INTREPID: A double-masked, sham-controlled dose-ranging study to evaluate the safety and efficacy of low-voltage stereotactic radiosurgery in patients with choroidal neovascularization secondary to age-related macular degeneration (PI: Professor Tariq Aslam)

LUMINOUS™: Study to observe the effectiveness and safety of ranibizumab through individualized patient treatment and associated outcomes. (PI: Mr Sajjad Mahmood)

Newtricious: Interventional study to assess the effect of daily consumption of a lutein-enriched egg beverage on maintenance of visual function in subjects with early signs of age-related macular degeneration. (PI: Dr Forbes Manson)

MERLOT: Macular EpiRetinal Brachytherapy versus Lucentis™ Only Treatment: A study of the VIDION™ system versus Lucentis™ monotherapy for the treatment of sub-foveal choroidal neovascularisation associated with wet age-related macular degeneration in patients who have commenced anti-VEGF therapy (PI: Professor Paulo Stanga)

MEM Study: Manchester Pascal Endpoint Management laser treatment of diffuse diabetic macular oedema: A safety and efficacy study (PI: Professor Paulo Stanga)

Mobile Vision Tests: The use of mobile vision tests in measurement of ophthalmic conditions. (PI: Professor Tariq Aslam)

p-EVES: The effectiveness of pEVES for near vision in visual impairment. (PI: Professor Chris Dickinson)

Prometheus: A 12-month randomized, double-masked, sham controlled, multi-centre study to evaluate the safety and efficacy of 0.5mg ranibizumab intravitreal injections in patients with visual impairment due to VEGF-driven macular oedema (PI: Mr Konstantinos Balaskas)

PRPhS: Pascal Pan-Retinal Photo-Stimulation in Pre-Proliferative Diabetic Retinopathy: a safety and efficacy Study. (PI: Professor Paulo Stanga)

REPARO: Evaluation of safety and efficacy of rhNGF in patients with stage 2 and 3 neurotrophic keratitis. (PI: Mrs Fiona Carley)

ROSA: An RCT of continuous positive airway pressure in patients with impaired vision due to diabetic retinopathy and concurrent obstructive sleep apnoea. (PI: Mrs Yvonne D'Souza)

VanSel-1: A Cancer Research UK Phase I dose escalation trial of the oral VEGFR and EGFR inhibitor vandetanib in combination with the oral MEK inhibitor selumetinib (VanSel-1) in solid tumours (dose escalation) and NSCLC (expansion cohort) (In association with the Christie Hospital)

In June 2014 the MREH 200 Bicentenary Academic Conference will be held at the Manchester Conference Centre; a major scientific meeting celebrating the clinical and research work of MREH and its alumni. Over 100 speakers, including several prestigious visitors and many friends and alumni will be involved in 14 specialist sessions over 4 days.

Cornea Team and Manchester Eye Bank

Consultants: Mr Arun Brahma, Mrs Fiona Carley, Mr Leon Au, Mr Tim de Klerk, (Mr Sus Biswas)

The corneal service at MREH was initiated by Alan Ridgway in the late 1970s and strongly reinforced by Andrew Tullo in the 1990s, and the adjacency of the Manchester Eye Bank has enabled strong clinical and research links. The service is now ably manned by Mr Arun Brahma (who successfully introduced laser refractive surgery to MREH), Mrs Fiona Carley (who also manages the Manchester Eye Bank), Mr Leon Au who combines corneal and glaucoma expertise, and in 2014 Mr Tim de Klerk has joined the team, also leading the cataract service at MREH. The specialist paediatric cornea clinic, run jointly by Fiona Carley and Sus Biswas, has evolved into a national referral centre for paediatric corneal transplantation. Research is developing novel treatments for ocular allergy and external eye diseases in children. The corneal team is one of the busiest in the UK, providing all forms of modern corneal transplantation including femtolaser based lamellar surgery, and has a strong research base in corneal grafting techniques, keratoconus, crosslinking and corneal segments. In 2013 the team performed 165 corneal transplants. More than 400 excimer/femtosecond laser refractive procedures per annum are performed in the Laser Refractive Suite. There are two clinical fellowship posts at MREH for cornea/refractive surgery and external eye disease. The corneal service has extensive research interests, collaborating with several teams at the University of Manchester, ongoing research projects including studies on stem cell regeneration with the departments of Optometry and Vision Science, University School of Dentistry, Material Sciences and Inflammation and Repair. There is also collaboration with Cardiff University on corneal structure research, Lancaster University on the development of artificial corneas, and Bradford University on studies into 3-dimensional corneal modelling.

The David Lucas Manchester Eye Bank (MEB) first opened in 1989, and goes from strength to strength while celebrating its 25th anniversary, preparing and distributing corneas and sclera for MREH, the North of England and beyond. Currently ably led by Dr Isaac Zambrano, his team of 6 occupy a specially designed suite within the new hospital. MEB is the largest eye bank in the UK and second largest in Europe: about 2,000 corneas were processed in 2013, and in November a substantial milestone was achieved when a total of 40,000 corneas had been made available for transplantation by MEB, an immense achievement. The MEB also provides eye tissue for research in retinal, genetic and corneal diseases and supports numerous training courses for corneal transplantation throughout the UK.

Dr Isaac Zambrano, Manager of Manchester Eye Bank

Glaucoma Team

Consultants: Miss Cecilia Fenerty, Miss Fiona Spencer, Mr Leon Au, Miss Eleni Nikita

The glaucoma team have recently expanded to meet the considerable challenges of new NICE standards for glaucoma management (a committee on which Cecilia Fenerty played a large part). A variety of innovative shared-care systems and stream-lined referral patterns have been initiated at MREH and several have been adopted widely elsewhere. The OLGA clinic and glaucoma referral refinement scheme have been introduced in tandem with enhanced training and accreditation for community optometrists, and these innovations have been a springboard for the greater involvement of optometrists in clinical care at MREH. The team have been leaders in the use of glaucoma drainage devices for complex paediatric and adult glaucoma, are leading the UK in minimally invasive glaucoma surgery, and were the first UK centre for the use of Schlemm canal stents. Leon Au is the co-lead for a trial of a new glaucoma drainage stent (the Hydrus) as part of a multicentre study. Manchester is the only UK centre using high-intensity focussed ultrasound for cycloablation. There is research into the future use of suprachoroidal stents, a completely new treatment for primary open-angle glaucoma. In summary, the MREH glaucoma team offer the largest glaucoma surgical portfolio in the UK and possibly in Europe. The Glaucoma Virtual Clinic commenced this year, permitting remote assessments, and the team are pioneering intraocular pressure self-checking devices for glaucoma patients, reducing the need for clinic attendance. The glaucoma team have research strengths in innovative methods of glaucoma management and in minimally invasive glaucoma surgery including iStenting. There are two glaucoma clinical fellowship posts at MREH.

Management Team

Mr Sus Biswas (Clinical Head of Division), Miss Cecilia Fenerty (Associate CHD), Mr Stephen Dickson (Division Director), Mrs Debra Armstrong (Lead Nurse)

In 2012, after 12 years in two periods as Clinical Director and latterly Clinical Head of Division, Barry Mills handed over a thriving hospital to Sus Biswas, who is ably supported by Cecilia Fenerty as Associate CHD. Mr Stephen Dickson joined MREH in 2012 to manage both MREH and the University Dental Hospital which are currently a joint Division within CMFT. The medical management tree comprises Clinical Leads Professor Chris Lloyd (Paediatric Ophthalmology and Neuro-ophthalmology); Mr Steve Charles (Retina); Miss Cecilia Fenerty (Associate Clinical Head of Division and Anterior Segment Lead); Saj Ataullah (Orbital and Oculoplastics); and Felipe Dhawahir-Scala (Emergency Services).

The Division Management Team oversee all activities within the hospital and liaise closely with Trust management to ensure corporate aims and objectives, and financial balance. In addition to the direct patient care activities of clinical staff, all outpatient and laser activity is booked by teams of clerical staff, surgical episodes by staff in the admissions office, a coding team classifies and records all activity, the hundreds of thousands of professional communications each year are produced by our medical secretariat, and the innumerable telephone calls answered by both secretarial and clerical staff. Laboratory and radiological services process tens of thousands of investigations yearly, and an offsite team manage a gigantic medical records storage facility. The Hospital has an audit and clinical governance team, and its senior staff participate in a wide variety of organisational and managerial roles in addition to their clinical responsibilities. The corridors are filled with the activities of stocking, re-stocking, disposal, cleaning and maintenance. The MREH is as busy a hospital as can be seen anywhere, not least because traditionally, ophthalmology is the busiest of all specialties, and also because MREH is amongst the busiest of all. The management team run a tight ship.

Manchester Centre for Vision

The private facility of MREH has been retained within the new Hospital, providing an outpatient consulting suite, day-case and inpatient bedroom facilities, and the refractive surgery suite. Located adjacent to both NHS ward and operating theatres, the suite provides convenience for consultants and enables MREH to continue to generate revenue from private medicine and surgery, which is reinvested into facilities for all Hospital services.

Manchester Uveitis Clinic

Mr Nicholas Jones, Miss Jane Ashworth, (Miss Cecilia Fenerty), (Mr Niall Patton), (Dr Alice Chieng)

The Manchester Uveitis Clinic was inaugurated in 1991 by this author and it is now internationally recognised as a centre of excellence in the management of intraocular inflammatory disease. The clinic provides tertiary care for difficult uveitis, for patients from the Northwest of England, North Wales and beyond, has so far seen about 3,500 new patients, and deals with about 5,000 patient visits annually. Data from the clinic have recently been published as the world's largest-ever epidemiological study on uveitis. The service provides training for three fellows in uveitis and medical retina, and produces a steady stream of research publications, current strengths including the diagnosis of sarcoid-associated uveitis, the diagnosis and management of tuberculosis-associated uveitis, and the management of secondary glaucoma in uveitis. Children with paediatric uveitis are cared for jointly by Nick Jones and Jane Ashworth, paediatric ophthalmologist. There is close liaison with Drs Alice Chieng and Phil Riley, consultant paediatric rheumatologists at the adjacent Royal Manchester Children's Hospital, including a monthly Joint-Eye Clinic, managing children with complex inflammatory disease and immunosuppression. Uveitis patients with complex glaucoma are managed by Cecilia Fenerty and team, and those with vitreoretinal problems by Niall Patton. Patients with Behçet's disease are managed together with Dr Rachel Gorodkin, Consultant Rheumatologist, and others in the Manchester Behçet's Disease Multidisciplinary Team; those with sarcoidosis and tuberculosis jointly with chest physicians Professor Mark Woodhead and Dr Chris Hardy; and those with systemic vasculitis with Dr Mike Venning, nephrologist. There is close liaison with a wide network of rheumatologists and physicians throughout the Northwest, providing combined care for those with multisystem disease.

Manchester Vision Regeneration Laboratory

The Manchester Vision Regeneration Laboratory (MVRL) was established in 2010 by Professor Paulo Stanga. The research team focuses on medical retinal and vitreoretinal conditions using advanced diagnostic and treatment devices in order to offer the best options for clinical care for those with profound visual loss. The MVRL is equipped with the latest diagnostic and research resources including Optomap® digital wide-angle multispectral imaging, 3D Fourier-domain and new infra-red swept-source OCT, green and yellow wavelength Pascal® laser with endpoint management® for sub-threshold treatment. The team is pioneering research into, amongst others, laser-tissue interaction, swept-source OCT imaging of the cortical vitreous, widefield Optos imaging versus standard ETDRS photography, anti-VEGF versus Pascal® laser therapy for diabetic macular oedema, development of an ultrasound-based probe for the surgical excision of vitreous and epiretinal membranes, and electronic epiretinal implants for artificial vision in patients with retinitis pigmentosa and age-related

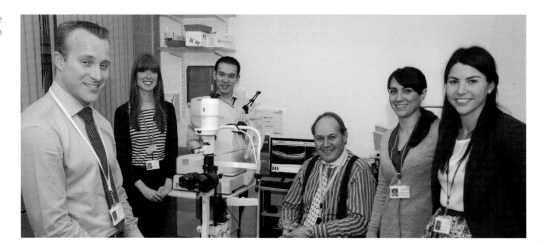

macular degeneration. The MRV Lab is the only site worldwide for some of these industry-sponsored research projects but also collaborates with research teams elsewhere in the UK and in the USA, Italy, Spain, Netherlands, Argentina, and Egypt. The MVRL provides three clinical research fellowship posts.

Medical Retina Team, including Macular Treatment Centre

Mr Saj Mahmood, Professor Paul Bishop, Professor Tariq Aslam, Professor Paulo Stanga, Mrs Yvonne D'Souza, Mr Konstantinos Balaskas, Mr Felipe Dhawahir-Scala

The medical retina team are responsible for a huge throughput of patients referred from a wide area, especially in the Macular Treatment Centre dealing with age-related macular degeneration and other maculopathies, where 11,000 intravitreal injections are administered per year. The high throughput has been accompanied by several high-profile treatment trials of anti-VEGF monoclonal antibody treatment, steroid implantation and targeted radiotherapy. The team run a wide variety of subspecialist clinics including Choroidal Naevus Clinic, Diabetic Retinopathy Clinic, Macula Clinic, Complex Macular Clinic, Radiotherapy Clinic, Macular Research Clinic, Retinal Genetic Clinic, and Virtual Macular Clinic. There are three medical retina clinical fellowship posts at MREH.

The team is engaged in an array of research work. Professor Aslam has a particular interest in the interface of computing and ophthalmology, inventing and developing original devices incorporating mobile vision testing, computerised genetic profiling, computerised visual field assessment, computerised amblyopia management, together with projects in image processing and machine vision. Professor Bishop and Mr Mahmood have led important macular degeneration research trials, and Professor Bishop continues studies into vitreous ultrastructure and biochemistry. Professor Stanga introduced Pattern-scanning retinal laser to MREH, the first European hospital to use the innovative technology, and developed new techniques for the management of diabetic retinopathy, making MREH a World leader in this area.

Neuro-ophthalmology Team

Mr Alec Ansons, Mr Mandagere Vishwanath, Dr Adam Zermansky

Consultant ophthalmologists Messrs Ansons and Vishwanath, together with consultant neurologist Dr Zermansky, provide 4 neuro-ophthalmology clinics weekly and the team also manage adult strabismus. A neurological screening clinic receives referrals of stroke and pituitary tumour patients. The team also specialises in the management of giant cell arteritis patients. Mr Vishwanath offers an expert ultrasound service. There is one neuro-ophthalmology clinical fellowship post at MREH.

Nursing Teams and Operating Theatres

Lead Nurse: Debra Armstrong

The current nursing body at MREH comprises 148 nurses and 48 healthcare support workers (previously known as auxiliary nurses). Nurses are involved in all aspects of ophthalmic care, inpatient, outpatient and surgical. The Inpatient Nursing

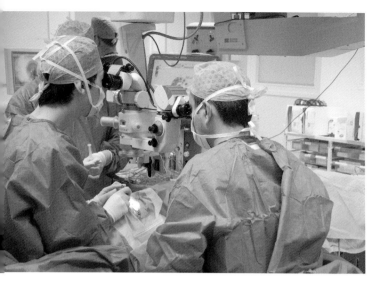

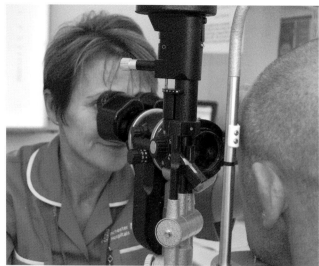

A typical MREH operating theatre at work

An MREH nurse practitioner at work

Team manage the ophthalmology ward which currently has 24 beds and houses those patients whose surgery mandates hospital stay, together with admission of patients with emergency conditions including severe ocular trauma, infection and inflammations. The Preadmission Clinic is nurse-led, where a team perform all necessary preoperative investigations including biometry. The Daycase Unit accommodates those great majority of patients visiting for surgery who do not require inpatient admission. There are 5 operating theatres at MREH and a sixth at the Withington Community Hospital. The main theatre suite has 65 staff including 45 nurses, the remainder comprising operating department assistants, technicians, care assistants and link workers. Two operating theatres deal predominantly with daycase anterior segment surgery, with three theatres supporting vitreoretinal, orbital and oculoplastic surgery. The theatre teams support over 11,000 operations annually. The Outpatient Nursing Team provide support for consultant clinics seeing approximately 3,000 patients each week, and several work as practitioners running parallel with doctor-led clinics.

This hospital was in the vanguard of the development of ophthalmic nurse practitioners, commencing with A&E nurse practitioners 22 years ago, and including a nurse sub-Tenon anaesthetist supporting cataract service operating lists. Now, there are over 30 practitioners and specialist nurses, including advanced practitioners and nurse prescribers, in the Emergency Eye Centre, in oculoplastic surgery, Preadmission Clinic, retina, cornea, glaucoma, paediatrics and uveitis. A nurse practitioner is about to begin intravitreal injections in the Macular Treatment Centre. Nurses from MREH have gone on to academic research and education, including Professors Marsden and Waterman at the Manchester Metropolitan University and Manchester University, respectively.

Ocular Prosthetics Department

The service is now provided by Andrea Morris and colleagues who custom-manufacture on-site in the MREH prosthetics laboratory, fit and maintain all ocular and oculofacial prosthesis for MREH patients, working closely with the oculoplastic and orbital team.

The MREH ocular prosthetics team

Ophthalmic Emergency Services

The MREH adult emergency services are managed by Mr Felipe Dhawahir-Scala. Since the introduction of A&E ophthalmic nurse practitioners in the 1990s, MREH has provided a two-tier emergency service; the Emergency Eye Centre (EEC) which is staffed by nurse practitioners (most of whom are now registered prescribers) and provides a service to walk-in patients; and the Acute Referral Centre (ARC), a consultant-led and partially consultant-delivered service for GP and other doctor referrals, and for patients referred on by EEC nurse practitioners. A total of about 35,000 urgent consultations are undertaken per year. Patients requiring further care by MREH ophthalmologists are now taken over by specialist teams rather than the consultant team on-call. Children with ophthalmic emergencies are seen by on-call ophthalmologists within the adjacent Royal Manchester Children's Hospital A&E Department, and admitted to a children's ward if necessary. Peripatetic services to other Manchester hospitals are provided on an on-call basis.

Ophthalmic Imaging

Since the first ophthalmic photographer was appointed in 1972, the need for ophthalmic imaging has grown out of all proportion, with new technologies including laser-scanning ophthalmoscopy, ultra-widefield imaging, fluorescein and indocyanine green angiography, corneal topography, microperimetry and high-resolution optical coherence tomography, both posterior and anterior segment. The enormous

An ophthalmic photographer at work

throughput within the Macular Treatment Centre has necessitated a burgeoning imaging facility. Currently there are 15 ophthalmic photographers, ably led by Jane Gray, and in addition to the main Ophthalmic Imaging Department at MREH these photographers work in 9 other locations including two outreach clinics. The practice of ophthalmology in 2014 is unthinkable without high-quality imaging and the department goes from strength to strength.

Professor Paulo Stanga has a substantial research interest in ophthalmic imaging, introducing OCT to the UK and Optos widefield imaging to MREH, and is currently researching high-resolution deep posterior segment OCT including

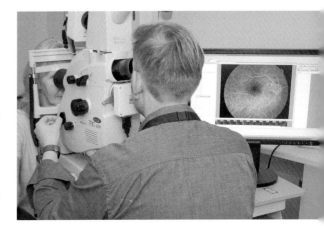

swept-source infrared devices. He has also researched intraoperative optical coherence tomography vitreoretinal imaging, slit-lamp fundus autofluorescence, slit-lamp retinal laser photocoagulation with simultaneous fundus autofluorescence and OCT imaging, amongst others. His research team are world leaders in these areas, and he is currently President of the Ophthalmic Imaging Association.

Ophthalmic Pathology

The Manchester Royal Eye Hospital houses one of only four National Specialist

Ophthalmic Pathology Service laboratories in the UK. Our two consultant ophthalmic pathologists, Dr Richard Bonshek and Dr Lucianne Dreher Irion, offer a comprehensive ocular and ophthalmic pathology service not only to the consultants of MREH, but also to other eye units in the Northwest, North and South Wales and elsewhere. A specialist forensic ocular pathology service is also provided. Over 1,000 specimens are processed annually. The department is active in research, particularly in relation to corneal and periocular disease.

Consultant ophthalmic pathologists Dr Richard Bonshek and Dr Lucianne Irion

Optometry Department

This essential and busy department comprises a team of 27 optometrists, led by Consultant Optometrists Dr Cindy Tromans and Dr Robert Harper. In addition to complex adult, and paediatric in-house refractions, the department provides several other services. The Contact Lens Clinics include a tertiary referral centre for complex contact lens work and paediatric contact lenses. The busy Low Vision Service is fully integrated with multidisciplinary care teams within and outside the Hospital, including a valued support service provided by Henshaw's Society for Blind People, led by Maggie Harrison. The department runs community clinics commissioned by Manchester and Trafford PCTs, including support for community orthoptic clinics and in special schools. The department plays an integral part at the Withington Cataract Centre, performing all routine post-operative assessments, providing a complex biometry service and training for nurse biometrists, and have initiated a direct cataract referral scheme from community optometrists. In the Macular Treatment Centre, optometrists lead the Macular Assessment Referral Refinement Clinic, receiving urgent new referrals of suspected wet age-related macular degeneration direct from community optometrists or GPs, and provide post-treatment assessments. Dr Tromans also offers an expert ophthalmic ultrasound service including colour Doppler imaging and ultrasound biomicroscopy of the anterior segment.

The Optometric Assessment Clinics (OptAC) allow triaged GP referrals to be seen

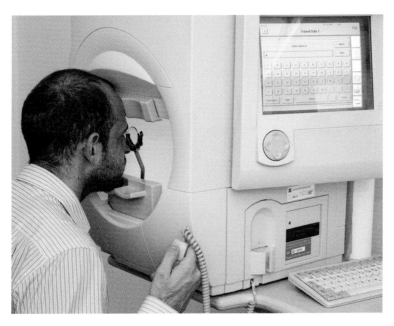

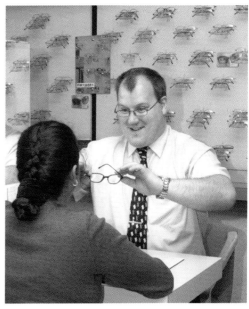

Visual field testing
underway in the
optometry department

Stephen Golding,
dispensing opticians
manager, at work

and managed by optometrists with further training who are registered prescribers. This
clinic is currently being merged into OLGA to provide a multi-purpose optometrist-led
outpatient service. The Optometry-Led Glaucoma Assessment Clinics (OLGA) have
provided, since 2003, assessment for patients with suspected glaucoma after direct
referral from trained community optometrists, and internal co-management with the

glaucoma team, of patients with glaucoma requiring regular assessment. Optometrists leading the clinic obtain higher qualification with the Diploma in Glaucoma offered by the College of Optometrists. New referrals are seen and fully assessed (including visual fields and disc photography) at a single visit. The Visual Fields Service is also managed within the Department of Optometry, as are day-phasing patients. Optometrists are now integrated into the Acute Referral Centre, independently managing and prescribing for new and follow-up patients.

Optometry contributes collaboratively to several research studies throughout the Division, including trials in the Macular Treatment Centre, glaucoma assessment studies with Professor Henson, and with the University of Manchester, especially with Professors Dickinson in the field of visual impairment and with Waterman in falls and adherence research. Optometry also has its own independent research programme, with several current funded studies.

The Manchester Royal Eye Hospital also has its own dispensing opticians, managed by Mr Stephen Golding whose staff of three dispenses about 3,000 prescriptions per annum, specialising in complex prescriptions for MREH patients. Services include handmade frames, safety eyewear for staff of the Trust services provider, Sodexo and a dispensing service for Trust staff. Mr Golding is also actively involved in low vision, assessing and dispensing electronic low vision aids and electronic CCTV.

Orthoptics and Vision Science

The orthoptic department continues to be one of the busiest in the UK, its acting manager at the moment being Mrs Alison Ansons. There are 11 orthoptists, dealing with about 15,000 patients per annum. In addition to paediatric work, orthoptists are

Members of the orthoptics department together with Messrs Ansons and Vishwanath, and Dr Neil Parry, Vision Scientist

involved in stroke clinics, neuro-ophthalmology and Botox strabismus clinics. The Vision Science unit, led by Dr Neil Parry, has 2 vision scientists and provides electrophysiology testing for patients from MREH and elsewhere.

Orbital, Lacrimal & Oculoplastic Team

Mr Saj Ataullah, Mr Brian Leatherbarrow, Mr Mohammed Sadiq, Miss Anne Cook, Mr Dan Nolan

The oculoplastic and orbital team have expanded enormously since Mr Leatherbarrow placed MREH onto the world map for this subspecialty 20 years ago. The team offer a Regional surgical service for periocular cancer including Mohs micrographic surgery, in tandem with Mohs surgical dermatologists Dr Nick Telfer and colleagues.

Mr Sadiq leads a multidisciplinary Facial Function Clinic together with expertise from otolaryngology, plastic surgery and facial physiotherapy. Miss Cook leads a multidisciplinary Thyroid Eye Disease Clinic. There are regular Orbital Radiology MDT meetings to discuss complex cases. There are two orbital & oculoplastic surgical fellowship posts at MREH.

Outreach Services, including Withington Cataract Centre

Outreach ophthalmology clinics in other Manchester hospitals have been a feature of MREH work for decades. Currently such services are provided at Wythenshawe, Trafford General and Altrincham General hospitals. The Community Eye Physician (CEP) service, initiated by David McLeod in 1994, continues to provide CEP clinics provided by Associate Specialist-grade ophthalmologists, to health centres in various parts of the city. The Withington Community Hospital DTC contains an ophthalmology clinic, day-case unit and operating theatre, and MREH staff provide a 5-day cataract surgery service in this location. In 2012 Trafford Hospitals became a part of CMFT and discussions are afoot to develop an outreach ophthalmology service from MREH. The future rationalisation of foundation trusts in Greater Manchester may provide opportunities for further outreach services from MREH.

Paediatric Ophthalmology and Ophthalmic Genetics

Professor Chris Lloyd (Team Lead), Mr Sus Biswas, Miss Jane Ashworth (Mrs Fiona Carley, Miss Cecilia Fenerty, Mr Nicholas Jones, Professor Paulo Stanga, Professor Graeme Black, Professor Jill Clayton-Smith)

Although a few consultants in the 1970s developed special expertise in strabismus surgery, paediatric ophthalmology as an area of special interest began to develop at MREH in the 1980s when Alan Ridgway built a practice in paediatric cataract, cornea and glaucoma, and Chris Dodd provided a service for the visually handicapped. It was in 1993 that a Paediatric Ophthalmology Centre was first developed to provide bespoke premises, and the first substantive appointment to the post of Paediatric Ophthalmologist was Chris Lloyd, who has gone on to lead what is now a centre of worldwide repute, especially in the field of paediatric cataract surgery. He is ably supported by Sus Biswas (who leads the retinopathy of prematurity service) and Jane Ashworth with whom he runs the Paediatric Cataract Clinic, and there is close liaison with other colleagues with subspecialist combined clinics; Paediatric Glaucoma Clinic (with Cecilia Fenerty); Paediatric Uveitis Clinic (with Nick Jones); Paediatric Immunology Clinic (with Dr Vibna Sharma); Paediatric Retina Clinic (with Professor Paulo Stanga); Paediatric Ophthalmology & Genetics (with Professors Graeme Black and Jill Clayton-Smith); and paediatric cornea (with Fiona Carley). Dr Neil Parry in the Vision Science Centre offers an integral electrophysiology service for paediatric patients. There are two paediatric ophthalmology clinical fellowship posts at MREH.

Inherited disease has a particular significance for paediatric ophthalmology, and the consultants at MREH work closely with colleagues at the Manchester Centre for Genomic Medicine at St. Mary's Hospital, especially with Professors Graeme Black and Jill Clayton-Smith. The ophthalmic genetics team have developed a national service in genetic testing for inherited retinal dystrophies and also provide reports internationally on request. They continue to lead research in this field, and have also made rapid developments in the identification of gene mutations causing anophthalmia and microphthalmia. The Manchester ophthalmic genetics team is at the forefront of next-generation sequencing for inherited eye disorders and are now introducing a new test to identify genes for congenital cataract. The test will analyse 115 genes in parallel and uses next generation DNA sequencing technology. These new techniques promise to revolutionise genetic testing and the Manchester team remain in the vanguard both in clinical ophthalmic genetics, and in research.

Vitreoretinal Surgical Unit

Mr Steve Charles (Team Lead), Mr George Turner, Professor Paulo Stanga, Mr Niall Patton, Mr Felipe Dhawahir-Scala

The Vitreoretinal (VR) unit provides a comprehensive tertiary referral service, receiving referrals from ophthalmologists throughout the Northwest of England. All vitreoretinal diseases are treated, including emergencies such as retinal detachment and serious eye injuries (referrals being seen daily in the VR Urgency Clinic), and elective work, especially macular disease (epiretinal membrane and macular hole surgery) and severe diabetic eye disease. Niall Patton provides VR surgery for the MREH uveitis service. Steve Charles and Felipe Dhawahir-Scala have led the development of macular hole surgery without post-operative posturing, achieve high success rates. Mr Dhawahir-Scala is also to conduct a trial at MREH of an implantable telescope for those with severe macular disease. Professor Stanga specialises in the medical and surgical management of vitreo-retinal disorders, developing new

Modern vitreoretinal surgery taking place at MREH

therapies including retrobulbar interferon alpha-2a, macular and retinal pigment epithelium translocation surgery, anti-angiogenic intravitreal drugs and high-speed phaco/vitrectomy surgical systems. He is the Manchester Principal Investigator for the Argus II (Bionic Eye) 10-centre international trial, which uses an epiretinal electronic implant to treat blindness in retinitis pigmentosa, and his surgery was the first to achieve word-reading, colour perception or face detection for treated patients. The Argus II is now also being trialled at MREH in a pilot study of severe age-related macular degeneration.

Vitreoretinal surgeons at MREH use gold-standard techniques including small-gauge sutureless vitrectomy and wide-angle intraoperative microscope viewing systems. The unit is recognised nationally and internationally as a prestigious training ground for aspiring VR surgeons, and the three VR fellowship training posts are subject to intense competition. By 2014 over 50 VR surgeons have been trained at MREH, and they now work in most major cities in the UK including Moorfields in London, and internationally in Australia, Canada, Greece, Ireland, Italy, Malaysia, New Zealand, Singapore, Spain and the USA. The unit was the first in the UK to enhance the care of VR patients by developing the role of the specialist VR nurse practitioner, the post held by Rita Mclauchlan.

The year 2014 marks an important milestone for the Manchester Royal Eye Hospital, and the event will be marked appropriately. Details are found on our bicentenary website, www.MREH200.org.uk. A major permanent exhibition of the history and current work of the Hospital will be displayed in the main atrium. The MREH 200 Bicentenary Academic Conference will showcase the work of MREH staff. The bicentenary day itself, October 21st 2014, will be marked by a Hospital Open Day for visitors, dignitaries and media, with organised tours of the Hospital for senior school and undergraduate groups. The day will end with a major evening celebration for all Hospital staff. This book will, it is hoped, will provide a permanent memento for those who have trained and worked at MREH, and a source of interest for those who follow the development of ophthalmology, medicine, science and Manchester history. All proceeds will go towards our bicentenary appeal, described below:

Each new development in medicine and ophthalmology involves capital, staff time, revenue and space. For many years, a substantial part of the finance of most new developments has come from donations or bequests to the hospital, and we have been fortunate to be able to secure such financial support. The recent developments in ophthalmic genetics have been little-short of mind-boggling, and the new forms of multi-gene testing for ophthalmic disorders offer a remarkable leap forward in the management of this important area of our work. To be delivered properly, a new Paediatric Ophthalmic Genetics Unit is being planned. We have chosen this particular project to be the subject of a Bicentenary Appeal: **"200 for 200"**. We are attempting to raise £200,000 towards the costs of the new Unit, to mark the

200th anniversary. Our appeals website is at www.cmftcharity.org.uk.This hospital in 1814 depended entirely on charitable donations for its survival. Throughout its two centuries of existence, the generosity of many people has permitted it firstly to remain in existence, and then after 1948, to enhance the quality of care provided, substantially beyond that supported by central NHS funding. We are confident that such generosity will continue, so that the Manchester Royal Eye Hospital can continue at the forefront of Manchester Medicine, and at the forefront of World Ophthalmology.

APPENDIX 1

Hospital Officers

Manchester Institution for Curing Diseases of the Eye (1814–1838); Manchester Eye Hospital (1838–1867); Manchester Royal Eye Hospital (1867–present)

A. Senior Medical Staff

Dates given are from the year of appointment to the most senior post at the hospital, until the date of retirement (or conversion to consulting surgeon). Early senior posts were named Honorary Surgeon, then from 1948, Consultant Surgeon. All are surgeons unless otherwise indicated. Honours, higher degrees and postgraduate diplomas, where known, are noted.

William James Wilson FRCS	1814–1827
John Hull MD LRCP (Honorary Physician)	1814–1838
Samuel Barton FRCS JP	1815–1844
John Windsor FRCS FLS	1818–1857
RW Robinson MD (Honorary Physician)	1838–1855
Richard Thomas Hunt MRCS LSA	1844–1867
John Walker	1844–1847 (died)
Charles Redfern	1857–1862
James Bent	1857–1864 (died)
Thomas Windsor	1862–1867
John Birch	1862–1863 (died)
Robert Heywood McKeand MRCS	1862–1872
Adolph Samelson MD	1862–1876
David Little MD FRCS(Ed)	1867–1902
Charles Edward Glascott MD FRCS	1873–1908
T C Morgan	1874–1875
Philip Henry Mules MRCS LSA	1875–1889
Abraham Emrys Jones MD JP	1882–1914
Alexander Hill Griffith MD FRCS	1889–1918
Edward Roberts MRCS LSA	1894–1910
John Gray Clegg MD FRCS	1902–1933
Harry Horsman McNabb MD	1908–1940
John Wharton MA MD	1910–1942
Thomas Milnes Bride MD FRCS	1914–1947
Harry V White	1919–1944
Donald E Core MD (Honorary Physician & Neurologist)	1920–1934 (died)
Sir Geoffrey Jefferson KBE FRS FRCS (Hon Neurosurgeon)	1924–1951
William Stirling MD DSc OBE	1924–1954

Gordon Renwick	1931–1959 (died)
CS Don MD (Honorary Physician)	1933–1935
HR Donald (Honorary Physician)	1935–1946
Ogilvie Maxwell Duthie MD FRCS	1941–1964
Alexander Stewart Scott	1947–1979
Sydney B Smith	1948–1972
Frederick Janus MD MRCS	1948–1975
Peter Llewellyn Blaxter FRCS	1954–1983
Alan Stanworth MD PhD DOMS	1954–1961
Roy Dalgleish FRCS FRCS(Ed)	1961–1988
Professor Calbert Phillips MD PhD FRCS FRCS(Ed) DO	1965–1972
Terence G Ramsell MD FRCS (Senior Lecturer)	1968
Emanuel Saul Rosen MD FRCS(Ed) FRCOphth FRPS	1971–1993
David Leighton FRCS	1972–1973
Dr David Lucas FRCPath (Consultant Ophthalmic Pathologist)	1972–1987
Alan Edward Andrew Ridgway FRCS FRCOphth DO	1974–2001
Satish Kumar Bhargava FRCS(Ed) FCOphth DO	1975–1991 (died)
Christopher Ledward Dodd FRCS FRCOphth	1976–2003
Joan Laura Noble FRCS (Ed) FRCOphth	1979–2007
Maeve McDermott FRCS	1980–1982
Keith Barry Mills FRCS FRCOphth DO	1981–2012
Professor David McLeod FRCS FRCOphth	1988–2006
Andrew Brent Tullo MD FRCOphth	1989–2006
Michael John Lavin FRCS FRCOphth	1990–
Nicholas Philip Jones FRCS(Ed) FRCOphth DO	1991–
Alec Michael Ansons FRCS FRCOphth DO	1991–
Brian Leatherbarrow FRCS FRCOphth DO	1992–
Dr Richard Bonshek MD CM FRCPath	
(Consultant Ophthalmic Pathologist)	1992–
George Stewart Turner MRCP FRCS FRCOphth	1993 -
Professor Ian Christopher Lloyd FRCS FRCOphth DO	1995–
Stephen John Charles MD FRCS(Glas) FRCOphth	1997–
Anne Fiona Spencer DM FRCS(Glas) FRCOphth FCOptom	1998–
Professor Paul N Bishop PhD FRCS FRCOphth	1998–
Eamonn O'Donoghue FRCOphth	1998–2001
Saghir Ahmed Sadiq DM FRCS(Ed) FRCOphth DO	1999–
Arun Kevin Brahma MD FRCOphth	2000–
Cecilia Helen Fenerty MD FRCOphth	2002–
Susmito Biswas FRCOphth	2002–
Sajid A M Ataullah FRCOphth	2002–
Professor Graeme C Black DPhil FRCOphth	
(Consultant Ophthalmic Geneticist)	2002–
Professor Paulo Eduardo Stanga MD	2003–
Fiona Carley FRCOphth	2006–
Anne Elizabeth Cook MD FRCS FRCOphth	2007–
Jane Louise Ashworth PhD FRCOphth	2007–
Niall Patton MD FRCOphth	2008–

Sajjad Mahmood MRCOphth	2008–
Mangadere Vishwanath FRCS(Ed) DOMS	2009–
Bruno Zuberbuhler MD FMHOphth EBO	2009–2012
Felipe Dhawahir-Scala FRCS(Ed) LMS	2010–
Professor Tariq Aslam PhD DM FRCS(Ed) DipIT	2010–
Leon Au FRCOphth	2010–
Yvonne D'Souza MD MS FRCS	2011–
Dr Lucianne Irion (Consultant Ophthalmic Pathologist)	2011–
Tomas Cudrnak MD FRCOphth FEBO	2011–2012
Daniel John Augustine Nolan FRCOphth	2012–
Eleni Nikita FRCOphth FEBO	2014–
Konstantinos Balaskas MD FEBO	2014–
Timothy de Klerk MRCOphth	2014–

B. Presidents of the hospital 1814–1948

Sir John Thomas Stanley (7th Baronet of Alderley)	1814–1842
Rev. Harry Grey, 8th Earl of Stamford, 4rd Earl of Warrington	1843–1847
James Prince Lee, Right Rev. Lord Bishop of Manchester	1848–1852
George Granville Francis Egerton, 2nd Earl of Ellesmere	1853–1862
Edward George Fitzalan-Howard 1st Baron Howard of Glossop	1863–1883
Edward Henry Stanley, 15th Earl of Derby	1884–1893
Frederick Arthur Stanley, 16th Earl of Derby	1894–1908
Edward George Villiers Stanley, 17th Earl of Derby	1909–1948

Owing to incomplete hospital records, some dates below are unknown and are marked (?)

C. Chairmen of the Hospital 1814–1966

William Fox	1814
Reverend Richard Bassnett MA	1848–1862
Henry Julius Leppoc JP	1863–1869
Philip Goldschmidt	1870–1889
David Bannerman JP	1890–1897
Philip William Kessler	1898–1920
Herman Julius Goldschmidt	1921–1941
John Wright Crewdson	1941–1946
Eric Evans	1946–1952
SH Hampson	1952–1956
HW Townley	1956–1966
Colin Midwood	1966–?

D. Hospital Managers

Rosemary Knights	1984–?
John Foster	?–?
Mary Roberts	?–1999
Karen Partington	1999–2004
Beth Weston	2005–2012
Stephen Dickson	2012–

E. Hospital Matrons (1839–1973); Senior Nursing Officers (1974–1984); Directors of Nursing (1984–1998); Lead Nurses (1998-present)

Frances Atkinson	1839–1850
Esther Morris	1850–1862
Mrs A Hall	1862–1866
Miss MA Bishop	1866–1872
Margaret Somerville	1872–1882
Mrs Mason	1882–1883
Mrs Atkin	1883–1889
Miss MV Black	1889–1895
Caroline Glover	1895–1898
Miss ME Bland	1898–1901
Margaret Sutherland	1901–1915
Miss AB Barter	1915–1939
Jane Reilly	1939–1941
Monica Rimmer	1942–1944
Winifred Heath	1944–1947
Miriam Howard	1947–1948
Miss CC Wheatcroft	1948–1960
Miss N Mustard	1961–1967
Mr S Richards	1967–1973
Miss G Khastagir	1974
Mrs Hamilton	1975–?
Rosemary Knights	?–1984
Jane Grabham	1984–1987
Giety Richards	1987–?
John Perry	?–1998
Jane Grabham	1998–2002
John Fletcher	2002–2006
Linda Adamson	2007–2012
Debra Armstrong	2013–

F. Clinical Directors; Clinical Heads of Division

David McLeod	1991–1994
Barry Mills	1994–1998
Nicholas Jones	1998–2000
Chris Lloyd	2001–2005
Barry Mills	2005–2012
Sus Biswas	2012–

Timeline

A resumé of important dates in ophthalmology, science, Manchester and political history

2000BC	Couching is used for cataract
80AD	Romans build a wooden fort at *Mamucium*
1227	Manceaster becomes a market town
1249	Roger Bacon invents spectacles
1515	Manchester Grammar School is created
1603	The Great Plague strikes Manchester. 1,000 (25%) die
1719	Manchester's first newspaper is published, the *Manchester Weekly Journal*
1729	Manchester's first Cotton Exchange is built
1748	Jacques Daviel introduces extracapsular cataract extraction
1752	Manchester Infirmary is created
1764	James Hargreaves invents the Spinning Jenny
1771	Arkwright's first water-powered mill
1792	Oil-fired street lamps are introduced to Manchester
1796	Belladonna drops first used to dilate the pupil for cataract surgery
1803	John Dalton publishes a prototype Periodic Table in Manchester
1805	The London Dispensary for the Relief of the Poor Afflicted with Diseases of the Eye and Ear (later to become Moorfields Eye Hospital) is created. Nelson dies at Trafalgar
1808	The West of England Eye Infirmary is created
1810	The Bristol Eye Hospital is created
1812	Napoleon invades Russia
1813	The Luddites are dispersed by the Army near Manchester
1814	Manchester Institution for Curing Diseases of the Eye is created. National Eye Hospital, Dublin is created. British troops occupy and torch Washington DC. Anglo-Dutch treaty
1815	Battle of Waterloo. Invention of the Davy safety lamp. First of the Corn Laws

1816	The year without a summer (eruption of Mt Tambora, Dutch East Indies)
1819	Peterloo massacre, Manchester
1820	New York Eye Infirmary is created
1821	The Plymouth Eye Dispensary is created. The *Manchester Guardian* is first published
1822	The Newcastle Infirmary for Diseases of the Eye is created
1823	The Birmingham & Midland Eye Hospital is created. One of the world's first public horse-drawn omnibus services opens, in Manchester
1824	Boston Eye Infirmary, Massachusetts USA, is created
1829	Robert Peel forms first police service in London. First electric motor.
1830	Opening of the Liverpool-Manchester railway, the world's first timetabled passenger railway
1832	Great Reform Act. The Sussex Eye Hospital is created. The Manchester cholera epidemic kills 700
1833	Abolition of Slavery Act
1834	The Wills Eye Institute is created. The Eye Infirmary of Edinburgh is created
1836	The Sunderland Eye Infirmary is created
1838	Anti-Corn Law League formed in Manchester
1841	First cylindrical spectacles to correct astigmatism
1843	The Central London Ophthalmic Hospital is created
1844	St. Mark's Ophthalmic Hospital, Dublin is created
1845	Irish famine begins. Many Irish emigrate to Manchester. Engels writes *The Condition of the Working Class in England* in Manchester. James Joule publishes on electromotive power in Manchester

1846	First use of ether for general anaesthesia
1847	First use of chloroform for general anaesthesia Charlotte Brontë publishes *Jane Eyre,* written mostly in Manchester. St. Mary's collegiate church in Manchester is made a cathedral
1848	The *Communist Manifesto* is published by Marx and Engels
1849	The Manchester Lunatic Asylum separates from the MRI and moves to Cheadle
1851	The Great Exhibition, London. Owen's College is created in Manchester (later to become its University). Von Helmholtz invents the ophthalmoscope
1852	Peter Mark Roget, previously Honorary Physician to the Manchester Infirmary, publishes his thesaurus
1853	First medical syringe invented. Robert wood invents the hypodermic cannula. Manchester is granted city status
1855	Bessemer converter is patented
1856	The Western Eye Infirmary is created
1857	The South London Ophthalmic Hospital is created. The Indian mutiny
1863	London underground begins
1865	Albrecht von Graefe introduces his *ab interno* cataract section First silk suture to close the cornea after cataract surgery
1866	First transatlantic telephone cable
1867	Joseph Lister introduces surgical antisepsis
1869	Manhattan Eye, Ear & Throat Hospital is created. The Suez canal opens
1870	Robert Koch's germ theory of disease
1871	St. Paul's Eye Hospital, Liverpool is created
1874	The Rotterdam Eye Hospital is created
1876	Queen Victoria becomes Empress of India
1879	Edison's first electric light bulb. Manchester opens the first telephone exchange in the UK
1880	First endotracheal tube for general anaesthesia. The Victoria University of Manchester is created
1882	The St. John's Ophthalmic Hospital, Jerusalem is created The Sydney Eye Hospital is created. British occupation of Egypt
1883	Krakatoa erupts

1884	Cocaine first used as local anaesthetic for cataract surgery
1886	Oxford Eye Hospital is created
1887	First contact lenses developed
1894	First gramophone recording. The Manchester Ship Canal opens (the largest navigable man-made waterway in the world)
1895	Wilhelm Röntgen discovers X-rays
1897	Royal Victoria Eye & Ear Hospital, Dublin is created by a hospital merger
1901	Blood group classification introduced
1905	Eduard Zirm performs the first corneal transplantation
1906	San Francisco is devastated by an earthquake
1907	Hans Geiger, working with Rutherford in Manchester, begins to develop his radiation counter
1908	First commercial radio
1909	The Royal Wurttemberg Eye Clinic, Tuebingen, is created
1910	Intracapsular cataract surgery gains popularity. Ernest Rutherford investigates alpha radiation at the University of Manchester
1914	van Lint introduces facial nerve anaesthesia using injected procaine. World War I begins
1917	Russian revolution
1918	World War I ends
1921	Irish Free State established. Dr Marie Stopes, first woman Lecturer at the University of Manchester, opens her birth control clinic
1925	The Wilmer Ophthalmological Institute, Baltimore USA, is created
1926	Gullstrand introduces the ophthalmic slit-lamp microscope
1929	Beginning of great depression
1930	Penicillin is first used in humans – successfully to treat ophthalmia neonatorum
1934	First use of an intravenous anaesthetic (sodium pentothal) for general anaesthesia
1935	Physostigmine introduced to treat glaucoma. First sulphonamide introduced
1936	The Jarrow march
1938	Cortisone discovered
1939	World War II begins
1940	Battle of Britain
1943	Lignocaine is synthesised
1945	Charles Schepens invents the binocular indirect ophthalmoscope

| | Central London Ophthalmic Hospital merges with Moorfields Eye Hospital | 1972 | Robert Machemer introduces pars plana vitrectomy |

1947 Indian independence. The transistor is invented

1948 Operating microscope first used for cataract surgery. Tom Kilburn invents the world's first stored-programme computer at Manchester University. Alan Turing moves to Manchester

1949 Harold Ridley implants the first intraocular lens, made by Rayner

1950 Single-strand virgin silk sutures (8/0) become available

1954 First successful human vascular organ transplant (kidney)

1955 Retrobulbar local anaesthesia is introduced

1956 Suez crisis
First commercially available Xenon arc retinal photocoagulator

1957 José Barraquer introduces chymotrypsin for intracapsular cataract extraction
Bernard Lovell builds the world's largest radio-telescope at Jodrell Bank for the University of Manchester

1958 Cassette tape invented. Integrated circuit invented

1960 Cornelius Binkhorst introduces the iris-clip intraocular lens. Krwawicz introduces cryoextraction of cataract. First human retinal fluorescein angiogram

1965 The first Olivetti personal computer is produced

1967 Charles Kelman experiments with phacoemulsification for cataract surgery

1968 Argon laser first used for human retinal disease. John Cairns introduces trabeculectomy for glaucoma. The National Eye Institute, Bethesda, USA is created

| | Central London Ophthalmic Hospital merges with Moorfields Eye Hospital |
World War II ends

1972 Robert Machemer introduces pars plana vitrectomy

1974 The three-day week

1975 Computerised tomography invented

1977 Steven Shearing introduces the posterior chamber lens
Nuclear Magnetic Resonance imaging (later MRI) introduced

1978 The first foldable intraocular lens is used

1980 Daniel Aron-Rosa introduces the Neodymium-YAG laser
Robert Stegmann first uses Sodium Hyaluronate in cataract surgery

1982 The first compact disc player is released

1983 HIV is identified

1985 Peribulbar local anaesthesia is introduced

1987 First excimer laser corneal refractive operation performed

1990 Sub-Tenon local anaesthesia is re-introduced. The first FDA-approved foldable silicone intraocular lens is released

1992 Topical anaesthesia alone was reintroduced for cataract surgery

1993 Optical coherence photography imaging of human retina introduced

1995 The first DVD is released

2008 Patterned scanning retinal laser treatment introduced

2010 Andre Geim and Konstantin Novoselov, at the University of Manchester, are awarded the Nobel Prize for work on graphene

2011 60-electrode retinal prosthetic implantation introduced

2013 Health & social care act: PCTs disbanded, "any willing provider" for services

2014 Manchester Royal Eye Hospital celebrates its bicentenary

Bibliography

Material for this book has been extensively harvested from (incomplete) archives of the Manchester Royal Eye Hospital and Royal Infirmary. Minor references have not been included here, but the following have provided important references or quotations:

Albert DM. 'Corneal surgery'. In: Albert DM, Edwards DD (Eds.) *The History of Ophthalmology*. Cambridge Mass, Blackwell 1996

Albert DM. 'The Ophthalmoscope and Retinovitreous Surgery'. In: Albert DM, Edwards DD (Eds.) *The History of Ophthalmology*. Cambridge Mass, Blackwell 1996

Anon. 'Manchester Institutions I: Consulting Time at the Eye Hospital'. *Manchester City News* 3/2/1877

Anon. 'Manchester Royal Eye Hospital'. In: *Manchester Faces and Places*. John Heywood, Manchester February 1892

Anon. *Dictionary of National Biography*. London, Smith Elder & Co. 1900

Armitage WJ, Moss SJ, Easty DL et al. 'Supply of corneal tissue in the United Kingdom'. *Br J Ophthalmol* 1990;74:685–7

Aston J. *The Manchester Guide: A Brief Historical Description of the Towns of Manchester and Salford, the Public Buildings and the Charitable and Literary Institutions*. Manchester 1804

Axon E. 'General and political history of Manchester'. In: *The book of Manchester and Salford*, Faulkner & Sons, Manchester 1929

Axon WE. *In memoriam Adolph Samelson. Papers of the Manchester Literary Club* Vol 14 p172–185

Baines E. *History, Directory & Gazetteer of the County Palatine of Lancaster Vol 2*. Wales & Co., Liverpool 1825

Barker JRV. *The Brontës*. Phoenix, London 1994

Birley AR. 'A case of eye disease (Lippitudo) on the Roman Frontier in Britain'. *Documenta Ophthalmologica* 1992;81:111–9

British Newspaper Archive www. Britishnewspaperarchive.co.uk

Brockbank EM. *Sketches of the lives and works of the honorary medical staff of the Manchester Infirmary, from its foundation in 1752 to 1830, when it became the Royal Infirmary*. Manchester University Press 1904

Brockbank EM. 'The history of collegiate teaching'. In: *The book of Manchester and Salford*, Faulkner & Sons, Manchester 1929

Brockbank EM. 'The hospitals of Manchester and Salford'. In: *The book of Manchester and Salford*, Faulkner & Sons, Manchester 1929

Brockbank EM. *A centenary history of the Manchester Medical Society*. Sherratt & Hughes, Manchester 1934

Brockbank W. *Portrait of a hospital 1752–1948 to commemorate the bicentenary of the Royal Infirmary, Manchester*. Heinemann, London 1952

Brockbank W. *The honorary medical staff of the Manchester Royal Infirmary 1830–1948*. Manchester University Press 1965

Bush M. *The Casualties of Peterloo*. Lancaster, Carnegie Publishing 2005

Carpenter MW. 'A cultural history of ophthalmology in nineteenth century Britain'. *Britain, Representation and Nineteenth Century History* (Felluga DF, Ed.) www.branchcollective.org

Coyne L, Doyle D, Pickstone JV. *A guide to the records of the health services in the Manchester region (Kendal to Crewe).* University of Manchester Institute of Science and Technology 1981

Crookes G. *Dublin's Eye & Ear: The Making of a Monument.* Dublin, Town House 1993

Donald GF. 'The history, clinical features and treatment of tinea capitis due to Trichophyton tonsurans and Trichophyton violaceum'. *Australasian Journal of Dermatology* 1959;5:90–102

Duke-Elder S. *System of Ophthalmology vols 1–15.* London, Henry Kimpton 1958–1976

Elwood WJ, Tuxford AF. *Some Manchester doctors: a biographical collection to mark the 150th anniversary of the Manchester Medical Society 1834–1984.* Manchester University Press 1984

Engels F. *The condition of the working class in England* (1845) D McLellan (Ed.) Oxford University Press 1993

Gaskell E. Mary Barton: *A Tale of Manchester Life.* London, Chapman 1848

Girouard M. *Cities and People: a Social and Architectural History.* Chicago University Press 1987

Gorsky M, Mohan J, Willis T. *Mutualism and Healthcare: British Hospital Contributory Schemes in the Twentieth Century.* Manchester University Press 2006

Hayes LM. *Reminiscences of Manchester and some of its Local Surroundings from the year 1840.* Sherratt & Hughes, Manchester 1905

House M, Storey G, Tillotson K (Eds.) *The letters of Charles Dickens Vol III (1842–1843).* Oxford, OUP 1974

Hunt DM, Dulai KS, Bowmaker JK & Mollon JD. *The Chemistry of John Dalton's Color Blindness.* Science 1995;267:984–8

Isherwood I. Historic address to the Manchester Medical Society, June 20th 1985

Kargon RH. *Science in Victorian Manchester: Enterprise and Expertise.* Manchester University Press 1977

Kay JP. T*he Moral & Physical Condition of the Working Classes Employed in the Cotton Manufacture in Manchester.* Ridgway, Manchester 1832

Keeler CR. 'A Brief History of the Ophthalmoscope'. *Optometry in Practice* 2003;4:137–45

Law FW. 'Egyptian Ophthalmia'. *Br J Ophthalmol* 1939:81–95

Little, David. 'On Extraction of Senile Cataract, with the Results of 1,248 Extractions'. *Br Med J* 1889;Feb23:407–9

Little, David. Observations on the Treatment of Certain Forms of Cataract. Presidential Address to the BMA Section of Ophthalmology. Br Med J 1896.Aug 8

Little, Dora. *Memoir of David Little MD FRCSE 1840–1902.* Tunbridge Wells, Baldwin 1947

McDonald L (Ed.) *Collected Works of Florence Nightingale: The Nightingale School.* Ontario, Wilfred Laurier 2009

Marmion VJ. *The Bristol Eye Hospital.* JCL Graphics, Bristol 1985

Marmion VJ. 'The origin of eye hospitals'. *British Journal of Ophthalmology* 2005;89:1396–7

Moore W. *The Knife Man.* London, Bantam Press 2005

Ott K, Serlin D, Mihm S (Eds.). *Artificial Parts, Practical Lives: Modern Histories of Prosthetics.* New York University Press 2002

Phillips CI. 'Could do better: a curious clinician looks back – and forward'. *Survey of Ophthalmology* 1993;38:75–84

Pickstone JV. *Medicine and Industrial Society.* Manchester University Press 1985

Pickstone JV. 'Medicine in Manchester: Manchester in Medicine, 1750–2005'. *Bulletin of the John Rylands University Library of Manchester* 2005;87:13–41

Porter R. *Quacks; Fakers and Charlatans in Medicine.* Stroud, Tempus 1989

Porter R. *Bodies politic: Disease, death and doctors in Britain 1650–1900.* Reaktion, London 2001

Reece R. *The Medical Guide.* London, Longman, Rees, Orme, Brown & Green 1824

Renaud F. *A short history of the rise and progress of the Manchester Royal Infirmary: from the year 1752 to 1877.* JE Cornish, Manchester 1898

Rutson James R. *Studies in the history of ophthalmology in England prior to the year 1800.* Cambridge University Press 1933

Samelson A. 'Reminiscences of a Four Months' Stay with Professor A. von Graefe in Berlin'. *Br Med J* 1866 Mar-Apr

Shapely P. 'Charity, status and leadership: charitable image and the Manchester man'. *Journal of Social History* 1998

Slugg JT. *Reminiscences of Manchester Fifty Years Ago.* JE Cornish, Manchester 1881

Smith M. *The Letters of Charlotte Brontë (Vol 1)* Oxford University Press 1995

Smith R. 'PFI: Perfidious Financial Idiocy'. *Br Med J* 1999;319:2–3

Sorsby A. 'Defunct London eye hospitals'. *British Journal of Ophthalmology* 1936;20:77–98

Sorsby A. 'Nineteenth century provincial eye hospitals (with special reference to those no longer extant)'. *British Journal of Ophthalmology* 1946;30:501–46

Stancliffe FS. *The Manchester Royal Eye Hospital 1814–1964; a Short History.* Manchester University Press 1964

Sumner J, Pickstone J. *John Dalton's Manchester.* Centre for the History of Science Technology & Medicine 2009

Sutton CW. *Dictionary of National Biography Vol 50.* London, Smith, Elder & Co. 1885–1900

Tallis R. *Hippocratic Oaths.* London, Atlantic Publishing 2004

Treacher Collins E. *The history and traditions of the Moorfields Eye Hospital.* HK Lewis, London 1929

Valier HK, Pickstone JV. *Community, Professions and Business: A History of the Central Manchester Teaching Hospitals and the National Health Service.* Carnegie Publishing, Lancaster 2008

Walker J. *The Oculist's Vade-mecum: a Complete Practical System of Ophthalmic Surgery (2nd edition).* London, Henry Renshaw 1857

Webb K. '"The most Stupid Place under the Sun": Medical Practice and Professional Aspirations in the Industrial Town 1820–60'. *Bulletin of the John Rylands University Library of Manchester* 2005;87:57–87

Wyke TJ. 'The Manchester & Salford Lock Hospital 1818–1917'. *Medical History* 1975;19:73–86

Wyman AL. *Benedict Duddell: Pioneer Oculist of the 18th Century.* JRSM 1992;85:412–5

Young JH. *St. Mary's Hospitals Manchester.* Livingstone, Edinburgh 1964